EVERYMAN'S LIBRARY
EDITED BY ERNEST RHYS

FOR YOUNG PEOPLE

THE WATER BABIES *and* GLAUCUS
BY CHARLES KINGSLEY
INTRODUCTION BY ROSE KINGSLEY

CHARLES KINGSLEY, born near Dartmoor in 1819, the son of a clergyman. Ordained in the Church of England in 1842. Professor of Modern History at Cambridge, 1860–9. Canon of Chester, 1869, and of Westminster, 1873. Died in 1875.

Everyman, I will go with thee, and be thy guide,
In thy most need to go by thy side.

This is No. 277 of Everyman's Library. A list of authors and their works in this series will be found at the end of this volume. The publishers will be pleased to send freely to all applicants a separate, annotated list of the Library.

J. M. DENT & SONS LIMITED
10–13 BEDFORD STREET LONDON W.C.2

E. P. DUTTON & CO. INC.
286–302 FOURTH AVENUE
NEW YORK

THE WATER BABIES
GLAUCUS

CHARLES KINGSLEY

LONDON: J. M. DENT & SONS LTD.
NEW YORK: E. P. DUTTON & CO. INC.

All rights reserved
Made in Great Britain
at The Temple Press Letchworth
and decorated by Eric Ravilious
for
J. M. Dent & Sons Ltd.
Aldine House Bedford St. London
First Published in this Edition 1908
Reprinted 1910, 1914, 1919, 1923, 1928,
1933, 1936

INTRODUCTION

ALTHOUGH at first sight these two books may seem to some to have little in common, the one a plea for the study of Natural Science, the other a fairy tale, yet they are profoundly similar in spirit ; for both are founded upon that deep and reverent love of nature which was so essential a part of my father's being.

It is a little difficult for the present generation with all its scientific equipment — its "nature study," its courses of botany, its "Bird and Tree" competitions, its cameras, its prizes, its articles on natural history in every parish magazine, its mania for shooting every rare bird, for collecting every rare butterfly, flower, and fern, to their utter destruction, alas ! in too many spots—it is difficult, I say, for this generation to believe the complete ignorance of cultivated, as well as uncultivated, English men and women on these subjects fifty years ago. For, when " Glaucus " was written in the winter of 1854-5, the " Study of Natural History " was an almost unknown quantity in the lives of all classes in England.

Therefore the aquarium which my father started for the amusement of his young children and to further his own scientific observations, during a long absence from Eversley at Torquay on account of my mother's health, was regarded as an extraordinary curiosity. So too were his dredging expeditions in Torbay ; and his wanderings with his children over the Livermead rocks or along the Paignton sands, hunting the pools for sea-anemones and strange sea-beasts, and the beds of ore-weed at low spring tides for living shells and sea weeds that were to be found there and there alone ; till the discovery of a new zoophyte in a rock pool, a rare shell on the sands, an unknown flower on the cliffs or fern in the woods, became a far greater and more exciting event to the small children than the finest pantomime can be to the rising generation of to-day. He himself referred to this happy time when he spoke of " wanderings among rock and pool, mixed up with holiest passages of friendship and of love, and the intercommunion of equal minds and sympathetic hearts, and of the laugh of children drinking in health from every breeze and instruction in every step, running ever and anon with proud delight to add their little treasure to their father's stock ; and of happy evenings spent over the microscope and the vase, in examining, arranging, preserving, and noting down in the diary the wonders and labours of the happy day."

The delight of these researches, and the close scientific study of the " wonders of the shore" that he discovered in such a happy hunting-ground as Torbay, found its expression in " Glaucus."

Brought up from his earliest childhood to be a keen and faithful observer of nature in all its phases—for my grandfather was not only a first-rate sportsman but an excellent naturalist, as was my grandmother, who loved every bird, and beast, and flower—my father was well qualified to reveal these wonders to the unseeing, unheeding thousands to whom he appeals in the first pages of " Glaucus," who too often wandered by the sea-shore in those days with

> " No speculation in those eyes
> Which they do glare withal."

And thus in helping them to see and love God's works to which they had hitherto been blind, he was in this, as in many other matters, a true pioneer. For the attention of his readers was so arrested by sound scientific facts put in such an attractive and often humorous form—as, for instance, the delightful description of the Holothuria's digestive arrangements, that "triumphant hygeist, *Cucumaria Hyndmanii*"—that they were impelled to observe for themselves.

To foster this delight in the wonders of nature and encourage sound scientific research, was one of my father's ceaseless aims.

Many a grown man recalls the days when, as a small schoolboy, his first interest in natural science was awakened in walks over the Hampshire moors catching butterflies with my father, or in long spring afternoons carrying his basket for him while he fished in the Itchen meadows. And townsmen of Reading or Winchester still say that their own delight in the study of natural history dates from hearing some of his lectures forty or fifty years ago, which revealed a new life to them ; while the now famous Natural Science Society of Chester is the outcome of a little botanical class for young men which he started in 1871, during the first term of his residence as Canon of Chester.

"Such," as Dean Stanley said long years after, "was the wakefulness, such the devouring curiosity, of him whose life and conversation, as he walked among ordinary men, was often as a waker among drowsy sleepers, as a watchful sentinel in advance of a slumbering host. . . . Perhaps even more than to the glories and wonders of man, he was, far beyond what falls to the lot of most, alive and awake in every pore to the beauty, the marvels of nature. That contrast of the old story of 'eyes and no eyes,' was the contrast between him and common men. That eagle eye seemed to discern every shade and form of animal and vegetable life. That listening ear, like that of the hero in the fairy tale, seemed almost to catch the growing of the grass and the opening of the shell. Nature to him was a companion speaking with a thousand voices. And Nature was to him also the voice of God, the face of the Eternal and Invisible, as it can only be to those who study and love and know it. For his was no idle dreamer's pleasure ; it was a wakefulness not only to the force and beauty of the outward world, but to the causes of its mysterious operations, to the explanations given by its patient students and explorers."[1]

To those who spent even an hour with him, these words must recall vividly that intense and reverent love of all created things as manifestations of the wisdom and love of God, which formed so remarkable a part of my father's daily life. But only those who lived in closest intimacy with him can realise to the full that in his noble ideal of the "perfect naturalist" in "Glaucus," he has, all unconsciously,

[1] "Letters and Memories," vol. i., p. 411.

drawn a more exact sketch of his own character than any that could be written of him.

If "Glaucus" represents the work of the pioneer, of the "waker among drowsy sleepers," "The Water-Babies" shows that of the naturalist in the plenitude of his strength, fearlessly, and yet tenderly, playing with the tremendous results of advanced science in the nineteenth century. For the nine years between 1854 and 1863 cover epoch-making developments in the scientific world. Darwin was "conquering everywhere, and rushing in like a flood, by the mere force of truth and fact," to use my father's own words ;[1] and with Lyell, Huxley, Wallace, Rolleston, Asa Gray, Bates, and many more giants of research and discovery, had changed the whole outlook of natural science.

The writing of "The Water-Babies" had for its reason a gentle reminder, one spring morning at breakfast, of an old promise, to the effect that as the three elder children had their book—"The Heroes"—the baby, my youngest brother, then four years old, "must have his." My father made no answer, "but got up at once and went into his study, locking the door," and in an hour came back with the first chapter of "The Water-Babies" in his hand, written exactly as it stands. At this pace, and with the same ease, the whole book was composed.

The year before, a fresh impetus had been given to his scientific studies by the meeting of the British Association at Cambridge, and the famous tournament between Owen and Huxley over the Hippocampus question—on which he wrote the delightful squib—the supposed speech of Lord Dundreary in Section D.[2] And with his mind full of the stupendous developments of modern natural science, aided by the rich store of facts he had observed for himself about botany and geology, and the habits of beasts and birds, fishes and insects, he gave reins to his imagination, with all reverence and tenderness and an intense sense of enjoyment, in the "Fairy Tale for a Land-Baby."

A visit to Mr. W. E. Forster in Wharfedale, and Mr. Morrison at Malham, in 1858, when he was thinking out a

---

[1] "Letters and Memories," vol ii., p. 171.
[2] Ibid., p. 140.

new novel (which was never finished) on the Pilgrimage of Grace, gave him the local setting of the beautiful opening chapters. For the grandeur of the scenery of Godale Scar and Malham Cove had made a profound impression upon him, as did the beauty of the Wharfe below Denton Park.

Places he had seen, and many more that he had read and dreamed of in his father's fine library of voyages and travels, fairies and men of science, fads and foibles, education true and false, sanitary science—a matter always dear to his heart—and Pandora's box, the ways of beasts and birds, fishes and insects, of plant and tree and rock, of river and tide, are all interwoven here with the deepest truths of life and living, of morals and religion. So that while the book enchants the child, it gives the wise man food for thought.

No wonder that the famous old Arctic voyager, Sir George Back, said in writing to a friend, " I think I told you that, no one, lady or gentleman, could give me anything like a satisfactory answer to the question of ' What is the story of "Water-Babies" about?' And now that I have read it the reason is clear enough, for in the playfulness of a charming fairy tale is included the most amusing allusions to different branches of science. Of plants fresh-water and sea, of water-flies, dear to an old fisherman, and especially the gorgeous dragon-fly, of fish, birds, and shells (I wish the large gull, burgomaster of Spitzbergen, had been mentioned), of species, gorillas, specific gravities, latitudes and longitudes, minute computations, philosophers, examiners, &c., &c., and some poetry that did one's heart good to read.

" I will honour the shadow of the shoe-tie of any landbaby, age *à discrétion*, who will do full justice to this extraordinary book."

While the child who reads "The Water-Babies" is carried in fancy from the right whales of Shiny Wall beyond the ice pack to Mount Erebus and the sperm whales, from the wicked otter in the Yorkshire salmon river to the sunfish from the Chesapeake, from St. Brandan's blessed isle guarded by its water-snakes to the Fish Market at Naples, to those who know what it means, a delightful under-current runs all through the book of allusions to Eversley and Eversley people—the home my father loved so well.

Many a time did he show his children, and other children too, the caddis-baits in the Long Pond in the glebe, building their cases, and, as in that particular May he mentions, starting a fashion of long tails by adding a straw to their houses. Many a time have they gone down to " Cordery's Moor to watch by the great withy pollard which hangs over the backwater," in hopes of seeing where the otters sometimes breed ; and listened to the noise " of the frogs on the Great-A, when they know it is going to be scorching hot to-morrow" ; and mourned over the unhappy eft that jumped out of the vivarium into somebody's work-box, to escape the handsome stickleback's cruel stabs.

Happy are the children who get their first ideas of the marvels of nature all around them from such a lesson-book as this. For no child who has read " The Water-Babies " is likely to forget the wonderful little brickmaker, with his " two big wheels, and one little one, all over teeth, spinning round and round like the wheels in a thrashing machine" ; or the delicious description of the otter and her young ones at play, as they race down the river in the thunderstorm ; or the shining silver salmon coming up proudly from the sea, as " the stream was clearing to a beautiful amber hue" ; or the caddis with her tightly-shut silken door that Tom so rudely pulled open ; or the transformation of the ugly, dirty, donkey-faced creature into the gorgeous dragon-fly, with its big short-sighted eyes that "shone like a thousand diamonds." Nor will they, when they have read the fight of the lobster and the otter and brave little Tom, puzzle over the mystery of how lobsters are kept in the pots, a matter which puzzled us sorely as small children, until our father shewed us the reason why down on the Livermead rocks.

And perchance when they are grown men and women, and like Tom have won their spurs in the great battle, they may look back with thankful hearts to certain pages in " The Water-Babies," which sank almost unconsciously into their minds, and taught them, while as little children they read a fairy tale, what a fine thing it is to love truth, mercy, justice, and courage.

ROSE G. KINGSLEY.

The following is a list of the works of Charles Kingsley :—
The Saint's Tragedy, 1848 ; Twenty-five Village Sermons,
1849 ; Alton Locke, 1850; Yeast, a Problem, 1851 (from
" Fraser's Magazine," 1848); Phaethon, or Loose Thoughts
for Loose Thinkers, 1852 ; Sermons on National Subjects,
1852, 1854 ; Hypatia, 1853 (from " Fraser's Magazine ");
Alexandria and her Schools (Lectures), 1854 ; Who causes
Pestilence? (four Sermons), 1854 ; Sermons for the Times,
1855 ; Westward Ho ! 1855 ; Glaucus, or the Wonders of the
Shore, 1855 ; The Heroes, or Greek Fairy Tales, 1856 ; Two
Years Ago, 1857 ; Andromeda, and Other Poems, 1858 ; The
Good News of God (Sermons), 1859 ; Miscellanies, 1859
Limits of Exact Science as applied to History (Inaugural
Address, Cambridge), 1860 ; Town and Country Sermons,
1861 ; Sermons on the Pentateuch, 1863 ; The Water-Babies,
1863 ; David (four Sermons), 1865 ; Hereward the Wake
1866 ; The Ancien Régime (Lectures), 1867 ; The Water of
Life and Other Sermons, 1867 ; The Hermits, 1868 ; Dis-
cipline and Other Sermons, 1868 ; Madam How and Lady
Why, 1869 (from " Good Words for the Young "); At Last :
A Christmas in the West Indies, 1871 ; Town Geology
(Lectures at Chester), 1872 ; Prose Idylls, 1873 ; Plays and
Puritans, 1873 ; Health and Education, 1874 ; Westminster
Sermons, 1874 ; Lectures delivered in America, 1875 ; All
Saints' Day and Other Sermons, 1878.

Letters and Memories of his Life (ed. by Mrs. Kingsley),
2 vols., 1876 ; 2 vols., Cabinet Edition, 1879 ; 1 vol., 1883.

CONTENTS

PAGE

THE WATER-BABIES: A FAIRY TALE FOR
A LAND-BABY   5

GLAUCUS; OR, THE WONDERS OF THE
SHORE   217

TO MY YOUNGEST SON

GRENVILLE ARTHUR

AND TO

ALL OTHER GOOD LITTLE BOYS

" Come read me my riddle, each good little man:
If you cannot read it, no grown-up folk can."

ERRATUM.—P. 47.

"Lizards . . . . had feathers."

This was written before Professor Owen's Memoir of November 20, 1862, showing that the Archæopteryx is certainly a bird; and was unfortunately overlooked in correcting the proofs.

CHAPTER I

" I heard a thousand blended notes,
While in a grove I sate reclined;
In that sweet mood when pleasant thoughts
Bring sad thoughts to the mind.

To her fair works did Nature link
The human soul that through me ran;
And much it grieved my heart to think,
What man has made of man."
—WORDSWORTH.

THE WATER-BABIES:

A FAIRY TALE FOR A LAND-BABY

CHAPTER I

ONCE upon a time there was a little chimney-sweep, and his name was Tom. That is a short name, and you have heard it before, so you will not have much trouble in remembering it. He lived in a great town in the North country, where there were plenty of chimneys to sweep, and plenty of money for Tom to earn and his master to spend. He could not read nor write, and did not care to do either; and he never washed himself, for there was no water up the court where he lived. He had never been taught to say his prayers. He never had heard of God, or of Christ, except in words which you never have heard, and which it would have been well if he had never heard. He cried half his time, and laughed the other half. He cried when he had to climb the dark flues, rubbing his poor knees and elbows raw; and when the soot got into his eyes, which it did every day in the week; and when his master beat him, which he did every day in the week; and when he had not enough to eat, which happened every day in the week likewise. And he laughed the other half of the day, when he was tossing half-pennies with the other boys, or playing leap-frog over the posts, or bowling stones at the horses' legs as they trotted by, which last was excellent fun, when there was a wall at hand behind which to hide. As for chimney-sweeping, and being hungry, and being beaten, he took all that for the way of the world, like the rain and snow and thunder, and stood manfully with his back to it till it was over, as his old donkey did to a hail-storm; and then shook his ears and was as jolly as ever; and thought of the fine times coming, when he would be a man, and a master sweep, and sit in the public-house with a quart of beer and a long pipe, and play cards for silver money, and wear velveteens and ankle-jacks, and keep a white bull-dog with one grey ear, and carry her puppies in his pocket, just like a man. And he would have apprentices, one, two, three, if he could. How he would bully them, and knock them about, just as his master did to him; and make them carry home the soot sacks, while he rode before them on his donkey, with a pipe in his mouth and a flower in his button-hole, like a king at the head of his army. Yes, there were good times coming; and, when his master let him have a pull at the leavings of his beer, Tom was the jolliest boy in the whole town.

One day a smart little groom rode into the court where Tom lived. Tom was just hiding behind a wall, to heave half a brick at his horse's legs, as is the custom of that country when they welcome strangers; but the groom saw him, and hallooed to him to know where Mr. Grimes, the chimney-sweep, lived. Now, Mr. Grimes was Tom's own master, and Tom was a good man of business, and always civil to customers, so he put the half-brick down quietly behind the wall, and proceeded to take orders.

Mr. Grimes was to come up next morning to Sir John Harthover's, at the Place, for his old chimney-sweep was gone to prison, and the chimneys wanted sweeping. And so he rode away, not giving Tom time to ask what the sweep had gone to prison for, which was a matter of interest to Tom, as he had been in prison once or twice himself. Moreover, the groom looked so very neat and clean, with his drab gaiters, drab breeches, drab jacket, snow-white tie with a smart pin in it, and clean round ruddy face, that Tom was offended and disgusted at his appearance, and considered him a stuck-up fellow, who gave himself airs because he wore smart clothes, and other people paid for them; and went behind the wall to fetch the half-brick after all: but did not, remembering that he had come in the way of business, and was, as it were, under a flag of truce.

His master was so delighted at his new customer that he knocked Tom down out of hand, and drank more beer that night than he usually did in two, in order to be sure of getting up in time next morning; for the more a man's head aches when he wakes, the more glad he is to turn out, and have a breath of fresh air. And, when he did get up at four the next morning, he knocked Tom down again, in order to teach him (as young gentlemen used to be taught at public schools) that he must be an extra good boy that day, as they were going to a very great house, and might make a very good thing of it, if they could but give satisfaction.

And Tom thought so likewise, and, indeed, would have done and behaved his best, even without being knocked down. For, of all places upon earth, Harthover Place (which he had never seen) was the most wonderful; and, of all men on earth, Sir John (whom he had seen, having been sent to gaol by him twice) was the most awful.

Harthover Place was really a grand place, even for the rich North country; with a house so large that in the frame-breaking riots, which Tom could just remember, the Duke of Wellington, with ten thousand soldiers and cannon to match, were easily housed therein; at least, so Tom believed; with a park full of deer, which Tom believed to be monsters who were in the habit of eating children; with miles of game-preserves, in which Mr. Grimes and the collier-lads poached at times, on which occasions Tom saw pheasants, and wondered what they tasted like; with a noble salmon-river, in which

Mr. Grimes and his friends would have liked to poach,
but then they must have got into cold water, and that
they did not like at all. In short, Harthover was a
grand place, and Sir John a grand old man, whom even
Mr. Grimes respected, for not only could he send Mr.
Grimes to prison when he deserved it, as he did once or
twice a week; not only did he own all the land about
for miles; not only was he a jolly, honest, sensible
squire as ever kept a pack of hounds, who would do
what he thought right by his neighbours, as well as get
what he thought right for himself, but, what was more,
he weighed full fifteen stone, was nobody knew how
many inches round the chest, and could have thrashed
Mr. Grimes himself in fair fight, which very few folk
round there could do, and which, my dear little boy,
would not have been right for him to do, as a great
many things are not which one both can do, and would
like very much to do. So Mr. Grimes touched his hat
to him when he rode through the town, and called him
a "buirdly awd chap," and his young ladies "gradely
lasses," which are two high compliments in the North
country; and thought that that made up for his poaching
Sir John's pheasants; whereby you may perceive that
Mr. Grimes had not been to a properly-inspected
Government National School.

Now, I dare say, you never got up at three o'clock on
a midsummer morning. Some people get up then because they want to catch salmon; and some, because
they want to climb Alps; and a great many more, because they must, like Tom. But, I assure you, that
three o'clock on a midsummer morning is the pleasantest
time of all the twenty-four hours, and all the three hundred and sixty-five days; and why every one does not
get up then, I never could tell, save that they are all
determined to spoil their nerves and their complexions,
by doing all night, what they might just as well do all
day. But Tom, instead of going out to dinner at half-
past eight at night, and to a ball at ten, and finishing off
somewhere between twelve and four, went to bed at
seven, when his master went to the public-house, and

slept like a dead pig: for which reason he was as piert as a game-cock (who always gets up early to wake the maids), and just ready to get up when the fine gentlemen and ladies were just ready to go to bed.

So he and his master set out; Grimes rode the donkey in front, and Tom and the brushes walked behind; out of the court, and up the street, past the closed window-shutters, and the winking weary policemen, and the roofs all shining grey in the grey dawn.

They passed through the pitmen's village, all shut up and silent now; and through the turnpike; and then they were out in the real country, and plodding along the black dusty road, between black slag walls, with no sound but the groaning and thumping of the pit-engine in the next field. But soon the road grew white, and the walls likewise; and at the wall's foot grew long grass and gay flowers, all drenched with dew; and instead of the groaning of the pit-engine, they heard the skylark saying his matins high up in the air, and the pit-bird warbling in the sedges, as he had warbled all night long.

All else was silent. For old Mrs. Earth was still fast asleep; and, like many pretty people, she looked still prettier asleep than awake. The great elm-trees in the gold-green meadows were fast asleep above, and the cows fast asleep beneath them; nay, the few clouds which were about were fast asleep likewise, and so tired that they had lain down on the earth to rest, in long white flakes and bars, among the stems of the elm-trees, and along the tops of the alders by the stream, waiting for the sun to bid them rise and go about their day's business in the clear blue overhead.

On they went; and Tom looked, and looked, for he never had been so far into the country before; and longed to get over a gate, and pick buttercups, and look for birds' nests in the hedge; but Mr. Grimes was a man of business, and would not have heard of that.

Soon they came up with a poor Irishwoman, trudging along with a bundle at her back. She had a grey shawl over her head, and a crimson madder petticoat; so you may be sure she came from Galway. She had neither shoes nor stockings, and limped along as if she were tired and footsore : but she was a very tall handsome woman, with bright grey eyes, and heavy black hair hanging about her cheeks. And she took Mr. Grimes's fancy so much, that when he came alongside he called out to her :

"This is a hard road for a gradely foot like that. Will ye up, lass, and ride behind me ? "

But, perhaps, she did not admire Mr. Grimes's look and voice ; for she answered quietly :

"No, thank you ; I'd sooner walk with your little lad here."

"You may please yourself," growled Grimes, and went on smoking.

So she walked beside Tom, and talked to him, and asked him where he lived, and what he knew, and all about himself, till Tom thought he had never met such a pleasant spoken woman. And she asked him, at last, whether he said his prayers ; and seemed sad when he told her that he knew no prayers to say.

Then he asked her where she lived ; and she said far away by the sea. And Tom asked her about the sea ; and she told him how it rolled and roared over the rocks in winter nights, and lay still in the bright summer days, for the children to bathe and play in it ; and many a story more, till Tom longed to go and see the sea, and bathe in it likewise.

At last, at the bottom of a hill, they came to a spring : not such a spring as you see here, which soaks up out of a white gravel in the bog, among red fly-catchers, and pink bottle-heath, and sweet white orchis ; nor such a one as you may see, too, here, which bubbles up under the warm sand-bank in the hollow lane, by the great tuft of lady ferns, and makes the sand dance reels at the bottom, day and night, all the year round . not such a spring as either of those : but a real North country limestone fountain, like one of those in Sicily or Greece, where the old heathen fancied the nymphs sat cooling themselves the hot summer's day, while the shepherds peeped at them from behind the bushes.

Out of a low cave of rock, at the foot of a limestone crag, the great fountain rose, quelling and bubbling, and gurgling, so clear that you could not tell where the water ended and the air began; and ran away under the road, a stream large enough to turn a mill; among blue geranium, and golden globe-flower, and wild raspberry, and the bird-cherry with its tassels of snow.

And there Grimes stopped, and looked; and Tom looked too. Tom was wondering whether anything lived in that dark cave, and came out at night to fly in the meadows. But Grimes was not wondering at all. Without a word, he got off his donkey, and clambered over the low road wall, and knelt down, and began dipping his ugly head into the spring—and very dirty he made it.

Tom was picking the flowers as fast as he could. The Irishwoman helped him, and showed him how to tie them up; and a very pretty nosegay they had made between them. But when he saw Grimes actually wash, he stopped, quite astonished; and when Grimes had finished, and began shaking his ears to dry them, he said:

"Why, master, I never saw you do that before."

"Nor will again, most likely. 'Twasn't for cleanliness I did it, but for coolness. I'd be ashamed to want washing every week or so, like any smutty collier-lad."

"I wish I might go and dip my head in," said poor little Tom. "It must be as good as putting it under the town-pump; and there is no beadle here to drive a chap away."

"Thou come along," said Grimes, "what dost want with washing thyself? Thou did not drink half a gallon of beer last night, like me."

"I don't care for you," said naughty Tom, and ran down to the stream, and began washing his face.

Grimes was very sulky, because the woman preferred Tom's company to his; so he dashed at him with horrid words, and tore him up from his knees, and began beating him. But Tom was accustomed to that, and got his head safe between Mr. Grimes's legs, and kicked his shins with all his might.

"Are you not ashamed of yourself, Thomas Grimes?" cried the Irishwoman over the wall.

Grimes looked up, startled at her knowing his name; but all he answered was, "No: nor never was yet;" and went on beating Tom.

"True for you. If you ever had been ashamed of yourself, you would have gone over into Vendale long ago."

"What do you know about Vendale?" shouted Grimes; but he left off beating Tom.

"I know about Vendale, and about you, too. I know, for instance, what happened in Aldermire Copse, by night, two years ago come Martinmas."

"You do?" shouted Grimes; and leaving Tom, climbed up over the wall, and faced the woman. Tom thought he was going to strike her; but she looked him too full and fierce in the face for that.

"Yes; I was there," said the Irishwoman, quietly.

"You are no Irishwoman, by your speech," said Grimes, after many bad words.

"Never mind who I am. I saw what I saw; and if you strike that boy again, I can tell what I know."

Grimes seemed quite cowed, and got on his donkey without another word.

"Stop!" said the Irishwoman. "I have one more word for you both; for you will both see me again, before all is over. Those that wish to be clean, clean they will be; and those that wish to be foul, foul they will be. Remember."

And she turned away, and through a gate into the meadow. Grimes stood still a moment, like a man who had been stunned. Then he rushed after her, shouting "You come back." But when he got into the meadow the woman was not there.

Had she hidden away? There was no place to hide in. But Grimes looked about, and Tom also, for he was as puzzled as Grimes himself, at her disappearing so suddenly; but look where they would, she was not there.

Grimes came back again, as silent as a post, for he

was a little frightened; and getting on his donkey, filled a fresh pipe, and smoked away, leaving Tom in peace.

And now they had gone three miles and more, and came to Sir John's lodge-gates.

Very grand lodges they were, with very grand iron gates, and stone gate-posts, and on the top of each a most dreadful bogy, all teeth, horns, and tail, which was the crest which Sir John's ancestors wore in the Wars of the Roses; and very prudent men they were to wear it, for all their enemies must have run for their lives at the very first sight of them.

Grimes rang at the gate, and out came a keeper on the spot, and opened.

" I was told to expect thee," he said. " Now, thou'lt be so good as to keep to the main avenue, and not let me find a hare or a rabbit on thee when thou comest back. I shall look sharp for one, I tell thee."

" Not if it's in the bottom of the soot-bag," quoth Grimes, and at that he laughed; and the keeper laughed and said—

" If that's thy sort, I may as well walk up with thee to the hall."

" I think thou best had. It's thy business to see after thy game, man, and not mine."

So the keeper went with them; and to Tom's surprise, he and Grimes chatted together all the way quite pleasantly. He did not know that a keeper is only a poacher turned outside in, and a poacher a keeper turned inside out.

They walked up a great lime-avenue, a full mile long, and between their stems Tom peeped trembling at the horns of the sleeping deer, which stood up among the ferns. Tom had never seen such enormous trees, and as he looked up he fancied that the blue sky rested on their heads. But he was puzzled very much by a strange murmuring noise, which followed them all the way. So much puzzled, that at last he took courage to ask the keeper what it was.

He spoke very civilly, and called him Sir, for he was horribly afraid of him, which pleased the keeper, and he told him that they were the bees about the lime-flowers.

"What are bees?" asked Tom.

"What make honey."

"What is honey?" asked Tom.

"Thou hold thy noise," said Grimes.

"Let the boy be," said the keeper. "He's a civil young chap now, and that's more than he'll be long, if he bides with thee."

Grimes laughed, for he took that for a compliment.

"I wish I were a keeper," said Tom, "to live in such a beautiful place, and wear green velveteens, and have a real dog-whistle at my button, like you."

The keeper laughed; he was a kind-hearted fellow enough.

"Let well alone, lad, and ill too, at times. Thy life's safer than mine at all events, eh, Mr. Grimes?"

And Grimes laughed again, and then the two men began talking quite low. Tom could hear, though, that it was about some poaching fight—and at last Grimes said surlily—

"Hast thou anything against me?"

"Not now."

"Then don't ask me any questions till thou hast, for I am a man of honour."

And at that they both laughed again, and thought it a very good joke.

And by this time they were come up to the great iron gates in front of the house; and Tom stared through them at the rhododendrons and azaleas, which were all in flower; and then at the house itself, and wondered how many chimneys there were in it, and how long ago it was built, and what was the man's name that built it, and whether he got much money for his job?

These last were very difficult questions to answer. For Harthover had been built at ninety different times, and in nineteen different styles, and looked as if some-body had built a whole street of houses of every imagi-nable shape, and then stirred them together with a spoon.

For the attics were Anglo-Saxon.

The third-floor Norman.

The second Cinque-cento.

The first-floor Elizabethan.

The right wing Pure Doric.

The centre Early English, with a huge portico, copied from the Parthenon.

The left wing Pure Bœotian, which the country folk admired most of all, because it was just like the new barracks in the town, only three times as big.

The grand staircase was copied from the Catacombs at Rome.

The back staircase from the Tajmahal at Agra. This was built by Sir John's great-great-great-uncle, who won, in Lord Clive's Indian wars, plenty of money, plenty of wounds, and no more taste than his betters.

The cellars were copied from the caves of Elephanta.

The offices from the Pavilion at Brighton.

And the rest from nothing in heaven, or earth, or under the earth.

So that Harthover House was a great puzzle to antiquarians, and a thorough Naboth's vineyard to critics, and architects, and all persons who like meddling with other men's business, and spending other men's money. So they all were setting upon poor Sir John, year after year, and trying to talk him into spending a hundred thousand pounds or so, in building to please them and not himself. But he always put them off, like a canny North-countryman as he was. One wanted him to build a Gothic house, but he said he was no Goth; and another to build an Elizabethan, but he said he lived under good Queen Victoria, and not good Queen Bess; and another was bold enough to tell him that his house was ugly, but he said he lived inside it, and not outside; and another, that there was no unity in it; but he said that that was just why he liked the old place. For he liked to see how each Sir John, and Sir Hugh, and Sir Ralph, and Sir Randal, had left his mark upon the place, each after his own taste; and he had no more notion of disturbing his ancestors' work than of disturbing their graves. For now the house looked like a real live house, that had a history, and had grown and grown as the world grew; and that it was only an upstart fellow who did not know who his own grandfather was, who would change it for some spick and span new Gothic or Elizabethan thing, which looked as if it had been all spawned in a night, as mushrooms are. From which you may collect (if you have wit enough), that Sir John was a very sound-headed, sound-hearted squire, and just the man to keep the country side in order, and show good sport with his hounds.

But Tom and his master did not go in through the great iron gates, as if they had been Dukes or Bishops, but round the back way, and a very long way round it was; and into a little back-door, where the ash-boy let them in, yawning horribly; and then in a passage the housekeeper met them, in such a flowered chintz dressing-gown, that Tom mistook her for My Lady herself, and she gave Grimes solemn orders about "You will take care of this, and take care of that," as if he was going up the chimneys, and not Tom. And Grimes listened, and said every now and then, under his voice, "You'll mind that, you little beggar?" and Tom did mind, at least all that he could. And then the housekeeper turned them into a grand room, all covered up in sheets of brown paper, and bade them begin, in a lofty and tremendous voice; and so after a whimper or two, and a kick from his master, into the grate Tom went, and up the chimney, while a housemaid stayed in the room to watch the furniture; to whom Mr. Grimes paid many playful and chivalrous compliments, but met with very slight encouragement in return.

How many chimneys he swept I cannot say: but he swept so many that he got quite tired, and puzzled too, for they were not like the town flues to which he was accustomed, but such as you would find—if you would only get up them and look, which perhaps you would not like to do—in old country-houses, large and crooked chimneys, which had been altered again and again, till they ran into one another, anastomosing (as Professor Owen would say) considerably. So Tom fairly lost his way in them; not that he cared much for that, though he was in pitchy darkness, for he was as much at home in a chimney as a mole is underground; but at last, coming down as he thought the right chimney, he came down the wrong one, and found himself standing on the hearthrug in a room the like of which he had never seen before.

Tom had never seen the like. He had never been in gentlefolks' rooms but when the carpets were all up, and the curtains down, and the furniture huddled together under a cloth, and the pictures covered with aprons and dusters; and he had often enough wondered what the rooms were like when they were all ready for the quality to sit in. And now he saw, and he thought the sight very pretty.

The room was all dressed in white; white window curtains, white bed curtains, white furniture, and white walls, with just a few lines of pink here and there. The carpet was all over gay little flowers; and the walls were hung with pictures in gilt frames, which amused Tom very much. There were pictures of ladies and gentlemen, and pictures of horses and dogs. The horses he liked; but the dogs he did not care for much, for there were no bull-dogs among them, not even a terrier. But the two pictures which took his fancy most were, one a man in long garments, with little children and their mothers round him, who was laying his hand upon the children's heads. That was a very pretty picture, Tom thought, to hang in a lady's room. For he could see that it was a lady's room by the dresses which lay about.

The other picture was that of a man nailed to a cross, which surprised Tom much. He fancied that he had seen something like it in a shop window. But why was it there? "Poor man," thought Tom, "and he looks so kind and quiet. But why should the lady have such a sad picture as that in her room? Perhaps it was some kinsman of hers, who had been murdered by the savages in foreign parts, and she kept it there for a remembrance." And Tom felt sad, and awed, and turned to look at something else.

The next thing he saw, and that too puzzled him, was
a washing-stand, with ewers and basons, and soap and
brushes, and towels; and a large bath, full of clean
water—what a heap of things all for washing! "She
must be a very dirty lady," thought Tom, "by my
master's rule, to want as much scrubbing as all that.
But she must be very cunning to put the dirt out of the
way so well afterwards, for I don't see a speck about the
room, not even on the very towels."

And then, looking toward the bed, he saw that dirty
lady, and held his breath with astonishment.

Under the snow-white coverlet, upon the snow-white
pillow, lay the most beautiful little girl that Tom had
ever seen. Her cheeks were almost as white as the
pillow, and her hair was like threads of gold spread all
about over the bed. She might have been as old as
Tom, or maybe a year or two older; but Tom did
not think of that. He thought only of her delicate skin
and golden hair, and wondered whether she were a
real live person, or one of the wax dolls he had seen
in the shops. But when he saw her breathe, he made
up his mind that she was alive, and stood staring at her,
as if she had been an angel out of heaven.

No. She cannot be dirty. She never could have been
dirty, thought Tom to himself. And then he thought,
"And are all people like that when they are washed?"
And he looked at his own wrist, and tried to rub the
soot off, and wondered whether it ever would come off.
"Certainly I should look much prettier then, if I grew
at all like her."

And looking round, he suddenly saw, standing close
to him, a little ugly, black, ragged figure, with bleared
eyes and grinning white teeth. He turned on it angrily.
What did such a little black ape want in that sweet
young lady's room? And behold, it was himself, reflected in a great mirror, the like of which Tom had
never seen before.

And Tom, for the first time in his life, found out that
he was dirty; and burst into tears with shame and anger;
and turned to sneak up the chimney again and hide,

and upset the fender, and threw the fire-irons down, with a noise as of ten thousand tin kettles tied to ten thousand mad dogs' tails.

Up jumped the little white lady in her bed, and, seeing Tom, screamed as shrill as any peacock. In rushed a stout old nurse from the next room, and seeing Tom likewise, made up her mind that he had come to rob, plunder, destroy, and burn ; and dashed at him, as he lay over the fender, so fast that she caught him by the jacket.

But she did not hold him. Tom had been in a policeman's hands many a time, and out of them too, what is more ; and he would have been ashamed to face his friends for ever if he had been stupid enough to be caught by an old woman : so he doubled under the good lady's arm, across the room, and out of the window in a moment.

He did not need to drop out, though he would have done so bravely enough. Nor even to let himself down a spout, which would have been an old game to him ; for once he got up by a spout to the church roof, he said to take jackdaws' eggs, but the policemen said to steal lead ; and when he was seen on high, sat there till the sun got too hot, and came down by another spout, leaving the policemen to go back to the station-house and eat their dinners.

But all under the window spread a tree, with great leaves, and sweet white flowers, almost as big as his head. It was a magnolia, I suppose ; but Tom knew nothing about that, and cared less ; for down the tree he went, like a cat, and across the garden lawn, and over the iron-railings, and up the park towards the wood, leaving the old nurse to scream murder and fire at the window.

The under gardener, mowing, saw Tom, and threw down his scythe ; caught his leg in it, and cut his shin open, whereby he kept his bed for a week : but in his hurry he never knew it, and gave chase to poor Tom. The dairymaid heard the noise, got the churn between her knees, and tumbled over it, spilling all the cream ; and yet she jumped up, and gave chase to

Tom. A groom cleaning Sir John's hack at the stables let him go loose, whereby he kicked himself lame in five minutes; but he ran out, and gave chase to Tom. Grimes upset the soot-sack in the new-gravelled yard, and spoilt it all utterly; but, he ran out and gave chase to Tom. The old steward opened the park gate in such a hurry, that he hung up his pony's chin upon the spikes, and for aught I know it hangs there still; but he jumped off, and gave chase to Tom. The ploughman left his horses at the headland, and one jumped over the fence, and pulled the other into the ditch, plough and all; but he ran on, and gave chase to Tom. The keeper, who was taking a stoat out of a trap, let the stoat go, and caught his own finger; but he jumped up and ran after Tom, and considering what he said, and how he looked, I should have been sorry for Tom if he had caught him. Sir John looked out of his study window (for he was an early old gentleman), and up at the nurse, and a marten dropt mud in his eye, so that he had at last to send for the doctor; and yet he ran out and gave chase to Tom. The Irishwoman, too, was walking up to the house to beg —she must have got round by some byway: but she threw away her bundle, and gave chase to Tom likewise. Only my lady did not give chase; for when she had put her head out of the window, her night-wig fell into the garden, and she had to ring up her lady's-maid, and send her down for it privately; which quite put her out of the running, so that she came in nowhere, and is consequently not placed.

In a word, never was there heard at Hall Place, not even when the fox was killed in the conservatory, among acres of broken glass, and tons of smashed flower-pots, such a noise, row, hubbub, babel, shindy, hullabaloo, stramash, charivari, and total contempt of dignity, repose, and order, as that day, when Grimes, the gardener, the groom, the dairymaid, Sir John, the steward, the ploughman, the keeper, and the Irish-woman, all ran up the park, shouting "Stop thief," in the belief that Tom had at least a thousand pounds' worth of jewels in his empty pockets; and the very magpies and jays followed Tom up, screaking and screaming, as if he were a hunted fox, beginning to droop his brush.

And all the while poor Tom paddled up the park with his little bare feet, like a small black gorilla fleeing to the forest. Alas for him! there was no big father gorilla therein to take his part; to scratch out the gardener's inside with one paw, toss the dairymaid into a tree with another, and wrench off Sir John's head with a third, while he cracked the keeper's scull with his teeth, as easily as if it had been a cocoa-nut or a paving-stone.

However, Tom did not remember ever having had a father; so he did not look for one, and expected to have to take care of himself; while as for running, he could keep up for a couple of miles with any stage-coach, if there was the chance of a copper or a cigar-end, and turn coach wheels on his hands and feet ten times following, which is more than you can do. Wherefore his pursuers found it very difficult to catch him; and we will hope that they did not catch him at all.

Tom, of course, made for the woods. He had never been in a wood in his life: but he was sharp enough to know that he might hide in a bush, or swarm up a tree, and, altogether, had more chance there than in the open. If he had not known that, he would have been foolisher than a mouse or a minnow.

But when he got into the wood, he found it a very different sort of place from what he had fancied. He pushed into a thick cover of rhododendrons, and found himself at once caught in a trap. The boughs laid hold of his legs and arms, poked him in his face and his stomach, made him shut his eyes tight (though that was no great loss, for he could not see at best a yard before his nose); and when he got through the rhododendrons, the hassock-grass and sedges tumbled him over, and cut his poor little fingers afterwards most spitefully; the birches birched him as soundly as if he had been a nobleman at Eton, and over the face too (which is not fair swishing, as all brave boys will agree); and the lawyers tripped him up, and tore his shins as if they had sharks' teeth—which lawyers are likely enough to have.

"I must get out of this," thought Tom, "or I shall stay here till somebody comes to help me—which is just what I don't want."

But how to get out was the difficult matter. And indeed I don't think he would ever have got out at all, but have staid there till the cock-robins covered him with leaves, if he had not suddenly run his head against a wall.

Now running your head against a wall is not pleasant, especially if it is a loose wall, with the stones all set on edge, and a sharp-cornered one hits you between the eyes, and makes you see all manner of beautiful stars. The stars are very beautiful, certainly : but unfortunately they go in the twenty-thousandth part of a split second, and the pain which comes after them does not. And so Tom hurt his head ; but he was a brave boy, and did not mind that a penny. He guessed that over the wall the cover would end ; and up it he went, and over like a squirrel.

And there he was, out on the great grouse-moors, which the country folk called Harthover Fell—heather and bog and rock, stretching away and up, up to the very sky.

Now, Tom was a cunning little fellow—as cunning as an old Exmoor stag. Why not ? Though he was but ten years old, he had lived longer than most stags, and had more wits to start with into the bargain.

He knew as well as a stag, that if he backed he might throw the hounds out. So the first thing he did when he was over the wall, was to make the neatest double sharp to his right, and run along under the wall for nearly half a mile.

Whereby Sir John, and the keeper, and the steward, and the gardener, and the ploughman, and the dairymaid, and all the hue-and-cry together, went on ahead half a mile in the very opposite direction, and inside the wall, leaving him a mile off on the outside, while Tom heard their shouts die away in the wood, and chuckled to himself merrily.

At last he came to a dip in the land, and went to the bottom of it, and then he turned bravely away from the wall, and up the moor; for he knew that he had put a hill between him and his enemies, and could go on without their seeing him.

But the Irishwoman, alone of them all, had seen which way Tom went. She had kept ahead of every one the whole time: and yet she neither walked or ran. She went along quite smoothly and gracefully, while her feet twinkled past each other so fast, that you could not see which was foremost; till every one asked the other who the strange woman was? and all agreed, for want of anything better to say, that she must be in league with Tom.

But when she came to the plantation they lost sight of her; and they could do no less. For she went quietly over the wall after Tom, and followed him wherever he went. Sir John and the rest saw no more of her; and out of sight was out of mind.

And now Tom was right away into the heather, over just such a moor as those in which you have been bred, except that there were rocks and stones lying about everywhere; and that instead of the moor growing flat as he went upwards, it grew more and more broken and hilly: but not so rough but that little Tom could jog along well enough, and find time, too, to stare about at the strange place, which was like a new world to him.

He saw great spiders there, with crowns and crosses marked on their backs, who sat in the middle of their webs, and when they saw Tom coming, shook them so fast that they became invisible. Then he saw lizards, brown, and grey, and green, and thought they were snakes, and would sting him: but they were as much frightened as he, and shot away into the heath. And then, under a rock, he saw a pretty sight—a great brown sharpnosed creature, with a white tag to her brush, and round her, four or five smutty little cubs, the funniest fellows Tom ever saw. She lay on her back, rolling about, and stretching out her legs, and head, and tail in the bright sunshine; and the cubs jumped over her, and ran round her, and nibbled her paws, and lugged her about by the tail; and she seemed to enjoy it mightily. But one selfish little fellow stole away from the rest to a dead crow close by, and dragged it off to hide it, though it was nearly as big as he was. Whereat all his little brothers set off after him in full cry, and saw Tom; and then all ran back, and up jumped Mrs. Vixen, and caught one up in her mouth, and the rest toddled after her, and into a dark crack in the rocks; and there was an end of the show.

And next he had a fright; for as he scrambled up a sandy brow—whirr-poof-poof-cock-cock-kick—something went off in his face, with a most horrid noise. He thought the ground had blown up, and the end of the world come.

And when he opened his eyes (for he shut them very tight), it was only an old cock-grouse, who had been washing himself in sand, like an Arab, for want of water; and who, when Tom had all but trodden on him, jumped up, with a noise like the express train, leaving his wife and children to shift for themselves, like an old coward, and went off, screaming "Cur-ru-u-uck, cur-ru-u-uck—murder, thieves, fire—cùr-u-uck-cock-kick—the end of the world is come—kick-kick-cock-kick." He was always fancying that the end of the world was come, when anything happened which was farther off than the end of his own nose. But the end of the world was not come, any more than the twelfth of August was; though the old grouse-cock was quite certain of it.

So the old grouse came back to his wife and family an hour afterwards, and said solemnly, "Cock-cock-kick; my dears, the end of the world is not quite come; but I assure you it is coming the day after to-morrow—cock." But his wife had heard that so often, that she knew all about it, and a little more. And, beside, she was the mother of a family, and had seven little poults to wash and feed every day;

and that made her very practical, and a little sharp-tempered; so all she answered was: "Kick-kick-kick —go and catch spiders, go and catch spiders—kick."

So Tom went on, and on, he hardly knew why: but he liked the great, wide, strange place, and the cool, fresh, bracing air. But he went more and more slowly as he got higher up the hill; for now the ground grew very bad indeed. Instead of soft turf and springy heather, he met great patches of flat limestone rock, just like ill-made pavements, with deep cracks between the stones and ledges, filled with ferns; so he had to hop from stone to stone, and now and then he slipped in between, and hurt his little bare toes, though they were tolerably tough ones: but still he would go on and up, he could not tell why.

What would Tom have said, if he had seen, walking over the moor behind him, the very same Irishwoman who had taken his part upon the road? But whether it was that he looked too little behind him, or whether it was that she kept out of sight behind the rocks and knolls, he never saw her, though she saw him.

And now he began to get a little hungry, and very thirsty; for he had run a long way, and the sun had risen high in heaven, and the rock was as hot as an oven, and the air danced reels over it, as it does over a limekiln, till everything round seemed quivering and melting in the glare.

But he could see nothing to eat anywhere, and still less to drink.

The heath was full of bilberries and whimberries: but they were only in flower yet, for it was June. And as for water, who can find that on the top of a limestone rock? Now and then he passed by a deep dark swallow-hole, going down into the earth, as if it was the chimney of some dwarf's house underground; and more than once, as he passed, he could hear water falling, trickling, tinkling, many many feet below. How he longed to get down to it, and cool his poor baked lips! But, brave little chimney-sweep as he was, he dared not climb down such chimneys as those.

So he went on, and on, till his head spun round with the heat, and he thought he heard church-bells ringing, a long way off.

"Ah!" he thought, "where there is a church, there will be houses and people; and, perhaps, some one will give me a bit and a sup." So he set off again, to look for the church; for he was sure that he heard the bells quite plain.

And in a minute more, when he looked round, he stopped again, and said, "Why, what a big place the world is!"

And so it was; for, from the top of the mountain, he could see—what could he not see?

Behind him, far below, was Harthover, and the dark woods, and the shining salmon river; and on his left, far below, was the town, and the smoking chimneys of the collieries; and far, far away, the river widened to the shining sea; and little white specks, which were ships, lay on its bosom. Before him lay, spread out like a map, great plains, and farms, and villages, amid dark knots of trees. They all seemed at his very feet; but he had sense to see that they were long miles away.

And to his right rose moor after moor, hill after hill, till they faded away, blue into blue sky. But between him and those moors, and really at his very feet, lay something, to which, as soon as Tom saw it, he determined to go, for that was the place for him.

A deep, deep green and rocky valley, very narrow, and filled with wood: but through the wood, hundreds of feet below him, he could see a clear stream glance. Oh, if he could but get down to that stream! Then, by the stream, he saw the roof of a little cottage, and a little garden, set out in squares and beds. And there was a tiny little red thing moving in the garden, no bigger than a fly. As Tom looked down, he saw that it was a woman in a red petticoat! Ah! perhaps she would give him something to eat. And there were the church bells ringing again. Surely there must be a village down there. Well, nobody would know him, or what had happened at the Place. The news could not have got there yet, even if Sir John had set all the policemen in the county after him; and he could get down there in five minutes.

Tom was quite right about the hue-and-cry not having got thither; for he had come, without knowing it, the best part of ten miles from Harthover: but he was wrong about getting down in five minutes, for the cottage was more than a mile off, and a good thousand feet below.

However, down he went, like a brave little man as he was, though he was very footsore, and tired, and hungry, and thirsty; while the church-bells rang so loud, he began to think that they must be inside his own head, and the river chimed and tinkled far below; and this was the song which it sang :—

> Clear and cool, clear and cool,
> By laughing shallow, and dreaming pool,
> Cool and clear, cool and clear,
> By shining shingle, and foaming wear;
> Under the crag where the ouzel sings,
> And the ivied wall where the church-bell rings,
> Undefiled, for the undefiled;
> Play by me, bathe in me, mother and child.
>
> Dank and foul, dank and foul,
> By the smoky town in its murky cowl;
> Foul and dank, foul and dank,
> By wharf and sewer and slimy bank;
> Darker and darker the further I go,
> Baser and baser the richer I grow;
> Who dare sport with the sin-defiled?
> Shrink from me, turn from me, mother and child.
>
> Strong and free, strong and free,
> The floodgates are open, away to the sea.
> Free and strong, free and strong,
> Cleansing my streams as I hurry along,
> To the golden sands, and the leaping bar,
> And the taintless tide that awaits me afar,
> As I lose myself in the infinite main,
> Like a soul that has sinned and is pardoned again.
> Undefiled, for the undefiled,
> Play by me, bathe in me, mother and child.

So Tom went down; and all the while he never saw the Irishwoman going down behind him.

CHAPTER II

"And is there care in heaven? and is there love
In heavenly spirits to these creatures base
That may compassion of their evils move?
There is :—else much more wretched were the case
Of men than beasts: But oh! the exceeding grace
Of Highest God that loves His creatures so,
And all His works with mercy doth embrace,
That blessed Angels He sends to and fro,
To serve to wicked man, to serve His wicked foe!"

—SPENSER.

CHAPTER II

MILE off, and a thousand feet down. So Tom found it; though it seemed as if he could have chucked a pebble on to the back of the woman in the red petticoat who was weeding in the garden, or even across the dale to the rocks beyond.

For the bottom of the valley was just one field broad, and on the other side ran the stream; and above it, grey crag, grey down, grey stair, grey moor, walled up to heaven.

A quiet, silent, rich, happy place; a narrow crack cut deep into the earth; so deep, and so out of the way, that the bad bogies can hardly find it out. The name of the place is Vendale; and if you want to see it for yourself, you must go up into the High Craven, and search from Bolland Forest north by Ingleborough, to the Nine Standards and Cross Fell; and if you have not found it, you must turn south, and search the Lake Mountains, down to Scaw Fell and the sea; and then if you have not found it, you must go northward again by merry Carlisle, and search the Cheviots all across, from Annan Water to Berwick Law; and then, whether you have found Vendale or not, you will have found such a country, and such a people, as ought to make you proud of being a British boy.

So Tom went to go down; and first he went down three hundred feet of steep heather, mixed up with loose brown gritstone, as rough as a file; which was not pleasant to his poor little heels, as he came bump, stump, jump, down the steep. And still he thought he could throw a stone into the garden.

Then he went down three hundred feet of limestone terraces, one below the other, as straight as if Mr. George White had ruled them with his ruler and then cut them out with his chisel. There was no heath there, but—

First, a little grass slope, covered with the prettiest flowers, rockrose and saxifrage, and thyme and basil, and all sorts of sweet herbs.

Then bump down a two-foot step of limestone

Then another bit of grass and flowers.

Then bump down a one-foot step.

Then another bit of grass and flowers for fifty yards. as steep as the house-roof, where he had to slide down on his dear little tail.

Then another step of stone, ten feet high ; and there he had to stop himself, and crawl along the edge to find a crack; for if he had rolled over, he would have rolled right into the old woman's garden, and frightened her out of her wits.

Then, when he had found a dark narrow crack, full of green-stalked fern, such as hangs in the basket in the drawing-room, and had crawled down through it, with knees and elbows, as he would down a chimney, there was another grass slope, and another step, and so on, till—oh, dear me ! I wish it was all over; and so did he. And yet he thought he could throw a stone into the old woman's garden.

At last he came to a bank of beautiful shrubs; whitebeam with its great silver-backed leaves, and mountain-ash, and oak ; and below them cliff and crag, cliff and crag, with great beds of crown-ferns and wood-sedge ; while through the shrubs he could see the stream sparkling, and hear it murmur on the white pebbles. He did not know that it was three hundred feet below.

You would have been giddy, perhaps, at looking down : but Tom was not. He was a brave little chimney-sweep ; and when he found himself on the top

of a high cliff, instead of sitting down and crying for
his baba (though he never had had any baba to cry
for), he said, "Ah, this will just suit me!" though
he was very tired; and down he went, by stock and
stone, sedge and ledge, bush and rush, as if he had
been born a jolly little black ape, with four hands
instead of two.

And all the while, he never saw the Irishwoman
coming down behind him.

But he was getting terribly tired now. The burning
sun on the fells had sucked him up; but the damp
heat of the woody crag sucked him up still more;
and the perspiration ran out of the ends of his fingers
and toes, and washed him cleaner than he had been for
a whole year. But, of course, he dirtied everything
terribly as he went. There has been a great black
smudge all down the crag ever since. And there have
been more black beetles in Vendale since than ever
were known before; all, of course, owing to Tom's
having blacked the original papa of them all, just as
he was setting off to be married, with a sky-blue coat
and scarlet leggings, as smart as a gardener's dog with
a polyanthus in his mouth.

At last he got to the bottom. But, behold, it was
not the bottom—as people usually find when they are
coming down a mountain. For at the foot of the crag
were heaps and heaps of fallen limestone of every size
from that of your head to that of a stage-waggon,
with holes between them full of sweet heath-fern; and
before Tom got through them, he was out in the bright
sunshine again; and then he felt, once for all and suddenly,
as people generally do, that he was b-e-a-t, beat.

You must expect to be beat a few times in your life,
little man, if you live such a life as a man ought to
live, let you be as strong and healthy as you may:
and when you are, you will find it a very ugly feeling.
I hope that that day you may have a stout staunch
friend by you who is not beat; for if you have not,
you had best lie where you are, and wait for better
times, as poor Tom did.

He could not get on. The sun was burning, and yet he felt chill all over. He was quite empty, and yet he felt quite sick. There was but two hundred yards of smooth pasture between him and the cottage, and yet he could not walk down it. He could hear the stream murmuring only one field beyond it, and yet it seemed to him as if it was a hundred miles off.

He lay down on the grass till the beetles ran over him, and the flies settled on his nose. I don't know when he would have got up again, if the gnats and the midges had not taken compassion on him. But the gnats blew their trumpets so loud in his ear, and the midges nibbled so at his hands and face wherever they could find a place free from soot, that at last he woke up, and stumbled away, down over a low wall, and into a narrow road, and up to the cottage door.

And a neat pretty cottage it was, with clipt yew hedges all round the garden, and yews inside too, cut into peacocks and trumpets and teapots and all kinds of queer shapes. And out of the open door came a noise like that of the frogs on the Great-A, when they know that it is going to be scorching hot to-morrow— and how they know that I don't know, and you don't know, and nobody knows.

He came slowly up to the open door, which was all hung round with clematis and roses; and then peeped in, half afraid.

And there sat by the empty fire-place, which was filled with a pot of sweet herbs, the nicest old woman that ever was seen, in her red petticoat, and short dimity bedgown, and clean white cap, with a black silk handkerchief over it, tied under her chin. At her feet sat the grandfather of all the cats; and opposite her sat, on two benches, twelve or fourteen neat rosy chubby little children, learning their Chris-cross-row; and gabble enough they made about it.

Such a pleasant cottage it was, with a shiny clean stone floor, and curious old prints on the walls, and an old black oak sideboard full of bright pewter and brass dishes, and a cuckoo clock in the corner, which began

shouting as soon as Tom appeared : not that it was
frightened at Tom, but that it was just eleven o'clock.

All the children started at Tom's dirty black figure ;
the girls began to cry, and the boys began to laugh,
and all pointed at him rudely enough : but Tom was
too tired to care for that.

"What art thou, and what dost want ?" cried the old
dame. "A chimney-sweep ! Away with thee. I'll have
no sweeps here."

"Water," said poor little Tom, quite faint.

"Water ? There's plenty i' the beck," she said, quite
sharply.

"But I can't get there ; I'm most clemmed with
hunger and drought." And Tom sank down upon the
door-step, and laid his head against the post.

And the old dame looked at him through her spectacles one minute, and two, and three ; and then she
said, "He's sick ; and a bairn's a bairn, sweep or none."

"Water," said Tom.

"God forgive me !" and she put by her spectacles,
and rose, and came to Tom. "Water's bad for thee ;
I'll give thee milk." And she toddled off into the next
room, and brought a cup of milk and a bit of bread.

Tom drank the milk off at one draught, and then looked
up, revived.

"Where didst come from ?" said the dame.

"Over Fell, there," said Tom, and pointed up into
the sky.

"Over Harthover? and down Lewthwaite Crag ?
Art sure thou art not lying ?"

"Why should I ?" said Tom, and leant his head
against the post.

"And how got ye up there ?"

"I came over from the Place," and Tom was so tired
and desperate he had no heart or time to think of a
story, so he told all the truth in a few words.

"Bless thy little heart ! And thou hast not been
stealing, then ?"

"No."

"Bless thy little heart ! and I'll warrant not. Why,

God's guided the bairn, because he was innocent! Away from the Place, and over Harthover Fell, and down Lewthwaite Crag! Who ever heard the like, if God hadn't led him? Why dost not eat thy bread?"

"I can't."

"It's good enough, for I made it myself."

"I can't," said Tom, and he laid his head on his knees, and then asked—

"Is it Sunday?"

"No, then; why should it be?"

"Because I hear the church bells ringing so."

"Bless thy pretty heart! The bairn's sick. · Come wi' me, and I'll hap thee up somewhere. If thou wert a bit cleaner I'd put thee in my own bed, for the Lord's sake. But come along here."

But when Tom tried to get up, he was so tired and giddy that she had to help him and lead him.

She put him in an outhouse upon soft sweet hay and an old rug, and bade him sleep off his walk, and she would come to him when school was over, in an hour's time.

And so she went in again, expecting Tom to fall fast asleep at once.

But Tom did not fall asleep.

Instead of it he turned and tossed and kicked about in the strangest way, and felt so hot all over that he longed to get into the river and cool himself; and then he fell half asleep, and dreamt that he heard the little white lady crying to him, "Oh, you're so dirty; go and be washed"; and then that he heard the Irishwoman saying, "Those that wish to be clean, clean they will be." And then he heard the church bells ring so loud, close to him, too, that he was sure it must be Sunday, in spite of what the old dame had said; and he would go to church, and see what a church was like inside, for he had never been in one, poor little fellow, in all his life. But the people would never let him come in, all over soot and dirt like that. He must go to the river and wash first. And he said out aloud again and again, though being half asleep he did not know it, "I must be clean, I must be clean."

And all of a sudden he found himself, not in the out-house on the hay, but in the middle of a meadow, over the road, with a stream just before him, saying continually, "I must be clean, I must be clean." He had got there on his own legs, between sleep and awake, as children will often get out of bed, and go about the room, when they are not quite well. But he was not a bit surprised, and went on to the bank of the brook, and lay down on the grass, and looked into the clear, clear limestone water, with every pebble at the bottom bright and clean, while the little silver trout dashed about in fright at the sight of his black face; and he dipped his hand in and found it so cool, cool, cool; and he said, "I will be a fish; I will swim in the water; I must be clean, I must be clean."

So he pulled off all his clothes in such haste that he tore some of them, which was easy enough with such ragged old things. And he put his poor hot sore feet into the water; and then his legs; and the further he went in, the more the church bells rang in his head.

"Ah," said Tom, "I must be quick and wash myself; the bells are ringing quite loud now: and they will stop soon, and then the door will be shut, and I shall never be able to get in at all."

Tom was mistaken: for in England the church doors are left open all service time, for everybody who likes to come in, Churchman or Dissenter; ay, even if he were a Turk or a Heathen; and if any man dared to turn him out, as long as he behaved quietly, the good old English law would punish that man, as he deserved, for ordering any peaceable person out of God's house, which belongs to all alike. But Tom did not know that, any more than he knew a great deal more which people ought to know.

And all the while he never saw the Irishwoman: not behind him this time, but before.

For just before he came to the river side, she had stept down into the cool clear water; and her shawl and her petticoat floated off her, and the green water-weeds floated round her sides, and the white water-lilies floated round her head, and the fairies of the stream came up from the bottom, and bore her away and down upon their arms;

for she was the Queen of them all ; and perhaps of more besides.

"Where have you been?" they asked her.

"I have been smoothing sick folk's pillows, and whispering sweet dreams into their ears ; opening cottage casements, to let out the stifling air ; coaxing little children away from gutters, and foul pools where fever breeds ; turning women from the gin-shop door, and staying men's hands as they were going to strike their wives ; doing all I can to help those who will not help themselves : and little enough that is, and weary work for me. But I have brought you a new little brother, and watched him safe all the way here."

Then all the fairies laughed for joy at the thought that they had a little brother coming.

"But mind, maidens, he must not see you, or know that you are here. He is but a savage now, and like the beasts which perish ; and from the beasts which perish he must learn. So you must not play with him, or speak to him, or let him see you : but only keep him from being harmed."

Then the fairies were sad, because they could not play with their new brother, but they always did what they were told.

And their Queen floated away down the river ; and whither she went, thither she came. But all this Tom, of course, never saw or heard : and perhaps if he had, it would have made little difference in the story ; for he was so hot and thirsty, and longed so to be clean for once, that he tumbled himself as quick as he could into the clear cool stream.

And he had not been in it two minutes before he fell fast asleep, into the quietest, sunniest, cosiest sleep that ever he had in his life ; and he dreamt about the green meadows by which he had walked that morning, and the tall elm-trees, and the sleeping cows ; and after that he dreamt of nothing at all.

The reason of his falling into such a delightful sleep is very simple ; and yet hardly any one has found it out. It was merely that the fairies took him.

Some people think that there are no fairies. Cousin Cramchild tells little folks so in his Conversations. Well, perhaps there are none—in Boston, U.S., where he was raised. There are only a clumsy lot of spirits there, who can't make people hear without thumping on the table: but they get their living thereby, and I suppose that is all they want. And Aunt Agitate, in her Arguments on political economy, says there are none. Well, perhaps there are none—in her political economy. But it is a wide world, my little man— and thank heaven for it, for else, between crinolines and theories, some of us would get squashed—and plenty of room in it for fairies, without people seeing them; unless, of course, they look in the right place. The most wonderful and the strongest things in the world, you know, are just the things which no one can see. There is life in you; and it is the life in you which makes you grow, and move, and think: and yet you can't see it. And there is steam in a steam-engine; and that is what makes it move: and yet you can't see it; and so there may be fairies in the world, and they may be just what makes the world go round to the old tune of

> " C'est l'amour, l'amour, l'amour
> Qui fait la monde à la ronde : "

and yet no one may be able to see them except those whose hearts are going round to that same tune. At all events, we will make believe that there are fairies in the world. It will not be the last time by many a one that we shall have to make believe. And yet, after all, there is no need for that. There must be fairies; for this is a fairy tale: and how can one have a fairy tale if there are no fairies?

You don't see the logic of that? Perhaps not. Then please not to see the logic of a great many arguments exactly like it, which you will hear before your beard is grey.

The kind old dame came back at twelve, when school was over, to look at Tom: but there was no Tom there. She looked about for his footprints; but the ground was so hard that there was no slot, as they say in dear old North Devon. And if you grow up to be a brave healthy man, you may know some day what no slot means, and know, too, I hope, what a slot does mean—a broad slot, with blunt claws, which makes a man put out his cigar, and set his teeth, and tighten his girths, when he sees it; and what his rights mean, if he has them, brow, bay, tray, and points; and see something worth seeing between Haddon Wood and Countisbury Cliff, with good Mr. Palk Collyns to show you the way, and mend your bones as fast as you smash them. Only when that jolly day comes, please don't break your neck: stogged in a mire you never will be, I trust; for you are a heath-cropper bred and born.

So the old dame went in again quite sulky, thinking that little Tom had tricked her with a false story, and shammed ill, and then run away again.

But she altered her mind the next day. For, when Sir John and the rest of them had run themselves out of breath, and lost Tom, they went back again, looking very foolish.

And they looked more foolish still when Sir John heard more of the story from the nurse; and more foolish still, again, when they heard the whole story from Miss Ellie, the little lady in white. All she had seen was a poor little black chimney-sweep, crying and sobbing, and going to get up the chimney again. Of course, she was very much frightened: and no wonder. But that was all. The boy had taken nothing in the room; by the mark of his little sooty feet, they could see that he had never been off the hearth-rug till the nurse caught hold of him. It was all a mistake.

So Sir John told Grimes to go home, and promised him five shillings if he would bring the boy quietly up to him, without beating him, that he might be sure of the truth. For he took for granted, and Grimes, too, that Tom had made his way home.

But no Tom came back to Mr. Grimes that evening; and he went to the police-office, to tell them to look out for the boy. But no Tom was heard of. As for his having gone over those great fells to Vendale, they no more dreamed of that than of his having gone to the moon.

So Mr. Grimes came up to Harthover next day with a very sour face; but when he got there, Sir John was over the hills and far away; and Mr. Grimes had to sit in the outer servants' hall all day, and drink strong ale to wash away his sorrows; and they were washed away, long before Sir John came back.

For good Sir John had slept very badly that night; and he said to his lady, "My dear, the boy must have got over into the grouse-moors, and lost himself; and he lies very heavily on my conscience, poor little lad. But I know what I will do."

So, at five the next morning up he got, and into his bath, and into his shooting-jacket and gaiters, and into the stable-yard, like a fine old English gentleman, with a face as red as a rose, and a hand as hard as a table, and a back as broad as a bullock's; and bade them bring his shooting pony, and the keeper to come on his pony, and the huntsman, and the first whip, and the second whip, and the under-keeper with the blood-hound in a leash—a great dog as tall as a calf, of the colour of a gravel walk, with mahogany ears and nose, and a throat like a church bell. They took him up to the place where Tom had gone into the wood; and there the hound lifted up his mighty voice, and told them all he knew.

Then he took them to the place where Tom had climbed the wall; and they shoved it down, and all got through.

And then the wise dog took them over the moor, and over the fells, step by step, very slowly; for the scent was a day old, you know, and very light from the heat and drought. But that was why cunning old Sir John started at five in the morning.

And at last he came to the top of Lewthwaite Crag, and there he bayed, and looked up in their faces, as much as to say, "I tell you he is gone down here!"

They could hardly believe that Tom would have gone

so far ; and when they looked at that awful cliff, they could never believe that he would have dared to face it. But if the dog said so, it must be true.

" Heaven forgive us ! " said Sir John. " If we find him at all, we shall find him lying at the bottom." And he slapped his great hand upon his great thigh, and said—

"Who will go down over Lewthwaite Crag, and see if that boy is alive? Oh that I were twenty years younger, and I would go down myself ! " And so he would have done, as well as any sweep in the county. Then he said—

" Twenty pounds to the man who brings me that boy alive ! " and as was his way, what he said he meant.

Now among the lot was a little groom-boy, a very little groom indeed ; and he was the same who had ridden up the court, and told Tom to come to the Hall ; and he said—

" Twenty pounds or none, I will go down over Lew-thwaite Crag, if it's only for the poor boy's sake. For he was as civil a spoken little chap as ever climbed a flue."

So down over Lewthwaite Crag he went : a very smart groom he was at the top, and a very shabby one at the bottom ; for he tore his gaiters, and he tore his breeches, and he tore his jacket, and he burst his braces, and he burst his boots, and he lost his hat, and what was worst of all, he lost his shirt pin, which he prized very much, for it was gold, and he had won it in a raffle at Malton, and there was a figure at the top of it of t'ould mare, noble old Beeswing herself, as natural as life ; so it was a really severe loss : but he never saw anything of Tom.

And all the while Sir John and the rest were riding round, full three miles to the right, and back again, to get into Vendale, and to the foot of the crag.

When they came to the old dame's school, all the children came out to see. And the old dame came out too ; and when she saw Sir John she curtsied very low for she was a tenant of his.

" Well, dame, and how are you ? " said Sir John.

" Blessings on you as broad as your back, Harth-over," says she—she didn't call him Sir John, but only Harthover, for that is the fashion in the North country—" and welcome into Vendale : but you're no hunting the fox this time of year ? "

" I am hunting, and strange game too," said he.

" Blessings on your heart, and what makes you look so sad the morn ? "

" I'm looking for a lost child, a chimney-sweep, that is run away."

" Oh Harthover, Harthover," says she, " ye were always a just man and a merciful ; and ye'll no harm the poor little lad if I give you tidings of him ? "

" Not I, not I, dame. I'm afraid we hunted him out of the house all on a miserable mistake, and the hound has brought him to the top of Lewthwaite Crag, and——"

Whereat the old dame broke out crying, without letting him finish his story.

" So he told me the truth after all, poor little dear ! Ah, first thoughts are best, and a body's heart'll guide them right, if they will but hearken to it." And then she told Sir John all.

" Bring the dog here, and lay him on," said Sir John, without another word, and he set his teeth very hard.

And the dog opened at once ; and went away at the back of the cottage, over the road, and over the meadow, and through a bit of alder copse ; and there, upon an alder stump, they saw Tom's clothes lying. And then they knew as much about it all as there was any need to know.

And Tom ?

Ah, now comes the most wonderful part of this wonderful story. Tom, when he woke, for of course he woke—children always wake after they have slept exactly as long as is good for them— found himself swimming about in the stream, being about four inches, or—that I may be accurate—3·87902 inches long, and having round the parotid region of his fauces a set of external gills (I hope you understand all the big words) just like those of a sucking eft, which he mistook for a lace frill, till he pulled at them, found he hurt himself, and made up his mind that they were part of himself, and best left alone.

In fact, the fairies had turned him into a water-baby.

A water-baby? You never heard of a water-baby. Perhaps not. That is the very reason why this story was written. There are a great many things in the world which you never heard of; and a great many more which nobody ever heard of; and a great many things, too, which nobody will ever hear of, at least until the coming of the Cocqcigrues, when man shall be the measure of all things.

" But there are no such things as water-babies."

How do you know that? Have you been there to see? And if you had been there to see, and had seen none, that would not prove that there were none. If Mr. Garth does not find a fox in Eversley Wood—as folks sometimes fear he never will—that does not prove that there are no such things as foxes. And as is Eversley Wood to all the woods in England, so are the waters we know to all the waters in the world. And no one has a right to say that no water-babies exist, till they have seen no water-babies existing; which is quite a different thing, mind, from not seeing water-babies; and a thing which nobody ever did, or perhaps ever will do.

"But surely if there were water-babies, somebody would have caught one at least?"

Well. How do you know that somebody has not?

" But they would have put it into spirits, or into the Illustrated News, or perhaps cut it into two halves, poor dear little thing, and sent one to Professor Owen, and one to Professor Huxley, to see what they would each say about it."

Ah, my dear little man! that does not follow at all, as you will see before the end of the story.

"But a water-baby is contrary to nature."

Well, but, my dear little man, you must learn to talk about such things, when you grow older, in a very different way from that. You must not talk about "ain't" and "can't" when you speak of this great wonderful world round you, of which the wisest man knows only the very smallest corner, and is, as the great Sir Isaac Newton said, only a child picking up pebbles on the shore of a boundless ocean.

You must not say that this cannot be, or that that is contrary to nature. You do not know what nature is, or what she can do; and nobody knows; not even Sir Roderick Murchison, or Professor Owen, or Professor Sedgwick, or Professor Huxley, or Mr. Darwin, or Professor Faraday, or Mr. Grove, or any other of the great men whom good boys are taught to respect. They are very wise men; and you must listen respectfully to all they say: but even if they should say, which I am sure they never would, "That cannot exist. That is contrary to nature," you must wait a little, and see; for perhaps even they may be wrong. It is only children who read Aunt Agitate's Arguments, or Cousin Cramchild's Conversations; or lads who go to popular lectures, and see a man pointing at a few big ugly pictures on the wall, or making nasty smells with bottles and squirts, for an hour or two, and calling that anatomy or chemistry—who talk about "cannot exist," and "contrary to nature." Wise men are afraid to say that there is anything contrary to nature, except what is contrary to mathematical truth; for two and two cannot make five, and two straight lines cannot join twice, and a part cannot be as great as the whole, and so on (at least, so it seems at present): but the wiser men are, the less they talk about "cannot." That is a very rash, dangerous word, that "cannot"; and if people use it too often, the Queen of all the Fairies, who makes the clouds thunder and the fleas bite, and takes just as much trouble about one as about the other, is apt to astonish them suddenly by showing them, that though they say she cannot, yet she can, and what is more, will, whether they approve or not.

And therefore it is, that there are dozens and hundreds of things in the world which we should certainly have said were contrary to nature, if we did not see them going on under our eyes all day long. If people had never seen little seeds grow into great plants and trees, of quite different shape from themselves, and these trees again produce fresh seeds, to grow into fresh trees, they would have said, "The thing cannot be; it is contrary to nature." And they would have been quite as right in saying so, as in saying that most other things cannot be.

Or suppose again, that you had come, like M. du Chaillu, a traveller from unknown parts; and that no human being had ever seen or heard of an elephant. And suppose that you described him to people, and said, "This is the shape, and plan, and anatomy of the beast, and of his feet, and of his trunk, and of his grinders, and of his tusks, though they are not tusks at all, but two fore teeth run mad; and this is the section of his skull, more like a mushroom than a reasonable skull of a reasonable or unreasonable beast; and so forth, and so forth; and though the beast (which I assure you I have seen and shot) is first cousin to the little hairy coney of Scripture, second cousin to a pig, and (I suspect) thirteenth or fourteenth cousin to a rabbit, yet he is the wisest of all beasts, and can do everything save read, write, and cast accounts." People would surely have said, "Nonsense; your elephant is contrary to nature"; and have thought you were telling stories—as the French thought of Le Vaillant when he came back to Paris and said that he had shot a giraffe; and as the king of the Cannibal Islands thought of the English sailor, when he said that in his country water turned to marble, and rain fell as feathers. They would tell you, the more they knew of science, "Your elephant is an impossible monster, contrary to the laws of comparative anatomy, as far as yet known." To which you would answer the less, the more you thought.

Did not learned men, too, hold, till within the last twenty-five years, that a flying dragon was an impossible monster? And do we not know now that there are hundreds of them found fossil up and down the world? People call them Pterodactyles : but that is only because they are ashamed to call them flying dragons, after denying so long that flying dragons could exist. And has not a German only lately discovered, what is most monstrous of all, that some of these flying dragons, lizards though they are, had feathers? And if that last is not contrary to what people mean by nature nowadays, one hardly knows what is.

The truth is, that folks' fancy that such and such things cannot be, simply because they have not seen them, is worth no more than a savage's fancy that there cannot be such a thing as a locomotive, because he never saw one running wild in the forest. Wise men know that their business is to examine what is, and not to settle what is not. They know that there are elephants; they know that there have been flying dragons; and the wiser they are, the less inclined they will be to say positively that there are no water-babies.

No water-babies, indeed? Why, wise men of old said that everything on earth had its double in the water; and you may see that that is, if not quite true, still quite as true as most other theories which you are likely to hear for many a day. There are land-babies —then why not water-babies? Are there not water-rats, water-flies, water-crickets, water-crabs, water-tortoises, water-scorpions, water-tigers and water-hogs, water-cats and water-dogs, sea-lions and sea-bears, sea-horses and sea-elephants, sea-mice and sea-urchins, sea-razors and sea-pens, sea-combs and sea-fans; and of plants, are there not water-grass, and water-crowfoot, water-milfoil, and so on, without end?

" But all these things are only nicknames; the water things are not really akin to the land things."

That's not always true. They are, in millions of cases, not only of the same family, but actually the same individual creatures. Do not even you know that a green drake, and an alder-fly, and a dragon-fly, live under water till they change their skins, just as Tom changed his? And if a water animal can continually change into a land animal, why should not a land animal sometimes change into a water animal? Don't be put down by any of Cousin Cramchild's arguments, but stand up to him like a man, and answer him (quite respectfully, of course) thus :—

If Cousin Cramchild says, that if there are water-babies, they must grow into water-men, ask him how he knows that they do not? and then, how he knows that they must, any more than the Proteus of the Adelsberg caverns grows into a perfect newt?

If he says that it is too strange a transformation for a land-baby to turn into a water-baby, ask him if he ever heard of the transformation of Syllis, or the Distomas, or the common jelly-fish, of which M. Quatrefages says excellently well—"who would not exclaim that a miracle had come to pass, if he saw a reptile come out of the egg dropped by the hen in his poultry-yard, and the reptile give birth at once to an indefinite number of fishes and birds? Yet the history of the jelly-fish is quite as wonderful as that would be." Ask him if he knows about all this; and if he does not, tell him to go and look for himself; and advise him (very respectfully, of course) to settle no more what strange things cannot happen, till he has seen what strange things do happen every day.

If he says that things cannot degrade, that is, change downwards into lower forms, ask him, who told him that water-babies were lower than land-babies? But even if they were, does he know about the strange degradation of the common goose-barnacles, which one finds sticking on ships' bottoms; or the still stranger degradation of some cousins of theirs, of which one hardly likes to talk, so shocking and ugly it is?

And, lastly, if he says (as he most certainly will) that these transformations only take place in the lower animals, and not in the higher, say that that seems to little boys, and to some grown people, a very strange fancy. For if the changes of the lower animals are so wonderful, and so difficult to discover, why should not there be changes in the higher animals far more wonderful, and far more difficult to discover? And may not man, the crown and flower of all things, undergo some change as much more wonderful than all the rest, as the Great Exhibition is more wonderful than a rabbit-burrow? Let him answer that. And if he says (as he will) that not having seen such a change in his experience, he is not bound to believe it, ask him respectfully where his microscope has been? Does not each of us, in coming into this world, go through a transformation just as wonderful as that of a sea-egg, or a butterfly? and does not reason and analogy, as well as Scripture, tell us that that transformation is not the last? and that, though what we shall be, we know not, yet we are here but as the crawling cater-pillar, and shall be hereafter as the perfect fly. The old Greeks, heathens as they were, saw as much as that two thousand years ago; and I care very little for Cousin Cramchild, if he sees even less than they. And so forth, and so forth, till he is quite cross. And then tell him that if there are no water-babies, at least, there ought to be; and that, at least, he cannot answer.

And meanwhile, my dear little man, till you know a great deal more about nature than Professor Owen and Professor Huxley, put together, don't tell me about what cannot be, or fancy that anything is too wonderful to be true. "We are fearfully and wonder-fully made," said old David; and so we are; and so is everything around us, down to the very deal table. Yes; much more fearfully and wonderfully made, already, is the table, as it stands now, nothing but a piece of dead deal wood, than if, as foxes say, and geese believe, spirits could make it dance, or talk to you by rapping on it.

Am I in earnest? Oh dear no. Don't you know that this is a fairy tale, and all fun and pretence; and that you are not to believe one word of it, even if it is true?

But at all events, so it happened to Tom. And, therefore, the keeper, and the groom, and Sir John, made a great mistake, and were very unhappy (Sir John, at least) without any reason, when they found a black thing in the water, and said it was Tom's body, and that he had been drowned. They were utterly mistaken. Tom was quite alive; and cleaner, and merrier, than he ever had been. The fairies had washed him, you see, in the swift river, so thoroughly, that not only his dirt, but his whole husk and shell had been washed quite off him, and the pretty little real Tom was washed out of the inside of it, and swam away, as a caddis does when its case of stones and silk is bored through, and away it goes on its back, paddling to the shore, there to split its skin, and fly away as a caperer, on four fawn-coloured wings, with long legs and horns. They are foolish fellows, the caperers, and fly into the candle at night, if you leave the door open. We will hope Tom will be wiser, now he has got safe out of his sooty old shell.

But good Sir John did not understand all this, not being a fellow of the Linnæan Society; and he took it into his head that Tom was drowned. When they looked into the empty pockets of his shell, and found no jewels there, nor money—nothing but three marbles, and a brass button with a string to it—then Sir John did something as like crying as ever he did in his life, and blamed himself more bitterly than he need have done. So he cried, and the groom-boy cried, and the huntsman cried, and the dame cried, and the little girl cried, and the dairymaid cried, and the old nurse cried (for it was somewhat her fault), and my lady cried, for though people have wigs, that is no reason why they should not have hearts: but the keeper did not cry, though he had been so good-natured to Tom the morning before; for he was so dried up with running after poachers, that you could no more get tears out of him than milk out of leather : and Grimes did not cry, for Sir John gave him ten pounds, and he drank it all in a week. Sir John sent, far and wide, to find Tom's father and mother : but he might have looked till Doomsday for them, for one was dead, and the other was in Botany Bay. And the little girl would not play with her dolls for a whole week, and never forgot poor little Tom. And soon my lady put a pretty little tombstone over Tom's shell in

the little churchyard in Vendale, where the old dales-
men all sleep side by side between the limestone crags.
And the dame decked it with garlands every Sunday,
till she grew so old that she could not stir abroad; then
the little children decked it for her. And always she
sung an old old song, as she sat spinning what she called
her wedding-dress. The children could not understand
it, but they liked it none the less for that; for it was
very sweet, and very sad; and that was enough for
them. And these are the words of it—

> " When all the world is young, lad,
>   And all the trees are green;
> And every goose a swan, lad,
>   And every lass a queen ;
> Then hey for boot and horse, lad,
>   And round the world away :
> Young blood must have its course, lad,
>   And every dog his day.
>
> When all the world is old, lad,
>   And all the trees are brown ;
> And all the sport is stale, lad,
>   And all the wheels run down ;
> Creep home, and take your place there,
>   The spent and maimed among :
> God grant you find one face there,
>   You loved when all was young."

Those are the words : but they are only the body of it :
the soul of the song was the dear old woman's sweet face,
and sweet voice, and the sweet old air to which she sang ;
and that, alas ! one cannot put on paper. And at last she
grew so stiff and lame, that the angels were forced to
carry her; and they helped her on with her wedding-
dress, and carried her up over Harthover Fells, and a
long way beyond that too ; and there was a new schoolmistress in Vendale, and we will hope that she was not
certificated.

And all the while Tom was swimming about in the
river, with a pretty little lace-collar of gills about his
neck, as lively as a grig, and as clean as a fresh-run
salmon.

Now if you don't like my story, then go to the school-room and learn your multiplication-table, and see if you like that better. Some people, no doubt, would do so. So much the better for us, if not for them. It takes all sorts, they say, to make a world.

CHAPTER III

" He prayeth well who loveth well,
Both men and bird and beast ;
He prayeth best who loveth best,
All things both great and small :
For the dear God who loveth us,
He made and loveth all."

—COLERIDGE.

CHAPTER III

OM was now quite amphibious. You do not know what that means? You had better, then, ask the nearest Government pupil-teacher, who may possibly answer you smartly enough, thus—

"Amphibious. Adjective, derived from two Greek words, *amphi*, a fish, and *bios*, a beast. An animal supposed by our ignorant ancestors to be compounded of a fish and a beast; which therefore, like the hippopotamus, can't live on the land, and dies in the water."

However that may be, Tom was amphibious; and what is better still, he was clean. For the first time in his life, he felt how comfortable it was to have nothing on him but himself. But he only enjoyed it: he did not know it, or think about it; just as you enjoy life and health, and yet never think about being alive and healthy: and may it be long before you have to think about it!

He did not remember having ever been dirty. Indeed, he did not remember any of his old troubles, being tired, or hungry, or beaten, or sent up dark chimneys. Since that sweet sleep, he had forgotten all about his master, and Harthover Place, and the little white girl, and in a word, all that had happened to him when he lived before; and what was best of all, he had forgotten all the bad words which he had learnt from Grimes, and the rude boys with whom he used to play.

That is not strange : for you know, when you came into this world, and became a land-baby, you remembered nothing. So why should he, when he became a water-baby?

Then have you lived before?

My dear child, who can tell? One can only tell that, by remembering something which happened where we lived before; and as we remember nothing, we know nothing about it; and no book, and no man, can ever tell us certainly.

There was a wise man once, a very wise man, and a very good man, who wrote a poem about the feelings which some children have about having lived before; and this is what he said—

> " Our birth is but a sleep and a forgetting ;
> The soul that rises with us, our life's star,
>   Hath elsewhere had its setting,
>   And cometh from afar :
>   Not in entire forgetfulness,
>   And not in utter nakedness,
> But trailing clouds of glory, do we come
>   From God, who is our home."

There, you can know no more than that. But if I was you, I would believe that. For then the great fairy Science, who is likely to be queen of all the fairies for many a year to come, can only do you good, and never do you harm ; and instead of fancying, with some people, that your body makes your soul, as if a steam-engine could make its own coke ; or, with some other people, that your soul has nothing to do with your body, but is only stuck into it like a pin into a pin-cushion, to fall out with the first shake ;—you will believe the one true,

orthodox,	inductive,
rational,	deductive,
philosophical,	seductive,
logical,	productive,
irrefragable,	salutary,
nominalistic,	comfortable,
realistic,	

and on-all-accounts-to-be-received

doctrine of this wonderful fairy tale; which is, that your soul makes your body, just as a snail makes his shell. For the rest, it is enough for us to be sure that whether or not we lived before, we shall live again; though not, I hope, as poor little heathen Tom did. For he went downward into the water: but we, I hope, shall go upward to a very different place.

But Tom was very happy in the water. He had been sadly overworked in the land-world; and so now, to make up for that, he had nothing but holidays in the water-world for a long, long time to come. He had nothing to do now but enjoy himself, and look at all the pretty things which are to be seen in the cool clear water-world, where the sun is never too hot, and the frost is never too cold.

And what did he live on? Water-cresses, perhaps; or perhaps water-gruel, and water-milk: too many land-babies do so likewise. But we do not know what one-tenth of the water things eat; so we are not answerable for the water-babies.

Sometimes he went along the smooth gravel water-ways, looking at the crickets which ran in and out among the stones, as rabbits do on land; or he climbed over the ledges of rock, and saw the sand-pipes hanging in thousands, with every one of them a pretty little head and legs peeping out; or he went into a still corner, and watched the caddises eating dead sticks as greedily as you would eat plum-pudding, and building their houses with silk and glue. Very fanciful ladies they were; none of them would keep to the same materials for a day. One would begin with some pebbles; then she would stick on a piece of green weed; then she found a shell, and stuck it on too; and the poor shell was alive, and did not like at all being taken to build houses with: but the caddis did not let him have any voice in the matter, being rude and selfish, as vain people are apt to be; then she stuck on a piece of rotten wood, then a very smart pink stone, and so on, till she was patched all over like an Irishman's coat. Then she found a long straw, five times as long as herself, and said, "Hurrah! my sister has a tail, and I'll have one too"; and she stuck it on her back, and marched about with it quite proud, though it was very inconvenient indeed. And, at that, tails became all the fashion among the caddis-baits in that pool, as they were at the end of the Long Pond last May, and they all toddled about with long straws sticking out behind, getting between each other's legs, and tumbling over each other, and looking so ridiculous, that Tom laughed at them till he cried, as we did. But they were quite right, you know; for people must always follow the fashion, even if it be spoon-bonnets.

Then sometimes he came to a deep still reach; and there he saw the water-forests. They would have looked to you only little weeds; but Tom, you must remember, was so little that everything looked a hundred times as big to him as it does to you, just as things do to a minnow, who sees and catches the little water-creatures which you can only see in a microscope.

And in the water-forest he saw the water-monkeys and water-squirrels (they had all six legs, though; everything almost has six legs in the water, except efts and water-babies); and nimbly enough they ran among the branches. There were water-flowers there, too, in thousands; and Tom tried to pick them: but as soon as he touched them, they drew themselves in and turned into knots of jelly; and then Tom saw that they were all alive— bells, and stars, and wheels, and flowers, of all beautiful shapes and colours; and all alive and busy, just as Tom was. So now he found that there was a great deal more in the world than he had fancied at first sight.

There was one wonderful little fellow, too, who peeped out of the top of a house built of round bricks. He had two big wheels, and one little one, all over teeth, spinning round and round like the wheels in a thrashing-machine; and Tom stood and stared at him, to see what he was going to make with his machinery. And what do you think he was doing? Brick-making. With his two big wheels he swept together all the mud which floated in the water: all that was nice in it he put into his stomach and ate; and all the mud he put into the little wheel on his breast, which really was a round hole set with teeth; and there he spun it into a neat hard round brick; and then he took it and stuck it on the top of his house-wall, and set to work to make another. Now was not he a clever little fellow?

Tom thought so: but when he wanted to talk to him, the brick-maker was much too busy and proud of his work to take notice of him.

Now you must know that all the things under the water talk: only not such a language as ours; but such as horses, and dogs, and cows, and birds talk to each other; and Tom soon learned to understand them and talk to them; so that he might have had very pleasant company if he had only been a good boy. But I am sorry to say, he was too like some other little boys, very fond of hunting and tormenting creatures for mere sport. Some people say that boys cannot help it; that it is nature, and only a proof that we are all originally descended from beasts of prey. But whether it is nature or not, little boys can help it, and must help it. For if they have naughty, low, mischievous tricks in their nature, as monkeys have, that is no reason why they should give way to those tricks like monkeys, who know no better. And therefore they must not torment dumb creatures; for if they do, a certain old lady who is coming will surely give them exactly what they deserve.

But Tom did not know that; and he pecked and howked the poor water things about sadly, till they were all afraid of him, and got out of his way, or crept into their shells; so he had no one to speak to or play with.

The water-fairies, of course, were very sorry to see him so unhappy, and longed to take him, and tell him how naughty he was, and teach him to be good, and to play and romp with him too: but they had been forbidden to do that. Tom had to learn his lesson for himself by sound and sharp experience, as many another foolish person has to do, though there may be many a kind heart yearning over them all the while, and longing to teach them what they can only teach themselves.

At last one day he found a caddis, and wanted it to peep out of its house: but its house-door was shut. He had never seen a caddis with a house-door before: so what must he do, the meddlesome little fellow, but pull it open, to see what the poor lady was doing inside. What a shame! How should you like to have any one breaking your bedroom-door in, to see how you looked when you were in bed? So Tom broke to pieces the door, which was the prettiest little grating of silk, stuck all over with shining bits of crystal; and when he looked in, the caddis poked out her head, and it had turned into just the shape of a bird's. But when Tom spoke to her she could not answer; for her mouth and face were tight tied up in a new nightcap of neat pink skin. However, if she didn't answer, all the other caddises did; for they held up their hands and shrieked like the cats in Struwel-peter: "Oh, you nasty, horrid boy; there you are at it again! And she had just laid herself up for a fortnight's sleep, and then she would have come out with such beautiful wings, and flown about, and laid such lots of eggs: and now you have broken her door, and she can't mend it because her mouth is tied up for a fortnight, and she will die. Who sent you here to worry us out of our lives?"

So Tom swam away. He was very much ashamed of himself, and felt all the naughtier; as little boys do when they have done wrong, and won't say so.

Then he came to a pool full of little trout, and began tormenting them, and trying to catch them: but they slipt through his fingers, and jumped clean out of water in their fright. But as Tom chased them, he came close to a great dark hover under an alder root, and out floushed a huge old brown trout ten times as big as he was, and ran right against him, and knocked all the breath out of his body; and I don't know which was the more frightened of the two.

Then he went on sulky and lonely, as he deserved to be; and under a bank he saw a very ugly dirty creature sitting, about half as big as himself; which had six legs, and a big stomach, and a most ridiculous head with two great eyes and a face just like a donkey's.

"Oh," said Tom, "you are an ugly fellow to be sure!"

and he began making faces at him; and put his nose close to him, and hallooed at him, like a very rude boy.

When, hey presto! all the thing's donkey-face came off in a moment, and out popped a long arm with a pair of pincers at the end of it, and caught Tom by the nose. It did not hurt him much; but it held him quite tight.

"Yah, ah! Oh, let me go!" cried Tom.

"Then let me go," said the creature. "I want to be quiet. I want to split."

Tom promised to let him alone, and he let go. "Why do you want to split?" said Tom.

"Because my brothers and sisters have all split, and turned into beautiful creatures with wings; and I want to split too. Don't speak to me. I am sure I shall split. I will split!"

Tom stood still, and watched him. And he swelled himself, and puffed, and stretched himself out stiff, and at last—crack, puff, bang—he opened all down his back, and then up to the top of his head.

And out of his inside came the most slender, elegant, soft creature, as soft and smooth as Tom: but very pale and weak, like a little child who has been ill a long time in a dark room. It moved its legs very feebly; and looked about it half ashamed, like a girl when she goes for the first time into a ball-room; and then it began walking slowly up a grass stem to the top of the water.

Tom was so astonished that he never said a word: but he stared with all his eyes. And he went up to the top of the water too, and peeped out to see what would happen.

And as the creature sat in the warm bright sun, a wonderful change came over it. It grew strong and firm; the most lovely colours began to show on its body, blue and yellow and black, spots and bars and rings; out of its back rose four great wings of bright brown gauze; and its eyes grew so large that they filled all its head, and shone like ten thousand diamonds.

"Oh, you beautiful creature!" said Tom; and he put out his hand to catch it.

But the thing whirled up into the air, and hung poised

on its wings a moment, and then settled down again by Tom quite fearless.

"No!" it said, "you cannot catch me. I am a dragon-fly now, the king of all the flies; and I shall dance in the sunshine, and hawk over the river, and catch gnats, and have a beautiful wife like myself. I know what I shall do. Hurrah!" And he flew away into the air, and began catching gnats.

"Oh! come back, come back," cried Tom, "you beautiful creature. I have no one to play with, and I am so lonely here. If you will but come back I will never try to catch you."

"I don't care whether you do or not," said the dragon-fly; "for you can't. But when I have had my dinner, and looked a little about this pretty place, I will come back; and have a little chat about all I have seen in my travels. Why, what a huge tree this is! and what huge leaves on it!"

It was only a big dock: but you know the dragon-fly had never seen any but little water-trees: starwort, and milfoil, and water-crowfoot, and such like; so it did look very big to him. Besides, he was very short-sighted, as all dragon-flies are; and never could see a yard before his nose; any more than a great many other folks, who are not half as handsome as he.

The dragon-fly did come back, and chatted away with Tom. He was a little conceited about his fine colours and his large wings; but you know, he had been a poor dirty ugly creature all his life before; so there were great excuses for him. He was very fond of talking about all the wonderful things he saw in the trees and the meadows; and Tom liked to listen to him, for he had forgotten all about them. So in a little while they became great friends.

And I am very glad to say, that Tom learnt such a lesson that day, that he did not torment creatures for a long time after. And then the caddises grew quite tame, and used to tell him strange stories about the way they built their houses, and changed their skins, and turned at last into winged flies; till Tom began to long to change his skin, and have wings like them some day.

And the trout and he made it up (for trout very soon forget, if they have been frightened and hurt). So Tom used to play with them at hare and hounds, and great fun they had; and he used to try to leap out of the water, head over heels, as they did before a shower came on: but somehow he never could manage it. He liked most, though, to see them rising at the flies, as they sailed round and round under the shadow of the great oak, where the beetles fell flop into the water, and the green caterpillars let themselves down from the boughs by silk ropes for no reason at all; and then changed their foolish minds for no reason at all either; and hauled themselves up again into the tree, rolling up the rope in a ball between their paws; which is a very clever rope-dancer's trick, and neither Blondin nor Leotard could do it: but why they should take so much trouble about it no one can tell; for they cannot get their living, as Blondin and Leotard do, by trying to break their necks on a string.

And very often Tom caught them just as they touched the water; and caught the alder flies, and the caperers, and the cock-tailed duns and spinners, yellow, and brown, and claret, and grey, and gave them to his friends the trout. Perhaps he was not quite kind to the flies; but one must do a good turn to one's friends when one can.

And at last he gave up catching even the flies; for he made acquaintance with one by accident, and found him a very merry little fellow. And this was the way it happened; and it is all quite true.

He was basking at the top of the water one hot day in July, catching duns and feeding the trout, when he saw a new sort, a dark grey little fellow with a brown head. He was a very little fellow indeed: but he made the most of himself, as people ought to do. He cocked up his head, and he cocked up his wings, and he cocked up his tail, and he cocked up the two whisks at his tail-end, and, in short, he looked the cockiest little man of all little men. And so he proved to be; for instead of getting away, he hopped upon Tom's finger, and sat there as bold as nine tailors; and he cried out in the tiniest, shrillest, squeakiest little voice you ever heard.

"Much obliged to you, indeed; but I don't want it yet."

"Want what?" said Tom, quite taken aback by his impudence.

"Your leg, which you are kind enough to hold out for me to sit on. I must just go and see after my wife for a few minutes. Dear me! what a troublesome business a family is!" (though the idle little rogue did nothing at all, but left his poor wife to lay all the eggs by herself.) "When I come back, I shall be glad of it, if you'll be so good as to keep it sticking out just so;" and off he flew.

Tom thought him a very cool sort of personage; and still more so, when in five minutes he came back, and said—"Ah, you were tired waiting? Well, your other leg will do as well."

And he popped himself down on Tom's knee, and began chatting away in his squeaking voice.

"So you live under the water? It's a low place. I lived there for some time; and was very shabby and dirty. But I didn't choose that that should last. So I turned respectable, and came up to the top, and put on this grey suit. It's a very business-like suit, you think, don't you?"

"Very neat and quiet indeed," said Tom.

"Yes, one must be quiet, and neat, and respectable, and all that sort of thing for a little, when one becomes a family man. But I'm tired of it, that's the truth. I've done quite enough business, I consider, in the last week, to last me my life. So I shall put on a ball-dress, and go out and be a smart man, and see the gay world, and have a dance or two. Why shouldn't one be jolly if one can?"

"And what will become of your wife?"

"Oh! she is a very plain stupid creature, and that's the truth; and thinks about nothing but eggs. If she chooses to come, why, she may; and if not, why, I go without her;—and here I go."

And, as he spoke, he turned quite pale, and then quite white.

"Why, you're ill!" said Tom. But he did not answer.

"You're dead," said Tom, looking at him as he stood on his knee as white as a ghost.

"No, I ain't!" answered a little squeaking voice over his head. "This is me up here, in my ball-dress: and that's my skin. Ha, ha! you could not do such a trick as that!"

And no more Tom could, nor Houdin, nor Robin, nor Frikell, nor all the conjurors in the world. For the little rogue had jumped clean out of his own skin, and left it standing on Tom's knee, eyes, wings, legs, tails, exactly as if it had been alive.

"Ha, ha!" he said, and he jerked and skipped up and down, never stopping an instant, just as if he had St. Vitus's dance. "Ain't I a pretty fellow now?"

And so he was; for his body was white, and his tail orange, and his eyes all the colours of a peacock's tail. And what was the oddest of all, the whisks at the end of his tail had grown five times as long as they were before.

"Ah!" said he, "now I will see the gay world. My living won't cost me much, for I have no mouth, you see, and no inside; so I can never be hungry, nor have the stomach-ache neither."

No more he had. He had grown as dry and hard and empty as a quill, as such silly shallow-hearted fellows deserve to grow.

But, instead of being ashamed of his emptiness, he was quite proud of it, as a good many fine gentlemen are, and began flirting and flipping up and down, and singing—

> " My wife shall dance, and I shall sing,
>   So merrily pass the day;
> For I hold it one of the wisest things,
>   To drive dull care away."

And he danced up and down for three days and three nights, till he grew so tired, that he tumbled

into the water, and floated down. But what became of
him Tom never knew, and he himself never minded;
for Tom heard him singing to the last, as he floated
down—

" To drive dull care away-ay-ay ! "

And if he did not care, why nobody else cared
either.

But one day Tom had a new adventure. He was
sitting on a water-lily leaf, he and his friend the dragon-
fly, watching the gnats dance. The dragon-fly had
eaten as many as he wanted, and was sitting quite still
and sleepy, for it was very hot and bright. The gnats
(who did not care the least for their poor brothers'
death), danced a foot over his head quite happily, and
a large black fly settled within an inch of his nose,
and began washing his own face and combing his hair
with his paws : but the dragon-fly never stirred, and
kept on chatting to Tom about the times when he lived
under the water.

Suddenly, Tom heard the strangest noise up the
stream ; cooing, and grunting, and whining, and squeaking, as if you had put into a bag two stock-doves,
nine mice, three guinea-pigs, and a blind puppy, and
left them there to settle themselves and make music.

He looked up the water, and there he saw a sight
as strange as the noise ; a great ball rolling over and
over down the stream, seeming one moment of soft
brown fur, and the next of shining glass : and yet it
was not a ball ; for sometimes it broke up and streamed
away in pieces, and then it joined again ; and all the
while the noise came out of it louder and louder.

Tom asked the dragon-fly what it could be : but, of
course, with his short sight, he could not even see it,
though it was not ten yards away. So he took the
neatest little header into the water, and started off to
see for himself ; and, when he came near, the ball
turned out to be four or five beautiful creatures, many
times larger than Tom, who were swimming about, and
rolling, and diving, and twisting, and wrestling, and

cuddling, and kissing, and biting, and scratching, in the most charming fashion that ever was seen. And if you don't believe me, you may go to the Zoological Gardens (for I am afraid that you won't see it nearer, unless, perhaps, you get up at five in the morning, and go down to Cordery's Moor, and watch by the great withy pollard which hangs over the backwater, where the otters breed sometimes), and then say, if otters at play in the water are not the merriest, lithest, gracefullest creatures you ever saw.

But, when the biggest of them saw Tom, she darted out from the rest, and cried in the water-language sharply enough, "Quick, children, here is something to eat, indeed!" and came at poor Tom, showing such a wicked pair of eyes, and such a set of sharp teeth in a grinning mouth, that Tom, who had thought her very handsome, said to himself, Handsome is that handsome does, and slipt in between the water-lily roots as fast as he could, and then turned round and made faces at her.

"Come out," said the wicked old otter, "or it will be worse for you."

But Tom looked at her from between two thick roots, and shook them with all his might, making horrible faces all the while, just as he used to grin through the railings at the old women, when he lived before. It was not quite well-bred, no doubt; but you know, Tom had not finished his education yet.

"Come away, children," said the otter in disgust, "it is not worth eating, after all. It is only a nasty eft, which nothing eats, not even those vulgar pike in the pond."

"I am not an eft!" said Tom; "efts have tails."

"You are an eft," said the otter, very positively; "I see your two hands quite plain, and I know you have a tail."

"I tell you I have not," said Tom. "Look here!" and he turned his pretty little self quite round; and, sure enough, he had no more tail than you.

The otter might have got out of it by saying that

Tom was a frog: but, like a great many other people, when she had once said a thing, she stood to it, right or wrong; so she answered:

"I say you are an eft, and therefore you are, and not fit food for gentlefolk like me and my children. You may stay there till the salmon eat you" (she knew the salmon would not, but she wanted to frighten poor Tom). "Ha! ha! they will eat you, and we will eat them;" and the otter laughed such a wicked cruel laugh—as you may hear them do sometimes; and the first time that you hear it you will probably think it is bogies.

"What are salmon?" asked Tom.

"Fish, you eft, great fish, nice fish to eat. They are the lords of the fish, and we are the lords of the salmon;" and she laughed again. "We hunt them up and down the pools, and drive them up into a corner, the silly things; they are so proud, and bully the little trout, and the minnows, till they see us coming, and then they are so meek all at once; and we catch them, but we disdain to eat them all; we just bite out their soft throats and suck their sweet juice—Oh, so good!"—(and she licked her wicked lips)—"and then throw them away, and go and catch another. They are coming soon, children, coming soon; I can smell the rain coming up off the sea, and then hurrah for a fresh, and salmon, and plenty of eating all day long."

And the otter grew so proud that she turned head over heels twice, and then stood upright half out of the water, grinning like a Cheshire cat.

"And where do they come from?" asked Tom, who kept himself very close, for he was considerably frightened.

"Out of the sea, eft, the great wide sea, where they might stay and be safe if they liked. But out of the sea the silly things come, into the great river down below, and we come up to watch for them; and when they go down again we go down and follow them. And there we fish for the bass and the pollock, and have jolly days along the shore, and toss and roll in the breakers, and sleep snug in the warm dry crags. Ah, that is a merry life too, children, if it were not for those horrid men."

"What are men?" asked Tom; but somehow he seemed to know before he asked.

"Two-legged things, eft: and, now I come to look at you, they are actually something like you, if you had not a tail" (she was determined that Tom should have a tail), "only a great deal bigger, worse luck for us; and they catch the fish with hooks and lines, which get into our feet sometimes, and set pots along the rocks to catch lobsters. They speared my poor dear husband as he went out to find something for me to eat. I was laid up among the crags then, and we were very low in the world, for the sea was so rough that no fish would come in shore. But they speared him, poor fellow, and I saw them carrying him away upon a pole. Ah, he lost his life for your sakes, my children, poor dear obedient creature that he was."

And the otter grew so sentimental (for otters can be very sentimental when they choose, like a good many people who are both cruel and greedy, and no good to anybody at all) that she sailed solemnly away down the burn, and Tom saw her no more for that time. And lucky it was for her that she did so; for no sooner was she gone, than down the bank came seven little rough terrier dogs, snuffing and yapping, and grubbing and splashing, in full cry after the otter. Tom hid among the water-lilies till they were gone; for he could not guess that they were the water-fairies come to help him.

But *He* could not help thinking of what the otter had said about the great river and the broad sea. And, as he thought, he longed to go and see them. He could not tell why; but the more he thought, the more he grew discontented with the narrow little stream in which he lived, and all his companions there; and wanted to get out into the wide wide world, and enjoy all the wonderful sights of which he was sure it was full.

And once he set off to go down the stream. But the stream was very low; and when he came to the shallows he could not keep under water, for there was no water left to keep under. So the sun burnt his back and made him sick; and he went back again and lay quiet in the pool for a whole week more.

And then, on the evening of a very hot day, he saw a sight.

He had been very stupid all day, and so had the trout; for they would not move an inch to take a fly, though there were thousands on the water, but lay dozing at the bottom under the shade of the stones; and Tom lay dozing too, and was glad to cuddle their smooth cool sides, for the water was quite warm and unpleasant.

But toward evening it grew suddenly dark, and Tom looked up and saw a blanket of black clouds lying right across the valley above his head, resting on the crags right and left. He felt not quite frightened, but very still; for everything was still. There was not a whisper of wind, nor a chirp of a bird to be heard; and next a few great drops of rain fell plop into the water, and one hit Tom on the nose and made him pop his head down quickly enough.

And then the thunder roared, and the lightning flashed, and leapt across Vendale and back again, from cloud to cloud, and cliff to cliff, till the very rocks in the stream seemed to shake; and Tom looked up at it through the water, and thought it the finest thing he ever saw in his life.

But out of the water he dared not put his head; for the rain came down by bucketsful, and the hail hammered like shot on the stream, and churned it into foam; and soon the stream rose, and rushed down, higher and higher, and fouler and fouler, full of beetles, and sticks, and straws, and worms, and addle-eggs, and wood-lice, and leeches, and odds and ends, and omniumgatherums, and this, that, and the other, enough to fill nine museums.

Tom could hardly stand against the stream, and hid

behind a rock. But the trout did not; for out they rushed from among the stones, and began gobbling the beetles and leeches in the most greedy and quarrelsome way, and swimming about with great worms hanging out of their mouths, tugging and kicking to get them away from each other.

And now, by the flashes of the lightning, Tom saw a new sight—all the bottom of the stream alive with great eels, turning and twisting along, all down stream and away. They had been hiding for weeks past in the cracks of the rocks, and in burrows in the mud; and Tom had hardly ever seen them, except now and then at night: but now they were all out, and went hurrying past him so fiercely and wildly that he was quite frightened. And as they hurried past he could hear them say to each other, " We must run, we must run. What a jolly thunderstorm! Down to the sea, down to the sea!"

And then the otter came by with all her brood, twining and sweeping along as fast as the eels themselves; and she spied Tom as she came by, and said :—

" Now is your time, eft, if you want to see the world. Come along, children, never mind those nasty eels : we shall breakfast on salmon to-morrow. Down to the sea, down to the sea!"

Then came a flash brighter than all the rest, and by the light of it—in the thousandth part of a second they were gone again—but he had seen them, he was certain of it—Three beautiful little white girls, with their arms twined round each other's necks, floating down the torrent, as they sang, " Down to the sea, down to the sea!"

" Oh stay! Wait for me!" cried Tom ; but they were gone : yet he could hear their voices clear and sweet through the roar of thunder and water and wind, singing as they died away, " Down to the sea!"

" Down to the sea?" said Tom ; "everything is going to the sea, and I will go too. Good-bye, trout." But the trout were so busy gobbling worms that they never turned to answer him ; so that Tom was spared the pain of bidding them farewell.

And now, down the rushing stream, guided by the bright flashes of the storm ; past tall birch-fringed rocks, which shone out one moment as clear as day, and the next were dark as night ; past dark hovers under swirling banks, from which great trout rushed out on Tom, thinking him to be good to eat, and turned back sulkily, for the fairies sent them home again with a tremendous scolding, for daring to meddle with a water-baby ; on through narrow strids and roaring cataracts, where Tom was deafened and blinded for a moment by the rushing waters ; along deep reaches, where the white water-lilies tossed and flapped beneath the wind and hail ; past sleeping villages ; under dark bridge-arches, and away and away to the sea.   And Tom could not stop, and did not care to stop ; he would see the great world below, and the salmon, and the breakers, and the wide, wide sea.

And when the daylight came, Tom found himself out in the salmon river.

And what sort of a river was it ?   Was it like an Irish stream, winding through the brown bogs, where the wild ducks squatter up from among the white water-lilies, and the curlews flit to and fro, crying " Tullie-wheep, mind your sheep " ; and Dennis tells you strange stories of the Peishtamore, the great bogy-snake which lies in the black peat pools, among the old pine stems, and puts his head out at night to snap at the cattle as they come down to drink ?—But you must not believe all that Dennis tells you, mind ; for if you ask him,

" Is there a salmon here, do you think, Dennis ? "

" Is it salmon, thin, your honour manes ?   Salmon ? Cartloads it is of thim, thin, an' ridgmens, shouldthering ache other out of water, av' ye'd but the luck to see thim."

Then you fish the pool all over, and never get a rise.

" But there can't be a salmon here, Dennis ! and, if you'll but think, if one had come up last tide, he'd be gone to the higher pools by now."

" Shure thin, and your honour's the thrue fisherman, and understands it all like a book.   Why, ye spake as if ye'd known the wather a thousand years !   As I said, how could there be a fish here at all, just now ? "

"But you said just now they were shouldering each other out of water?"

And then Dennis will look up at you with his handsome, sly, soft, sleepy, good-natured, untrustable, Irish grey eye, and answer with the prettiest smile:

"Shure, and didn't I think your honour would like a pleasant answer?"

So you must not trust Dennis, because he is in the habit of giving pleasant answers: but, instead of being angry with him, you must remember that he is a poor Paddy, and knows no better; so you must just burst out laughing; and then he will burst out laughing too, and slave for you, and trot about after you, and show you good sport if he can—for he is an affectionate fellow, and as fond of sport as you are—and if he can't, tell you fibs instead, a hundred an hour; and wonder all the while why poor ould Ireland does not prosper like England and Scotland, and some other places, where folk have taken up a ridiculous fancy that honesty is the best policy.

Or was it like a Welsh salmon river, which is remarkable chiefly (at least, till this last year) for containing no salmon, as they have been all poached out by the enlightened peasantry, to prevent the Cythrawl Sassenach (which means you, my little dear, your kith and kin, and signifies much the same as the Chinese Fan Quei) from coming bothering into Wales, with good tackle, and ready money, and civilisation, and common honesty, and other like things of which the Cymry stand in no need whatsoever?

Or was it such a salmon stream as I trust you will see among the Hampshire water-meadows before your hairs are grey, under the wise new fishing laws?—when Winchester apprentices shall covenant, as they did three hundred years ago, not to be made to eat salmon more than three days a week; and fresh-run fish shall be as plentiful under Salisbury spire as they are in Hollyhole at Christchurch; in the good time coming, when folks shall see that, of all Heaven's gifts of food, the one to be protected most carefully is that worthy gentleman salmon, who is generous enough to go down to the sea weighing five ounces, and to come back next year weighing five pounds, without having cost the soil or the state one farthing?

Or was it like a Scotch stream, such as Arthur Clough drew in his "Bothie":—

> "Where over a ledge of granite
> Into a granite bason the amber torrent descended. . . .
> Beautiful there for the colour derived from green rocks under;
> Beautiful most of all, where beads of foam uprising
> Mingle their clouds of white with the delicate hue of the stillness. . . .
> Cliff over cliff for its sides, with rowan and pendant birch boughs.". . .

Ah, my little man, when you are a big man, and fish such a stream as that, you will hardly care, I think, whether she be roaring down in full spate, like coffee covered with scald cream, while the fish are swirling at your fly as an oar-blade swirls in a boat-race, or flashing up the cataract like silver arrows, out of the fiercest of the foam; or whether the fall be dwindled to a single thread, and the shingle below be as white and dusty as a turnpike road, while the salmon huddle together in one dark cloud in the clear amber pool, sleeping away their time till the rain creeps back again off the sea. You will not care much, if you have eyes and brains; for you will lay down your rod contentedly, and drink in at your eyes the beauty of that glorious place; and listen to the water-ouzel piping on the stones, and watch the yellow roes come down to drink, and look up at you with their great soft trustful eyes, as much as to say, "You could not have the heart to shoot at us?" And then, if you have sense, you will turn and talk to the great giant of a gilly who lies basking on the stone beside you. He will tell you no fibs, my little man; for he is a Scotchman, and fears God, and not the priest; and, as you talk with him, you will be surprised more and more at his knowledge, his sense, his humour, his courtesy; and you will find out—unless you have found it out before—that a man may learn from his Bible to be a more thorough gentleman than if he had been brought up in all the drawing-rooms in London.

No. It was none of these, the salmon stream at Harthover. It was such a stream as you see in dear old Bewick ; Bewick, who was born and bred upon them. A full hundred yards broad it was, sliding on from broad pool to broad shallow, and broad shallow to broad pool, over great fields of shingle, under oak and ash coverts, past low cliffs of sandstone, past green meadows, and fair parks, and a great house of grey stone, and brown moors above, and here and there against the sky the smoking chimney of a colliery. You must look at Bewick to see just what it was like, for he has drawn it a hundred times with the care and the love of a true north countryman ; and, even if you do not care about the salmon river, you ought, like all good boys, to know your Bewick.

At least, so old Sir John used to say, and very sensibly he put it too, as he was wont to do—

"If they want to describe a finished young gentleman in France, I hear, they say of him, ' Il sait son Rabelais.' But if I want to describe one in England, I say, ' He knows his Bewick.' And I think that is the higher compliment."

But Tom thought nothing about what the river was like. All his fancy was, to get down to the wide wide sea.

And after a while he came to a place where the river spread out into broad still shallow reaches, so wide that little Tom, as he put his head out of the water, could hardly see across.

And there he stopped. He got a little frightened. "This must be the sea," he thought. "What a wide place it is. If I go on into it I shall surely lose my way, or some strange thing will bite me. I will stop here and look out for the otter, or the eels, or some one to tell me where I shall go."

So he went back a little way, and crept into a crack of the rock, just where the river opened out into the wide shallows, and watched for some one to tell him his way : but the otter and the eels were gone on miles and miles down the stream.

There he waited, and slept too, for he was quite tired

with his night's journey; and, when he woke, the stream was clearing to a beautiful amber hue, though it was still very high. And after a while he saw a sight which made him jump up; for he knew in a moment it was one of the things which he had come to look for.

Such a fish! ten times as big as the biggest trout, and a hundred times as big as Tom, sculling up the stream past him, as easily as Tom had sculled down.

Such a fish! shining silver from head to tail, and here and there a crimson dot; with a grand hooked nose, and grand curling lip, and a grand bright eye, looking round him as proudly as a king, and surveying the water right and left as if it all belonged to him. Surely he must be the salmon, the king of all the fish.

Tom was so frightened that he longed to creep into a hole; but he need not have been; for salmon are all true gentlemen, and, like true gentlemen, they look noble and proud enough, and yet, like true gentlemen, they never harm or quarrel with any one, but go about their own business, and leave rude fellows to themselves.

The salmon looked him full in the face, and then went on without minding him, with a swish or two of his tail which made the stream boil again. And in a few minutes came another, and then four or five, and so on; and all passed Tom, rushing and plunging up the cataract with strong strokes of their silver tails, now and then leaping clean out of water and up over a rock, shining gloriously for a moment in the bright sun; while Tom was so delighted that he could have watched them all day long.

And at last one came up bigger than all the rest; but he came slowly, and stopped, and looked back, and seemed very anxious and busy. And Tom saw that he was helping another salmon, an especially handsome one, who had not a single spot upon it, but was clothed in pure silver from nose to tail.

" My dear," said the great fish to his companion, " you really look dreadfully tired, and you must not over-exert yourself at first. Do rest yourself behind this rock;"

and he shoved her gently with his nose, to the rock where Tom sat.

You must know that this was the salmon's wife. For salmon, like other true gentlemen, always choose their lady, and love her, and are true to her, and take care of her, and work for her, and fight for her, as every true gentleman ought; and are not like vulgar chub and roach and pike, who have no high feelings, and take no care of their wives.

Then he saw Tom, and looked at him very fiercely one moment, as if he was going to bite him.

"What do you want here?" he said, very fiercely.

"Oh, don't hurt me!" cried Tom. "I only want to look at you; you are so handsome."

"Ah?" said the salmon, very stately but very civilly. "I really beg your pardon; I see what you are, my little dear. I have met one or two creatures like you before, and found them very agreeable and well-behaved. Indeed, one of them showed me a great kindness lately, which I hope to be able to repay. I hope we shall not be in your way here. As soon as this lady is rested, we shall proceed on our journey."

What a well-bred old salmon he was!

"So you have seen things like me before?" asked Tom.

"Several times, my dear. Indeed, it was only last night that one at the river's mouth came and warned me and my wife of some new stake-nets which had got into the stream, I cannot tell how, since last winter, and showed us the way round them, in the most charmingly obliging way."

"So there are babies in the sea?" cried Tom, and clapped his little hands. "Then I shall have some one to play with there? How delightful!"

"Were there no babies up this stream?" asked the lady salmon.

"No; and I grew so lonely. I thought I saw three last night: but they were gone in an instant, down to the sea. So I went too; for I had nothing to play with but caddises and dragon-flies and trout."

"Ugh!" cried the lady, "what low company!"

"My dear, if he has been in low company, he has certainly not learnt their low manners," said the salmon.

"No, indeed, poor little dear: but how sad for him to live among such people as caddises, who have actually six legs, the nasty things; and dragon-flies, too! why they are not even good to eat; for I tried them once, and they are all hard and empty; and, as for trout, every one knows what they are." Whereon she curled up her lip, and looked dreadfully scornful, while her husband curled up his too, till he looked as proud as Alcibiades.

"Why do you dislike the trout so?" asked Tom.

"My dear, we do not even mention them, if we can help it; for I am sorry to say they are relations of ours who do us no credit. A great many years ago they were just like us; but they were so lazy, and cowardly, and greedy, that instead of going down to the sea every year to see the world and grow strong and fat, they chose to stay and poke about in the little streams and eat worms and grubs: and they are very properly punished for it; for they have grown ugly and brown and spotted and small; and are actually so degraded in their tastes, that they will eat our children."

"And then they pretend to scrape acquaintance with us again," said the lady. "Why, I have actually known one of them propose to a lady salmon, the little impudent little creature."

"I should hope," said the gentleman, "that there are very few ladies of our race who would degrade themselves by listening to such a creature for an instant. If I saw such a thing happen, I should consider it my duty to put them both to death upon the spot." So the old salmon said, like an old blue-blooded hidalgo of Spain: and what is more, he would have done it too. For you must know, no enemies are so bitter against each other as those who are of the same race; and a salmon looks on a trout, as some great folks look on some little folks, as something just too much like himself to be tolerated.

CHAPTER IV

" Sweet is the lore which Nature brings ;
Our meddling intellect
Mis-shapes the beauteous forms of things
We murder to dissect.

Enough of science and of art :
Close up these barren leaves ;
Come forth, and bring with you a heart
That watches and receives."

—WORDSWORTH.

CHAPTER IV

SO the salmon went up, after Tom had warned them of the wicked old otter; and Tom went down, but slowly and cautiously, coasting along the shore. He was many days about it, for it was many miles down to the sea; and perhaps he would never have found his way, if the fairies had not guided him, without his seeing their fair faces, or feeling their gentle hands.

And, as he went, he had a very strange adventure. It was a clear still September night, and the moon shone so brightly down through the water, that he could not sleep, though he shut his eyes as tight as possible. So at last he came up to the top, and sat upon a little point of rock, and looked up at the broad yellow moon, and wondered what she was, and thought that she looked at him. And he watched the moonlight on the rippling river, and the black heads of the firs, and the silver-frosted lawns, and listened to the owl's hoot, and the snipe's bleat, and the fox's bark, and the otter's laugh; and smelt the soft perfume of the birches, and the wafts of heather honey off the grouse-moor far above; and felt very happy, though he could not well tell why. You, of course, would have been very cold sitting there on a September night, without the least bit of clothes on your wet back; but Tom was a water-baby, and therefore felt cold no more than a fish.

Suddenly, he saw a beautiful sight. A bright red light moved along the river side, and threw down into

the water a long tap-root of flame. Tom, curious little
rogue that he was, must needs go and see what it was ;
so he swam to the shore, and met the light as it stopped
over a shallow run at the edge of a low rock.

And there, underneath the light, lay five or six great
salmon, looking up at the flame with their great goggle
eyes, and wagging their tails, as if they were very much
pleased at it.

Tom came to the top, to look at this wonderful light
nearer, and made a splash.

And he heard a voice say :—

" There was a fish rose."

He did not know what the words meant : but he
seemed to know the sound of them, and to know the
voice which spoke them ; and he saw on the bank three
great two-legged creatures, one of whom held the light,
flaring and sputtering, and another a long pole. And
he knew that they were men, and was frightened, and
crept into a hole in the rock, from which he could see
what went on.

The man with the torch bent down over the water,
and looked earnestly in ; and then he said :

" Tak that muckle fellow, lad ; he's ower fifteen
punds ; and haud your hand steady."

Tom felt that there was some danger coming, and
longed to warn the foolish salmon, who kept staring up
at the light as if he was bewitched. But, before he
could make up his mind, down came the pole through
the water ; there was a fearful splash and struggle, and
Tom saw that the poor salmon was speared right through,
and was lifted out of the water.

And then, from behind, there sprung on these three
men three other men ; and there were shouts, and blows,
and words which Tom recollected to have heard before ;
and he shuddered and turned sick at them now, for
he felt somehow that they were strange, and ugly, and
wrong, and horrible. And it all began to come back to
him. They were men ; and they were fighting ; savage,
desperate, up-and-down fighting, such as Tom had seen
too many times before.

And he stopped his little ears, and longed to swim away; and was very glad that he was a water-baby, and had nothing to do any more with horrid dirty men, with foul clothes on their backs, and foul words on their lips: but he dared not stir out of his hole; while the rock shook over his head with the trampling and struggling of the keepers and the poachers.

All of a sudden there was a tremendous splash, and a frightful flash, and a hissing, and all was still.

For into the water, close to Tom, fell one of the men; he who held the light in his hand. Into the swift river he sank, and rolled over and over in the current. Tom heard the men above run along, seemingly looking for him: but he drifted down into the deep hole below, and there lay quite still, and they could not find him.

Tom waited a long time, till all was quiet; and then he peeped out, and saw the man lying. At last he screwed up his courage, and swam down to him. "Perhaps," he thought, "the water has made him fall asleep, as it did me."

Then he went nearer. He grew more and more curious, he could not tell why. He must go and look at him. He would go very quietly, of course; so he swam round and round him, closer and closer; and, as he did not stir, at last he came quite close and looked him in the face.

The moon shone so bright that Tom could see every feature; and, as he saw, he recollected, bit by bit. It was his old master, Grimes.

Tom turned tail, and swam away as fast as he could.

"Oh dear me!" he thought, "now he will turn into a water-baby. What a nasty troublesome one he will be! And perhaps he will find me out, and beat me again."

So he went up the river again a little way, and lay there the rest of the night under an alder root; but, when morning came, he longed to go down again to the big pool, and see whether Mr. Grimes had turned into a water-baby yet.

So he went very carefully, peeping round all the rocks, and hiding under all the roots. Mr. Grimes lay there

still; he had not turned into a water-baby. In the
afternoon Tom went back again. He could not rest
till he had found out what had become of Mr. Grimes.
But this time Mr. Grimes was gone; and Tom made up
his mind that he was turned into a water-baby.

He might have made himself easy, poor little man;
Mr. Grimes did not turn into a water-baby, or anything like one at all. But he did not make himself
easy; and a long time he was fearful lest he should meet
Grimes suddenly in some deep pool. He could not
know that the fairies had carried him away, and put
him, where they put everything which falls into the
water, exactly where it ought to be. But, do you know,
what had happened to Mr. Grimes had such an effect
on him, that he never poached salmon any more. And
it is quite certain that, when a man becomes a con-
firmed poacher, the only way to cure him is to put him
under water for twenty-four hours, like Grimes. So,
when you grow to be a big man, do you behave as all
honest fellows should; and never touch a fish or a head
of game which belongs to another man without his express leave; and then people will call you a gentleman,
and treat you like one; and perhaps give you good
sport: instead of hitting you into the river, or calling
you a poaching snob.

Then Tom went on down, for he was afraid of staying
near Grimes; and as he went, all the vale looked sad.
The red and yellow leaves showered down into the river;
the flies and beetles were all dead and gone; the chill
autumn fog lay low upon the hills, and sometimes spread
itself so thickly on the river, that he could not see his way.
But he felt his way instead, following the flow of the
stream, day after day, past great bridges, past boats and
barges, past the great town, with its wharfs, and mills,
and tall smoking chimneys, and ships which rode at
anchor in the stream; and now and then he ran against
their hawsers, and wondered what they were, and peeped
out, and saw the sailors lounging on board, smoking their
pipes; and ducked under again, for he was terribly afraid
of being caught by man and turned into a chimney-sweep

once more. He did not know that the fairies were close
to him always, shutting the sailors' eyes lest they should
see him, and turning him aside from millraces, and sewer-
mouths, and all foul and dangerous things. Poor little
fellow, it was a dreary journey for him; and more than
once he longed to be back in Vendale, playing with the
trout in the bright summer sun. But it could not be.
What has been once can never come over again. And
people can be little babies, even water-babies, only once
in their lives.

Besides, people who make up their minds to go and
see the world, as Tom did, must needs find it a weary
journey. Lucky for them if they do not lose heart and
stop half way, instead of going on bravely to the end as
Tom did. For then they will remain neither boys nor
men, neither fish, flesh, nor good red herring; having
learnt a great deal too much, and yet not enough; and
sown their wild oats, without having the advantage of
reaping them.

But Tom was always a brave, determined little English
bull-dog, who never knew when he was beaten; and on
and on he held, till he saw a long way off the red buoy
through the fog. And then he found, to his surprise, the
stream turned round, and running up inland.

It was the tide, of course: but Tom knew nothing of
the tide. He only knew that in a minute more the water,
which had been fresh, turned salt all round him. And
then there came a change over him. He felt as strong,
and light, and fresh, as if his veins had run champagne;
and gave, he did not know why, three skips out of the
water, a yard high, and head over heels, just as the salmon
do when they first touch the noble rich salt water, which,
as some wise men tell us, is the mother of all living
things.

He did not care now for the tide being against him.
The red buoy was in sight, dancing in the open sea; and
to the buoy he would go, and to it he went. He passed
great shoals of bass and mullet, leaping and rushing in
after the shrimps, but he never heeded them, or they him;
and once he passed a great black shinning seal, who was

coming in after the mullet. The seal put his head and shoulders out of water, and stared at him, looking exactly like a fat old greasy negro with a grey pate. And Tom, instead of being frightened, said, "How d'ye do, sir; what a beautiful place the sea is!" And the old seal, instead of trying to bite him, looked at him with his soft sleepy winking eyes, and said, "Good tide to you, my little man; are you looking for your brothers and sisters? I passed them all at play outside."

"Oh, then," said Tom, "I shall have playfellows at last!" and he swam on to the buoy, and got upon it (for he was quite out of breath) and sat there, and looked round for water-babies : but there were none to be seen.

The sea-breeze came in freshly with the tide, and blew the fog away; and the little waves danced for joy around the buoy, and the old buoy danced with them. The shadows of the clouds ran races over the bright blue bay, and yet never caught each other up; and the breakers plunged merrily upon the wide white sands, and jumped up over the rocks, to see what the green fields inside were like, and tumbled down and broke themselves all to pieces, and never minded it a bit, but mended themselves and jumped up again. And the terns hovered over Tom like huge white dragon-flies with black heads, and the gulls laughed like girls at play, and the sea-pies, with their red bills and legs, flew to and fro from shore to shore, and whistled sweet and wild. And Tom looked and looked, and listened; and he would have been very happy, if he could only have seen the water-babies. Then, when the tide turned, he left the buoy, and swam round and round in search of them : but in vain. Sometimes he thought he heard them laughing : but it was only the laughter of the ripples. And sometimes he thought he saw them at the bottom : but it was only white and pink shells. And once he was sure he had found one, for he saw two bright eyes peeping out of the sand. So he dived down, and began scraping the sand away, and cried, "Don't hide; I do want some one to play with so much!" And out jumped a great turbot, with his ugly eyes and mouth all awry, and flopped away along the bottom, knocking poor Tom over. And he sat down at the bottom of the sea, and cried salt tears from sheer disappointment.

To have come all this way, and faced so many dangers, and yet to find no water-babies! How hard! Well, it did seem hard: but people, even little babies, cannot have all they want without waiting for it, and working for it too, my little man, as you will find out some day.

And Tom sat upon the buoy long days, long weeks, looking out to sea, and wondering when the water-babies would come back; and yet they never came.

Then he began to ask all the strange things which came in out of the sea if they had seen any; and some said "Yes," and some said nothing at all.

He asked the bass and the pollock; but they were so greedy after the shrimps that they did not care to answer him a word.

Then there came in a whole fleet of purple sea-snails, floating along each on a sponge full of foam, and Tom said, "Where do you come from, you pretty creatures? and have you seen the water-babies?"

And the sea-snails answered, "Whence we come we know not; and whither we are going, who can tell? We float out our little life in the mid-ocean, with the warm sunshine above our heads, and the warm gulf stream below; and that is enough for us. Yes, perhaps we have seen the water-babies. We have seen many strange things as we sailed along." And they floated away, the happy stupid things, and all went ashore upon the sands.

Then there came in a great lazy sunfish, as big as a fat pig cut in half; and he seemed to have been cut in half too, and squeezed in a clothes-press till he was flat; but to all his big body and big fins he had only a little rabbit's mouth, no bigger than Tom's; and, when Tom questioned him, he answered in a little squeaky, feeble voice:

"I'm sure I don't know, I've lost my way. I meant to go to the Chesapeake, and I'm afraid I've got wrong, somehow. Dear me! it was all by following that pleasant warm water. I'm sure I've lost my way."

And, when Tom asked him again, he could only answer, "I've lost my way. Don't talk to me, I want to think."

But, like a good many other people, the more he tried to think the less he could think; and Tom saw him blundering about all day, till the coast-guardsmen saw his big fin above the water, and rowed out, and struck a boat-hook into him, and took him away. They took him up to the town and showed him for a penny a head, and made a good day's work of it. But of course Tom did not know that.

Then there came by a shoal of porpoises, rolling as they went—papas, and mammas, and little children— and all quite smooth and shiny, because the fairies French-polish them every morning; and they sighed so softly as they came by, that Tom took courage to speak to them: but all they answered was, "Hush hush, hush"; for that was all they had learnt to say.

And then there came a shoal of basking sharks, some of them as long as a boat, and Tom was frightened at them. But they were very lazy, good-natured fellows, not greedy tyrants, like white sharks and blue sharks and ground sharks and hammer-heads, who eat men, or saw-fish and threshers and ice-sharks, who hunt the poor old whales. They came and rubbed their great sides against the buoy, and lay basking in the sun with their backfins out of water; and winked at Tom: but he never could get them to speak. They had eaten so many herrings that they were quite stupid; and Tom was glad when a collier brig came by, and frightened them all away; for they did smell most horribly, certainly, and he had to hold his nose tight as long as they were there.

And then there came by a beautiful creature, like a ribbon of pure silver with a sharp head and very long teeth: but seemed very sick and sad. Sometimes it rolled helpless on its side; and then it dashed away glittering like white fire; and then it lay sick again and motionless.

"Where do you come from?" asked Tom. "And why are you so sick and sad?"

"I come from the warm Carolinas, and the sand-banks fringed with pines; where the great owl-rays leap and

flap, like giant bats, upon the tide. But I wandered north and north, upon the treacherous warm gulf stream, till I met with the cold icebergs, afloat in the mid-ocean. So I got tangled among the icebergs, and chilled with their frozen breath. But the water-babies helped me from among them, and set me free again. And now I am mending every day; but I am very sick and sad; and perhaps I shall never get home again to play with the owl-rays any more."

"Oh!" cried Tom. "And you have seen water-babies? Have you seen any near here?"

"Yes; they helped me again last night, or I should have been eaten by a great black porpoise."

How vexatious! The water-babies close to him, and yet he could not find one.

And then he left the buoy, and used to go along the sands and round the rocks, and come out in the night—like the forsaken Merman in Mr. Arnold's beautiful, beautiful poem, which you must learn by heart some day—and sit upon a point of rock, among the shining sea-weeds, in the low October tides, and cry and call for the water-babies: but he never heard a voice call in return. And, at last, with his fretting and crying, he grew quite lean and thin.

But one day among the rocks he found a playfellow. It was not a water-baby, alas! but it was a lobster; and a very distinguished lobster he was; for he had live barnacles on his claws, which is a great mark of distinction in lobsterdom, and no more to be bought for money than a good conscience or the Victoria Cross.

Tom had never seen a lobster before; and he was mightily taken with this one; for he thought him the most curious, odd, ridiculous creature he had ever seen; and there he was not far wrong; for all the ingenious men, and all the scientific men, and all the fanciful men, in the world, with all the old German bogy-painters into the bargain, could never invent, if all their wits were boiled into one, anything so curious, and so ridiculous, as a lobster.

He had one claw knobbed and the other jagged; and

Tom delighted in watching him hold on to the sea-weed with his knobbed claw, while he cut up salads with his jagged one, and then put them in his mouth, after smelling at them, like a monkey. And always the little barnacles threw out their casting nets and swept the water, and came in for their share of whatever there was for dinner.

But Tom was most astonished to see how he fired himself off—snap! like the leap-frogs which you make out of a goose's breast-bone. Certainly he took the most wonderful shots, and backwards, too. For, if he wanted to go into a narrow crack ten yards off, what do you think he did? If he had gone in head foremost, of course he could not have turned round. So he used to turn his tail to it, and lay his long horns, which carry his sixth sense in their tips (and nobody knows what that sixth sense is), straight down his back to guide him, and twist his eyes back till they almost came out of their sockets, and then make ready, present, fire, snap!—and away he went, pop into the hole ; and peeped out and twiddled his whiskers, as much as to say, " You couldn't do that."

Tom asked him about water-babies. " Yes," he said. He had seen them often. But he did not think much of them. They were meddlesome little creatures, that went about helping fish and shells which got into scrapes. Well, for his part, he should be ashamed to be helped by little soft creatures that had not even a shell on their backs. He had lived quite long enough in the world to take care of himself.

He was a conceited fellow, the old lobster, and not very civil to Tom ; and you will hear how he had to alter his mind before he was done, as conceited people generally have. But he was so funny, and Tom so lonely, that he could not quarrel with him ; and they used to sit in holes in the rocks, and chat for hours.

And about this time there happened to Tom a very strange and important adventure—so important, indeed, that he was very near never finding the water-babies at all ; and I am sure you would have been sorry for that.

I hope that you have not forgotten the little white lady all this while. At least, here she comes, looking like a clean white good little darling, as she always was, and always will be. For it befel in the pleasant short December days, when the wind always blows from the south-west, till Old Father Christmas comes and spreads the great white tablecloth, ready for little boys and girls to give the birds their Christmas dinner of crumbs—it befel (to go on) in the pleasant December days, that Sir John was so busy hunting that nobody at home could get a word out of him. Four days a week he hunted, and very good sport he had; and the other two he went to the bench and the board of guardians, and very good justice he did; and, when he got home in time, he dined at five; for he hated this absurd new fashion of dining at eight in the hunting season, which forces a man to make interest with the footman for cold beef and beer as soon as he comes in, and so spoil his appetite, and then sleep in an arm-chair in his bedroom, all stiff and tired, for two or three hours before he can get his dinner like a gentleman. And do you be like Sir John, my dear little man, when you are your own master; and, if you want either to read hard or ride hard, stick to the good old Cambridge hours of breakfast at eight and dinner at five, by which you may get two days' work out of one. But, of course, if you find a fox at three in the afternoon and run him till dark, and leave off twenty miles from home, why you must wait for your dinner till you can get it, as better men than you have done. Only see that, if you go hungry, your horse does not: but give him his warm gruel and beer, and take him gently home, remembering that good horses don't grow on the hedge like blackberries.

It befel (to go on a second time) that Sir John, hunting all day and dining at five, fell asleep every evening, and snored so terribly that all the windows in Harthover shook, and the soot fell down the chimneys. Whereon My Lady, being no more able to get conversation out of him than a song out of a dead nightingale, determined to go off and leave him, and the doctor, and

Captain Swinger the agent, to snore in concert every
evening to their hearts' content. So she started for the
sea-side with all the children, in order to put herself and
them into condition by mild applications of iodine.
She might as well have stayed at home and used Parry's
liquid horse-blister, for there was plenty of it in the
stables; and then she would have saved her money,
and saved the chance, also, of making all the children
ill instead of well (as hundreds are made), by taking
them to some nasty smelling undrained lodging, and
then wondering how they caught scarlatina and diph-
theria : but people won't be wise enough to understand
that till they are all dead of bad smells, and then it will be
too late : besides, you see, Sir John did certainly snore
very loud.

But where she went to nobody must know, for fear
young ladies should begin to fancy that there are water-
babies there ; and so hunt and howk after them (besides
raising the price of lodgings), and keep them in aqua-
riums, as the ladies at Pompeii (as you may see by the
paintings) used to keep Cupids in cages. But nobody
ever heard that they starved the Cupids, or let them
die of dirt and neglect, as English young ladies do by
the poor sea-beasts. So nobody must know where My
Lady went. Letting water-babies die is as bad as taking
singing-birds' eggs ; for, though there are thousands, ay,
millions, of both of them in the world, yet there is not
one too many.

Now it befel that, on the very shore, and over the
very rocks, where Tom was sitting with his friend the
lobster, there walked one day the little white lady, Ellie
herself, and with her a very wise man indeed—Professor
Ptthmllnsprts.

His mother was a Dutchwoman, and therefore he was
born at Curacao (of course you have learnt your geography, and therefore know why); and his father a Pole,
and therefore he was brought up at Petropaulowski (of
course you have learnt your modern politics, and therefore know why) : but for all that he was as thorough an
Englishman as ever coveted his neighbour's goods. And

his name, as I said, was Professor Ptthmllnsprts, which is a very ancient and noble Polish name.

He was, as I said, a very great naturalist, and chief professor of Necrobioneopalæonthydrochthonanthropopithekology in the new university which the king of the Cannibal Islands had founded; and, being a member of the Acclimatisation Society, he had come here to collect all the nasty things which he could find on the coast of England, and turn them loose round the Cannibal Islands, because they had not nasty things enough there to eat what they left.

But he was a very worthy kind good-natured little old gentleman; and very fond of children (for he was not the least a cannibal himself); and very good to all the world as long as it was good to him. Only one fault he had, which cock-robins have likewise, as you may see if you look out of the nursery window—that, when any one else found a curious worm, he would hop round them, and peck them, and set up his tail, and bristle up his feathers, just as a cock-robin would; and declare that he found the worm first; and that it was his worm: and, if not, that then it was not a worm at all.

He had met Sir John at Scarborough, or Fleetwood, or somewhere or other (if you don't care where, nobody else does), and had made acquaintance with him, and become very fond of his children. Now, Sir John knew nothing about sea-cockyolybirds, and cared less, provided the fishmonger sent him good fish for dinner; and My Lady knew as little: but she thought it proper that the children should know something. For in the stupid old times, you must understand, children were taught to know one thing, and to know it well: but in these enlightened new times they are taught to know a little about everything, and to know it all ill; which is a great deal pleasanter and easier, and therefore quite right.

So Ellie and he were walking on the rocks, and he was showing her about one in ten thousand of all the beautiful and curious things which are to be seen there. But little Ellie was not satisfied with them at all. She liked much better to play with live children, or even

with dolls, which she could pretend were alive; and at
last she said honestly, "I don't care about all these
things, because they can't play with me, or talk to me.
If there were little children now in the water, as there
used to be, and I could see them, I should like that."

"Children in the water, you strange little duck?"
said the professor.

"Yes," said Ellie. "I know there used to be children in the water, and mermaids too, and mermen. I
saw them all in a picture at home, of a beautiful lady
sailing in a car drawn by dolphins, and babies flying
round her, and one sitting in her lap; and the mermaids
swimming and playing, and the mermen trumpeting on
conch-shells; and it is called 'The Triumph of Galatea';
and there is a burning mountain in the picture behind.
It hangs on the great staircase, and I have looked at it
ever since I was a baby, and dreamt about it a hundred
times; and it is so beautiful, that it must be true."

Ah, you dear little Ellie, fresh out of heaven! when
will people understand that one of the deepest and
wisest speeches which can come out of a human mouth
is that—"It is so beautiful that it must be true."

Not till they give up believing that Mr. John Locke
(good man and honest though he was) was the wisest
man that ever lived on earth : and recollect that a wiser
man than he lived long before him; and that his name
was Plato the son of Ariston.

But the professor was not in the least of that opinion.
He held very strange theories about a good many things.
He had even got up once at the British Association,
and declared that apes had hippopotamus majors in
their brains just as men have. Which was a shocking
thing to say; for, if it were so, what would become of
the faith, hope, and charity of immortal millions? You
may think that there are other more important differ-
ences between you and an ape, such as being able to
speak, and make machines, and know right from wrong,
and say your prayers, and other little matters of that
kind : but that is a child's fancy, my dear. Nothing is
to be depended on but the great hippopotamus test. If

you have a hippopotamus major in your brain, you are no ape, though you had four hands, no feet, and were more apish than the apes of all aperies. But, if a hippopotamus major is discovered in one single ape's brain, nothing will save your great-great-great-great-great-great-great-great-great-great-great-greater-greatest-grandmother from having been an ape too. No, my dear little man; always remember that the one true, certain, final, and all-important difference between you and an ape is, that you have a hippopotamus major in your brain, and it has none; and that, therefore, to discover one in its brain will be a very wrong and dangerous thing, at which every one will be very much shocked, as we may suppose they were at the professor.—Though really, after all, it don't much matter: because—as Lord Dundreary and others would put it—nobody but men have hippopotamuses in their brains; so, if a hippopotamus was discovered in an ape's brain, why it would not be one, you know, but something else.

But the professor had gone, I am sorry to say, even further than that; for he had read at the British Association at Melbourne, Australia, in the year 1999, a paper, who assured every one who found himself the better or wiser for the news, that there were not, never had been, and could not be, any rational or half-rational beings except men, anywhere, anywhen, or anyhow; that nymphs, satyrs, fauns, inui, dwarfs, trolls, elves, gnomes, fairies, brownies, nixes, wilis, kobolds, leprechaunes, cluricaunes, banshees, will-o'-the-wisps, follets, lutins, magots, goblins, afrits, marids, jinns, ghouls, peris, deevs, angels, archangels, imps, bogies, or worse, were nothing at all, and pure bosh and wind. And he had to get up very early in the morning to prove that, and to eat his breakfast overnight: but he did it, at least to his own satisfaction. Whereon a certain great divine, and a very clever divine was he, called him a regular Sadducee; and probably he was quite right. Whereon the professor, in return, called him a regular Pharisee; and probably he was quite right too. But they did not quarrel in the least; for, when men are men of the world, hard words run off them like water off a duck's back. So the professor and the divine met at dinner that evening, and sat together on the sofa afterwards for an hour, and talked over the state of female labour on the antarctic continent (for nobody talks shop after his claret,) and each vowed that the other was the best company he ever met in his life. What an advantage it is to be men of the world !

From all which you may guess that the professor was not the least of little Ellie's opinion. So he gave her a succinct compendium of his famous paper at the British Association, in a form suited for the youthful mind. But, as we have gone over his arguments against water-babies once already, which is once too often, we will not repeat them here.

Now little Ellie was, I suppose, a stupid little girl ; for, instead of being convinced by Professor Ptthmllnsprts' arguments, she only asked the same question over again.

"But why are there not water-babies ? "

I trust and hope that it was because the professor trod at that moment on the edge of a very sharp mussel, and hurt one of his corns sadly, that he answered quite sharply, forgetting that he was a scientific man, and therefore ought to have known that he couldn't know ; and that he was a logician, and therefore ought to have known that he could not prove an universal negative—I say, I trust and hope it was because the mussel hurt his corn, that the professor answered quite sharply—

"Because there ain't."

Which was not even good English, my dear little boy ; for, as you must know from Aunt Agitate's Arguments, the professor ought to have said, if he was so angry as to say anything of the kind—Because there are not : or are none : or are none of them ; or (if he had been reading Aunt Agitate too), because they do not exist.

And he groped with his net under the weeds so violently, that, as it befel, he caught poor little Tom.

He felt the net very heavy ; and lifted it out quickly, with Tom all entangled in the meshes.

"Dear me !" he cried. "What a large pink Holothurian; with hands, too! It must be connected with Synapta."

And he took him out.

"It has actually eyes!" he cried. "Why, it must be a Cephalopod! This is most extraordinary!"

"No, I ain't!" cried Tom, as loud as he could; for he did not like to be called bad names.

"It is a water-baby!" cried Ellie; and of course it was.

"Water-fiddlesticks, my dear!" said the professor; and he turned away sharply.

There was no denying it. It was a water-baby: and he had said a moment ago that there were none. What was he to do?

He would have liked, of course, to have taken Tom home in a bucket. He would not have put him in spirits. Of course not. He would have kept him alive, and petted him (for he was a very kind old gentleman), and written a book about him, and given him two long names, of which the first would have said a little about Tom, and the second all about himself; for of course he would have called him Hydrotecnon Ptthmllnsprtsianum, or some other long name like that; for they are forced to call everything by long names now, because they have used up all the short ones, ever since they took to making nine species out of one. But—what would all the learned men say to him after his speech at the British Association? And what would Ellie say, after what he had just told her?

There was a wise old heathen once, who said, "Maxima debetur pueris reverentia"—The greatest reverence is due to children; that is, that grown people should never say or do anything wrong before children, lest they should set them a bad example.—Cousin Cramchild says it means, "The greatest respectfulness is expected from little boys." But he was raised in a country where little boys are not expected to be respectful, because all of them are as good as the President :—Well, every one knows his own concerns best; so perhaps they are. But poor Cousin Cramchild, to do him justice, not being of that opinion, and having a moral mission, and being no scholar to speak of, and hard up for an authority—why, it was a very great temptation for him.   But some people, and I am afraid the professor was one of them, interpret that in a more strange, curious, one-sided, left-handed, topsy-turvy, inside-out, behind-before fashion, than even Cousin Cramchild ; for they make it mean, that you must show your respect for children, by never confessing yourself in the wrong to them, even if you know that you are so, lest they should lose confidence in their elders.

Now, if the professor had said to Ellie, " Yes, my darling, it is a water-baby, and a very wonderful thing it is ; and it shows how little I know of the wonders of nature, in spite of forty years' honest labour.   I was just telling you that there could be no such creatures : and, behold ! here is one come to confound my conceit, and show me that Nature can do, and has done, beyond all that man's poor fancy can imagine.   So, let us thank the Maker, and Inspirer, and Lord of Nature for all His wonderful and glorious works, and try and find out something about this one : "—I think that, if the professor had said that, little Ellie would have believed him more firmly, and respected him more deeply, and loved him better, than ever she had done before.   But he was of a different opinion.   He hesitated a moment.   He longed to keep Tom, and yet he half wished he never had caught him ; and, at last, he quite longed to get rid of him.   So he turned away, and poked Tom with his finger, for want of anything better to do ; and said carelessly, " My dear little maid, you must have dreamt of water-babies last night, your head is so full of them."

Now Tom had been in the most horrible and unspeakable fright all the while ; and had kept as quiet as he could, though he was called a Holothurian and a Cephalopod ; for it was fixed in his little head that if a man with clothes on caught him, he might put clothes on him too, and make a dirty black chimney-sweep of him again. But when the professor poked him, it was more than he could bear ; and, between fright and rage, he turned to bay as valiantly as a mouse in a corner, and bit the professor's finger till it bled.

"Oh! ah! yah!" cried he; and glad of an excuse to be rid of Tom, dropped him on to the sea-weed, and thence he dived into the water, and was gone in a moment.

"But it was a water-baby, and I heard it speak!" cried Ellie. "Ah, it is gone!" And she jumped down off the rock to try and catch Tom before he slipt into the sea.

Too late! and what was worse, as she sprang down, she slipped, and fell some six feet, with her head on a sharp rock, and lay quite still.

The professor picked her up, and tried to waken her, and called to her, and cried over her, for he loved her very much: but she would not waken at all. So he took her up in his arms, and carried her to her governess, and they all went home; and little Ellie was put to bed, and lay there quite still; only now and then she woke up, and called out about the water-baby: but no one knew what she meant, and the professor did not tell, for he was ashamed to tell.

And, after a week, one moonlight night, the fairies came flying in at the window, and brought her such a pretty pair of wings, that she could not help putting them on; and she flew with them out of the window, and over the land, and over the sea, and up through the clouds, and nobody heard or saw anything of her for a very long while.

And this is why they say that no one has ever yet seen a water-baby. For my part, I believe that the naturalists get dozens of them when they are out dredging: but they say nothing about them, and throw them overboard again, for fear of spoiling their theories. But, you see the professor was found out, as every one is in due time. A very terrible old fairy found the professor out; she felt his bumps, and cast his nativity, and took the lunars of him carefully inside and out; and so she knew what he would do as well as if she had seen it in a print book, as they say in the dear old west country; and he did it; and so he was found out beforehand, as everybody always is; and the old fairy will find out the naturalists some day, and put them in the *Times;* and then on whose side will the laugh be?

So the old fairy took him in hand very severely there and then. But she says she is always most severe with the best people, because there is most chance of curing them, and therefore they are the patients who pay her best; for she has to work on the same salary as the Emperor of China's physicians (it is a pity that all do not), no cure, no pay.

So she took the poor professor in hand: and because he was not content with things as they are, she filled his head with things as they are not, to try if he would like them better; and because he did not choose to believe in a water-baby when he saw it, she made him believe in worse things than water-babies—in unicorns, firedrakes, manticoras, basilisks, amphisbœnas, griffins, phœnixes, rocs, orcs, dogheaded men, three-headed dogs, three-bodied geryons, and other pleasant creatures, which folks think never existed yet, and which folks hope never will exist, though they know nothing about the matter, and never will; and these creatures so upset, terrified, flustered, aggravated, confused, astounded, horrified, and totally flabbergasted the poor professor, that the doctors said that he was out of his wits for three months; and, perhaps, they were right, as they are now and then.

So all the doctors in the county were called in, to make a report on his case; and of course every one of them flatly contradicted the other: else what use is there in being men of science? But at last the majority agreed on a report, in the true medical language, one half bad Latin, the other half worse Greek, and the rest what might have been English, if they had only learnt to write it. And this is the beginning thereof—

" The subanhypaposupernal anastomoses of peritomic diacellurite in the encephalo digital region of the distin-guished individual of whose symptomatic phænomena we had the melancholy honour (subsequently to a preliminary diagnostic inspection) of making an inspectorial diagnosis, presenting the interexclusively quadrilateral and antino-mian diathesis known as Bumpsterhausen's blue follicles, we proceeded "—

But what they proceeded to do my lady never knew ; for she was so frightened at the long words that she ran for her life, and locked herself into her bedroom, for fear of being squashed by the words and strangled by the sentence. A boa constrictor, she said, was bad company enough ; but what was a boa constrictor made of paving-stones ?

"It was quite shocking! What can they think is the matter with him ?" said she to the old nurse.

"That his wit's just addled ; may be wi' unbelief and heathenry," quoth she.

"Then why can't they say so ?"

And the heaven, and the sea, and the rocks, and the vales re-echoed—"Why indeed?" But the doctors never heard them.

So she made Sir John write to the *Times* to command the Chancellor of the Exchequer for the time being to put a tax on long words ;—

A light tax on words over three syllables, which are necessary evils, like rats : but like them, must be kept down judiciously.

A heavy tax on words over four syllables, as heterodoxy, spontaneity, spiritualism, spuriosity, &c.

And on words over five syllables (of which I hope no one will wish to see any examples), a totally prohibitory tax.

And a similar prohibitory tax on words derived from three or more languages at once ; words derived from two languages having become so common, that there was no more hope of rooting out them than of rooting out peth-winds.

The Chancellor of the Exchequer, being a scholar and a man of sense, jumped at the notion ; for he saw in it the one and only plan for abolishing Schedule D : but when he brought in his bill, most of the Irish members, and (I am sorry to say) some of the Scotch likewise, opposed it most strongly, on the ground that in a free country no man was bound either to understand himself or to let others understand him. So the bill fell through on the first reading ; and the Chancellor, being a philosopher, comforted himself with the thought, that it was not the first time that a woman had hit off a grand idea, and the men turned up their stupid noses thereat.

Now the doctors had it all their own way; and to work they went in earnest, and they gave the poor professor divers and sundry medicines, as prescribed by the ancients and moderns, from Hippocrates to Feuchtersleben, as below, viz. :—

1. Hellebore, to wit—

    Hellebore of Æta.

    Hellebore of Galatia.

    Hellebore of Sicily.

    And all other Hellebores, after the method of the Helleborising Helleborists of the Helleboric era. But that would not do. Bumpsterhausen's blue follicles would not stir an inch out of his encephalo digital region.

2. Trying to find out what was the matter with him; after the method of—

    Hippocrates.

    Aretæus.

    Celsus.

    Cœlius Aurelianus.

    And Galen : but they found that a great deal too much trouble, as most people have since ; and so had recourse to—

3. Borage.

    Cauteries.

    Boring a hole in his head to let out fumes, which (says Gordonius) "will, without doubt, do much good." But it didn't.

    Bezoar stone.

    Diamargaritum.

    A ram's brain boiled in spice.

    Oil of wormwood.

    Water of Nile.

    Capers.

    Good wine (but there was none to be got).

    The water of a smith's forge.

    Hops.

    Ambergris.

Mandrake pillows.

Dormouse' fat.

Hares' ears.

Starvation.

Camphor.

Salts and Senna.

Musk.

Opium.

Strait-waistcoats.

Bullyings.

Bumpings.

Blisterings.

Bleedings.

Bucketings with cold water.

Knockings down.

Kneeling on his chest till they broke it in, &c., &c., after the mediæval or monkish method: but that would not do. Bumpsterhausen's blue follicles stuck there still.

Then—

4. Coaxing.

Kissing.

Champagne and turtle.

Red herrings and soda water.

Good advice.

Gardening.

Croquet.

Musical soirées.

Aunt Sally.

Mild tobacco.

The Saturday Review.

A carriage with outriders, &c., &c., after the modern method. But that would not do.

And if he had but been a convict lunatic, and had shot at the Queen, killed all his creditors to avoid paying them, or indulged in any other little amiable eccentricity of that kind, they would have given him in addition—

The healthiest situation in England, on Easthampstead Plain.

Free run of Windsor Forest.

The Times every morning.

A double-barrelled gun and pointers, and leave to shoot three Wellington College boys a week (not more) in case black game were scarce.

But as he was neither mad enough nor bad enough to be allowed such luxuries, they grew desperate, and fell into bad ways, viz. :—

5. Suffumigations of sulphur.

Heerwiggius his " Incomparable drink for madmen " : only they could not find out what it was.

Suffumigation of the liver of the fish * * * only they had forgotten its name, so Dr. Gray could not well procure them a specimen.

Metallic tractors.

Holloway's Ointment.

Electro-biology.

Valentine Greatrakes his Stroking Cure.

Spirit-rapping.

Holloway's Pills.

Table-turning.

Morrison's Pills.

Homœopathy.

Parr's Life Pills

Mesmerism.

Pure Bosh.

Exorcisms, for which they read Malleus Maleficarum, Nideri Formicarium, Delrio, Wierus, &c., but could not get one that mentioned water-babies.

Hydropathy.

Madame Rachel's Elixir of Youth.

The Poughkeepsie Seer his Prophecies.

The distilled liquor of addle eggs.

Pyropathy, as successfully employed by the old inquisitors to cure the malady of thought, and now by the Persian Mollahs to cure that of rheumatism.

Geopathy, or burying him.

Atmopathy, or steaming him.

Sympathy, after the method of Basil Valentine his Triumph of Antimony, and Kenelm Digby his

Weapon-salve, which some call a hair of the dog that bit him.

Hermopathy, or pouring mercury down his throat, to move the animal spirits.

Meteoropathy, or going up to the moon to look for his lost wits, as Ruggiero did for Orlando Furioso's: only, having no hippogriff, they were forced to use a balloon; and, falling into the North Sea, were picked up by a Yarmouth herring-boat, and came home much the wiser, and all over scales.

Antipathy, or using him like "a man and a brother."

Apathy, or doing nothing at all.

With all other ipathies and opathies which Noodle has invented, and Foodle tried, since black-fellows chipped flints at Abbeville—which is a considerable time ago, to judge by the Great Exhibition.

But nothing would do; for he screamed and cried all day for a water-baby, to come and drive away the monsters; and of course they did not try to find one, because they did not believe in them, and were thinking of nothing but Bumpsterhausen's blue follicles; having, as usual, set the cart before the horse, and taken the effect for the cause.

So they were forced at last to let the poor professor ease his mind by writing a great book, exactly contrary to all his old opinions; in which he proved that the moon was made of green cheese, and that all the mites in it (which you may see sometimes quite plain through a telescope, if you will only keep the lens dirty enough, as Mr. Weekes kept his voltaic battery) are nothing in the world but little babies, who are hatching and swarming up there in millions, ready to come down into this world whenever children want a new little brother or sister.

Which must be a mistake, for this one reason: that, there being no atmosphere round the moon (though some one or other says there is, at least on the other side, and that he has been round at the back of it to see, and found that the moon was just the shape of a Bath bun, and so wet that the man in the moon went about on Midsummer-day in Macintoshes and Cording's boots, spearing eels and sneezing); that therefore, I say, there being no atmosphere, there can be no evaporation; and, therefore, the dew-point can never fall below 71·5 below zero of Fahrenheit; and, therefore, it cannot be cold enough there about four o'clock in the morning to condense the babies' mesenteric apophthegms into their left ventricles; and, therefore, they can never catch the hooping-cough; and if they do not have hooping-cough, they cannot be babies at all; and, therefore, there are no babies in the moon.—Q. E. D.

Which may seem a roundabout reason; and so, perhaps, it is: but you will have heard worse ones in your time, and from better men than you are.

But one thing is certain; that, when the good old doctor got his book written, he felt considerably relieved from Bumpsterhausen's blue follicles, and a few things infinitely worse; to wit, from pride and vain-glory, and from blindness and hardness of heart; which are the true causes of Bumpsterhausen's blue follicles, and of a good many other ugly things beside. Whereon the foul flood-water in his brains ran down, and cleared to a fine coffee colour, such as fish like to rise in, till very fine clean fresh-run fish did begin to rise in his brains; and he caught two or three of them (which is exceedingly fine sport, for brain rivers), and anatomised them carefully, and never mentioned what he found out from them, except to little children; and became ever after a sadder and a wiser man; which is a very good thing to become, my dear little boy, even though one has to pay a heavy price for the blessing.

CHAPTER V

" Stern Lawgiver! yet thou dost wear
The Godhead's most benignant grace;
Nor know we anything so fair
As is the smile upon thy face:
Flowers laugh before thee on their beds;
And fragrance in thy footing treads;
Thou dost preserve the stars from wrong;
And the most ancient Heavens, through Thee are fresh and strong."
—WORDSWORTH, " Ode to Duty."

CHAPTER V

BUT what became of little Tom?

He slipt away off the rocks into the water, as I said before. But he could not help thinking of little Ellie. He did not remember who she was; but he knew that she was a little girl, though she was a hundred times as big as he. This is not surprising: size has nothing to do with kindred. A tiny weed may be first cousin to a great tree; and a little dog like Vick knows that Lioness is a dog too, though she is twenty times larger than herself. So Tom knew that Ellie was a little girl, and thought about her all that day, and longed to have her to play with; but he had very soon to think of something else. And here is the account of what happened to him, as it was published next morning in the Waterproof Gazette, on the finest watered paper, for the use of the great fairy, Mrs. Bedonebyasyoudid, who reads the news very carefully every morning, and especially the police cases, as you will hear very soon.

He was going along the rocks in three-fathom water, watching the pollock catch prawns, and the wrasses nibble barnacles off the rocks, shells and all, when he saw a round cage of green withes; and inside it, looking very much ashamed of himself, sat his friend the lobster, twiddling his horns, instead of thumbs.

"What, have you been naughty, and have they put you in the lock-up?" asked Tom.

The lobster felt a little indignant at such a notion, but he was too much depressed in spirits to argue; so he only said, "I can't get out."

"Why did you get in?"

"After that nasty piece of dead fish." He had thought it looked and smelt very nice when he was outside, and so it did, for a lobster: but now he turned round and abused it because he was angry with himself.

"Where did you get in?"

"Through that round hole at the top."

"Then why don't you get out through it?"

"Because I can't;" and the lobster twiddled his horns more fiercely than ever, but he was forced to confess.

"I have jumped upwards, downwards, backwards, and sideways, at least four thousand times; and I can't get out: I always get up underneath there, and can't find the hole."

Tom looked at the trap, and having more wit than the lobster, he saw plainly enough what was the matter; as you may if you will look at a lobster-pot.

"Stop a bit," said Tom. "Turn your tail up to me, and I'll pull you through hindforemost, and then you won't stick in the spikes."

But the lobster was so stupid and clumsy that he couldn't hit the hole. Like a great many fox-hunters, he was very sharp as long as he was in his own country: but as soon as they get out of it they lose their heads; and so the lobster, so to speak, lost his tail.

Tom reached and clawed down the hole after him, till he caught hold of him; and then, as was to be expected, the clumsy lobster pulled him in head foremost.

"Hullo! here is a pretty business," said Tom. "Now take your great claws, and break the points off those spikes, and then we shall both get out easily."

"Dear me, I never thought of that," said the lobster; "and after all the experience of life that I have had!"

You see, experience is of very little good unless a man, or a lobster, has wit enough to make use of it. For a good many people, like old Polonius, have seen all the world, and yet remain little better than children after all.

But they had not got half the spikes away, when they

saw a great dark cloud over them; and lo and behold, it was the otter.

How she did grin and girn when she saw Tom. "Yar!" said she, "you little meddlesome wretch, I have you now! I will serve you out for telling the salmon where I was!" And she crawled all over the pot to get in.

Tom was horribly frightened, and still more frightened when she found the hole in the top, and squeezed herself right down through it, all eyes and teeth. But no sooner was her head inside than valiant Mr. Lobster caught her by the nose, and held on.

And there they were all three in the pot, rolling over and over, and very tight packing it was. And the lobster tore at the otter, and the otter tore at the lobster, and both squeezed and thumped poor Tom till he had no breath left in his body; and I don't know what would have happened to him if he had not at last got on the otter's back, and safe out of the hole.

He was right glad when he got out: but he would not desert his friend who had saved him; and the first time he saw his tail uppermost he caught hold of it, and pulled with all his might.

But the lobster would not let go.

"Come along," said Tom; "don't you see she is dead?" And so she was, quite drowned and dead.

And that was the end of the wicked otter.

But the lobster would not let go.

"Come along, you stupid old stick-in-the-mud," cried Tom, "or the fisherman will catch you!" And that was true, for Tom felt some one above beginning to haul up the pot.

But the lobster would not let go.

Tom saw the fisherman haul him up to the boatside, and thought it was all up with him. But when Mr. Lobster saw the fisherman, he gave such a furious and tremendous snap, that he snapped out of his hand, and out of the pot, and safe into the sea. But he left his knobbed claw behind him; for it never came into his stupid head to let go after all, so he just shook his claw off as the easier method. It was something of a bull, that; but you must know the lobster was an Irish lobster, and was hatched off Island Magee at the mouth of Belfast Lough.

Tom asked the lobster why he never thought of letting go. He said very determinedly that it was a point of honour among lobsters. And so it is, as the mayor of Plymouth found out once to his cost—eight or nine hundred years ago, of course ; for if it had happened lately it would be personal to mention it.

For one day he was so tired with sitting on a hard chair, in a grand furred gown, with a gold chain round his neck, hearing one policeman after another come in and sing, "What shall we do with the drunken sailor, so early in the morning ? " and answering them each exactly alike— " Put him in the round house till he gets sober, so early in the morning "—

That, when it was over, he jumped up, and played leapfrog with the town-clerk till he burst his buttons, and then had his luncheon, and burst some more buttons, and then said : " It is a low spring tide ; I shall go out this afternoon and cut my capers."

Now he did not mean to cut such capers as you eat with boiled mutton. It was the commandant of artillery at Valetta who used to amuse himself with cutting them, and who stuck upon one of the bastions a notice, "No one allowed to cut capers here but me," which greatly edified the midshipmen in port, and the Maltese on the Nix Mangiare stairs. But all that the mayor meant was that he would go and have an afternoon's fun, like any school-boy, and catch lobsters with an iron hook.

So to the Mewstone he went, and for lobsters he looked. And, when he came to a certain crack in the rocks, he was so excited, that, instead of putting in his hook, he put in his hand ; and Mr. Lobster was at home, and caught him by the finger, and held on.

" Yah ! " said the mayor, and pulled as hard as he dared : but the more he pulled the more the lobster pinched, till he was forced to be quiet.

Then he tried to get his hook in with his other hand ; but the hole was too narrow.

Then he pulled again, but he could not stand the pain.

Then he shouted and bawled for help : but there was no one nearer him than the men-of-war inside the breakwater.

Then he began to turn a little pale; for the tide flowed, and still the lobster held on.

Then he turned quite white; for the tide was up to his knees, and still the lobster held on.

Then he thought of cutting off his finger; but he wanted two things to do it with—courage and a knife; and he had got neither.

Then he turned quite yellow; for the tide was up to his waist, and still the lobster held on.

Then he thought over all the naughty things he ever had done : all the sand which he had put in the sugar, and the sloe-leaves in the tea, and the water in the treacle, and the salt in the tobacco (because his brother was a brewer, and a man must help his own kin).

Then he turned quite blue; for the tide was up to his breast, and still the lobster held on.

Then, I have no doubt, he repented fully of all the said naughty things which he had done, and promised to mend his life, as too many do when they think they have no life left to mend. Whereby, as they fancy, they make a very cheap bargain. But the old fairy with the birch rod soon undeceives them.

And then he grew all colours at once, and turned up his eyes like a duck in thunder; for the water was up to his chin, and still the lobster held on.

And then came a man-of-war's boat round the Mewstone, and saw his head sticking up out of the water. One said it was a keg of brandy, and another that it was a cocoanut, and another that it was a buoy loose, and another that it was a black diver, and wanted to fire at it, which would not have been pleasant for the mayor : but just then such a yell came out of a great hole in the middle of it that the midshipman in charge guessed what it was, and bade pull up to it as fast as they could. So somehow or other the Jack-tars got the lobster out, and set the mayor free, and put him ashore at the Barbican. He never went lobster-catching again; and we will hope he put no more salt in the tobacco, not even to sell his brother's beer.

And that is the story of the Mayor of Plymouth, which has two advantages—first, that of being quite true ; and second, that of having (as folks say all good stories ought to have) no moral whatsoever : no more, indeed, has any part of this book, because it is a fairy tale, you know.

And now happened to Tom a most wonderful thing ; for he had not left the lobster five minutes before he came upon a water-baby.

A real live water-baby, sitting on the white sand, very busy about a little point of rock.   And when it saw Tom it looked up for a moment, and then cried, " Why, you are not one of us.   You are a new baby !   Oh, how delightful ! "

And it ran to Tom, and Tom ran to it, and they hugged and kissed each other for ever so long, they did not know why.   But they did not want any introductions there under the water.

At last Tom said, " Oh, where have you been all this while ?   I have been looking for you so long, and I have been so lonely."

" We have been here for days and days.   There are hundreds of us about the rocks.   How was it you did not see us, or hear us when we sing and romp every evening before we go home ? "

Tom looked at the baby again, and then he said :

" Well, this is wonderful !   I have seen things just like you again and again, but I thought you were shells, or sea-creatures.   I never took you for water-babies like myself."

Now, was not that very odd ?   So odd, indeed, that you will, no doubt, want to know how it happened, and why Tom could never find a water-baby till after he had got the lobster out of the pot.   And, if you will read this story nine times over, and then think for yourself, you will find out why.   It is not good for little boys to be told everything, and never to be forced to use their own wits.   They would learn, then, no more than they do at Dr. Dulcimer's famous suburban establishment for the idler members of the youthful aristocracy, where the

masters learn the lessons, and the boys hear them—
which saves a great deal of trouble—for the time being.

"Now," said the baby, "come and help me, or I shall
not have finished before my brothers and sisters come,
and it is time to go home."

"What shall I help you at?"

"At this poor dear little rock; a great clumsy boulder
came rolling by in the last storm, and knocked all its
head off, and rubbed off all its flowers. And now I must
plant it again with sea-weeds, and coralline, and anemones,
and I will make it the prettiest little rock-garden on all
the shore."

So they worked away at the rock, and planted it, and
smoothed the sand down round it, and capital fun they
had till the tide began to turn. And then Tom heard
all the other babies coming, laughing and singing and
shouting and romping; and the noise they made was
just like the noise of the ripple. So he knew that he had
been hearing and seeing the water-babies all along; only
he did not know them, because his eyes and ears were
not opened.

And in they came, dozens and dozens of them, some
bigger than Tom and some smaller, all in the neatest little
white bathing dresses; and when they found that he was
a new baby they hugged him and kissed him, and then
put him in the middle and danced round him on the
sand, and there was no one ever so happy as poor
little Tom.

"Now then," they cried all at once, "we must come
away home, we must come away home, or the tide will
leave us dry. We have mended all the broken sea-weed,
and put all the rock pools in order, and planted all the
shells again in the sand, and nobody will see where the
ugly storm swept in last week."

And this is the reason why the rock pools are always
so neat and clean; because the water-babies come in
shore after every storm, to sweep them out, and comb
them down, and put them all to rights again.

Only where men are wasteful and dirty, and let sewers
run into the sea, instead of putting the stuff upon the

fields like thrifty reasonable souls; or throw herrings' heads, and dead dog-fish, or any other refuse, into the water; or in any way make a mess upon the clean shore, there the water-babies will not come, sometimes not for hundreds of years (for they cannot abide anything smelly or foul): but leave the sea-anemones and the crabs to clear away everything, till the good tidy sea has covered up all the dirt in soft mud and clean sand, where the water-babies can plant live cockles and whelks and razor shells and sea-cucumbers and golden-combs, and make a pretty live garden again, after man's dirt is cleared away. And that, I suppose, is the reason why there are no water-babies at any watering-place which I have ever seen.

And where is the home of the water-babies? In St. Brandan's fairy isle.

Did you never hear of the blessed St. Brandan, how he preached to the wild Irish, on the wild wild Kerry coast; he and five other hermits, till they were weary, and longed to rest? For the wild Irish would not listen to them, or come to confession and to mass, but liked better to brew potheen, and dance the pater o'pee, and knock each other over the head with shillelaghs, and shoot each other from behind turf-dykes, and steal each other's cattle, and burn each other's homes; till St. Brandan and his friends were weary of them, for they would not learn to be peaceable Christians at all.

So St. Brandan went out to the point of old Dunmore, and looked over the tide-way roaring round the Blasquets, at the end of all the world, and away into the ocean, and sighed—"Ah that I had wings as a dove!" And far away, before the setting sun, he saw a blue fairy sea, and golden fairy islands, and he said, "Those are the islands of the blest." Then he and his friends got into a hooker, and sailed away and away to the westward, and were never heard of more. But the people who would not hear him were changed into gorillas, and gorillas they are until this day.

And when St. Brandan and the hermits came to that fairy isle, they found it overgrown with cedars, and full of beautiful birds; and he sat down under the cedars, and preached to all the birds in the air. And they liked his sermons so well that they told the fishes in the sea; and they came, and St. Brandan preached to them; and the fishes told the water-babies, who live in the caves under the isle; and they came up by hundreds every Sunday, and St. Brandan got quite a neat little Sunday-school. And there he taught the water-babies for a great many hundred years, till his eyes grew too dim to see, and his beard grew so long that he dared not walk for fear of treading on it, and then he might have tumbled down. And at last he and the five hermits fell fast asleep under the cedar shades, and there they sleep unto this day. But the fairies took to the water-babies, and taught them their lessons themselves.

And some say that St. Brandan will awake, and begin to teach the babies once more: but some think that he will sleep on, for better for worse, till the coming of the Cocqcigrues. But, on still clear summer evenings, when the sun sinks down into the sea, among golden cloud-capes and cloud-islands, and locks and friths of azure sky, the sailors fancy that they see, away to westward, St. Brandan's fairy isle.

But whether men can see it or not, St. Brandan's Isle once actually stood there; a great land out in the ocean, which has sunk and sunk beneath the waves. Old Plato called it Atlantis, and told strange tales of the wise men who lived therein, and of the wars they fought in the old times. And from off that island came strange flowers, which linger still about this land:—the Cornish heath, and Cornish moneywort, and the delicate Venus's hair, and the London-pride which covers the Kerry mountains, and the little pink butterwort of Devon, and the great blue butterwort of Ireland, and the Connemara heath, and the bristle-fern of the Turk waterfall, and many a strange plant more; all fairy tokens left for wise men and good children from off St. Brandan's Isle.

Now when Tom got there, he found that the isle stood all on pillars, and that its roots were full of caves. There were pillars of black basalt, like Staffa; and pillars of green and crimson serpentine, like Kynance; and pillars ribboned with red and white and yellow sandstone, like Livermead ; and there were blue grottoes, like Capri ; and white grottoes, like Adelsberg ; all curtained and draped with seaweeds, purple and crimson, green and brown ; and strewn with soft white sand, on which the water-babies sleep every night. But, to keep the place clean and sweet, the crabs picked up all the scraps off the floor, and ate them like so many monkeys ; while the rocks were covered with ten thousand sea-anemones, and corals and madrepores, who scavenged the water all day long, and kept it nice and pure. But, to make up to them for having to do such nasty work, they were not left black and dirty, as poor chimney-sweeps and dustmen are. No ; the fairies are more considerate and just than that ; and have dressed them all in the most beautiful colours and patterns, till they look like vast flower-beds of gay blossoms. If you think I am talking nonsense, I can only say that it is true ; and that an old gentleman named Fourier used to say that we ought to do the same by chimney-sweeps and dustmen, and honour them instead of despising them ; and he was a very clever old gentleman : but unfortunately for him and the world, as mad as a March hare.

And, instead of watchmen and policemen to keep out nasty things at night, there were thousands and thousands of water-snakes, and most wonderful creatures they were. They were all named after the Nereids, the sea fairies who took care of them, Eunice and Polynoe, Phyllodoce and Psamathe, and all the rest of the pretty darlings who swim round their Queen Amphitrite, and her car of cameo shell. They were dressed in green velvet, and black velvet, and purple velvet ; and were all jointed in rings ; and some of them had three hundred brains apiece, so that they must have been uncommonly shrewd detectives ; and some had eyes in their tails ; and some had eyes in every joint, so that they kept a very sharp look-out ; and when they wanted a baby-snake, they just grew one at the end of their own tails, and when it was able to take care of itself it dropped off ; so that they brought up their families very cheaply. But if any nasty thing came by, out they rushed upon it; and then out of each of their hundreds of feet there sprang a whole cutler's shop of

Scythes,	Javelins,
Billhooks,	Lances,
Pickaxes,	Halberts,
Forks,	Gisarines,
Penknives,	Poleaxes,
Rapiers,	Fishhooks,
Sabres,	Bradawls,
Yataghans,	Gimblets,
Creeses,	Corkscrews,
Ghoorka swords,	Pins,
Tucks,	Needles,

And so forth,

which stabbed, shot, poked, pricked, scratched, ripped, pinked, and crimped those naughty beasts so terribly, that they had to run for their lives, or else be chopped into small pieces and be eaten afterwards. And, if that is not all, every word, true, then there is no faith in microscopes, and all is over with the Linnæan Society.

And there were the water-babies in thousands, more than Tom, or you either, could count.—All the little children whom the good fairies take to, because their cruel mothers and fathers will not; all who are untaught and brought up heathens, and all who come to grief by ill-usage or ignorance or neglect; all the little children who are overlaid, or given gin when they are young, or are let to drink out of hot kettles, or to fall into the fire; all the little children in alleys and courts, and tumble-down cottages, who die by fever, and cholera, and measles, and scarlatina, and nasty complaints which no one has any business to have, and which no one will have some day, when folks have common sense; and all the little children who have been killed by cruel masters, and wicked soldiers; they were all there, except, of course, the babes of Bethlehem who were killed by wicked King Herod; for they were taken straight to heaven long ago, as everybody knows, and we call them the Holy Innocents.

But I wish Tom had given up all his naughty tricks, and left off tormenting dumb animals, now that he had plenty of playfellows to amuse him.   Instead of that, I am sorry to say, he would meddle with the creatures, all but the water-snakes, for they would stand no nonsense.   So he tickled the madrepores, to make them shut up ; and frightened the crabs, to make them hide in the sand and peep out at him with the tips of their eyes ; and put stones into the anemones' mouths to make them fancy that their dinner was coming.

The other children warned him, and said, "Take care what you are at.   Mrs. Bedonebyasyoudid is coming." But Tom never heeded them, being quite riotous with high spirits and good luck, till, one Friday morning early, Mrs. Bedonebyasyoudid came indeed.

A very tremendous lady she was ; and when the children saw her, they all stood in a row, very upright indeed, and smoothed down their bathing dresses, and put their hands behind them, just as if they were going to be examined by the inspector.

And she had on a black bonnet, and a black shawl, and no crinoline at all ; and a pair of large green spectacles, and a great hooked nose, hooked so much that the bridge of it stood quite up above her eyebrows ; and under her arm she carried a great birch-rod.   Indeed, she was so ugly, that Tom was tempted to make faces at her : but did not ; for he did not admire the look of the birch-rod under her arm.

And she looked at the children one by one, and seemed very much pleased with them, though she never asked them one question about how they were behaving ; and then began giving them all sorts of nice sea-things—sea-cakes, sea-apples, sea-oranges, sea-bullseyes, sea-toffee ; and to the very best of all she gave sea-ices, made out of sea-cows' cream, which never melt under water.

And, if you don't quite believe me, then just think— What is more cheap and plentiful than sea-rock ? Then why should there not be sea-toffee as well ? And every one can find sea-lemons (ready quartered too) if they will look for them at low tide ; and sea-grapes too sometimes, hanging in bunches ; and, if you will go to Nice, you will find the fish-market full of sea-fruit, which they call "frutta di mare": though I suppose they call them "fruits de mer" now, out of compliment to that most successful, and therefore most immaculate, potentate who is seemingly desirous of inheriting the blessing pronounced on those who remove their neighbours' landmark. And, perhaps, that is the very reason why the place is called Nice, because there are so many nice things in the sea there: at least, if it is not, it ought to be.

Now little Tom watched all these sweet things given away, till his mouth watered, and his eyes grew as round as an owl's. For he hoped that his turn would come at last; and so it did. For the lady called him up, and held out her fingers with something in them, and popped it into his mouth; and, lo and behold, it was a nasty cold hard pebble.

"You are a very cruel woman," said he, and began to whimper.

"And you are a very cruel boy; who puts peebles into the sea-anemones' mouths, to take them in, and make them fancy that they had caught a good dinner? As you did to them, so I must do to you."

"Who told you that?" said Tom.

"You did yourself, this very minute."

Tom had never opened his lips; so he was very much taken aback indeed.

"Yes; every one tells me exactly what they have done wrong; and that without knowing it themselves. So there is no use trying to hide anything from me. Now go, and be a good boy, and I will put no more pebbles in your mouth, if you put none in other creatures'."

"I did not know there was any harm in it," said Tom.

"Then you know now. People continually say that to me: but I tell them, if you don't know that fire burns, that is no reason that it should not burn you; and if you don't know that dirt breeds fever, and that is no reason why the fevers should not kill you. The lobster did not know that there was any harm in getting into the lobster pot; but it caught him all the same."

"Dear me," thought Tom, "she knows everything!" And so she did, indeed.

"And so, if you do not know that things are wrong, that is no reason why you should not be punished for them; though not as much, not as much, my little man" (and, the lady looked very kindly, after all), "as if you did know."

"Well, you are a little hard on a poor lad," said Tom.

"Not at all; I am the best friend you ever had in all your life.   But I will tell you; I cannot help punishing people when they do wrong.   I like it no more than they do; I am often very, very sorry for them, poor things: but I cannot help it.   If I tried not to do it, I should do it all the same.   For I work by machinery, just like an engine; and am full of wheels and springs inside; and am wound up very carefully, so that I cannot help going."

"Was it long ago since they wound you up?" asked Tom.   For he thought, the cunning little fellow, "She will run down some day: or they may forget to wind her up, as old Grimes used to forget to wind up his watch when he came in from the public-house: and than I shall be safe."

"I was wound up once and for all, so long ago that I forget all about it."

"Dear me," said Tom, "you must have been made a long time!"

"I never was made, my child; and I shall go for ever and ever; for I am as old as Eternity, and yet as young as Time."

And there came over the lady's face a very curious expression—very solemn, and very sad; and yet very, very sweet.   And she looked up and away, as if she were gazing through the sea, and through the sky, at something far, far off; and as she did so, there came such a quiet, tender, patient, hopeful smile over her face, that Tom thought for the moment that she did not look ugly at all.   And no more she did; for she was like a great many people who have not a pretty feature in their faces, and yet are lovely to behold, and draw little children's hearts to them at once; because, though the house is plain enough, yet from the windows a beautiful and good spirit is looking forth.

And Tom smiled in her face, she looked so pleasant for the moment. And the strange fairy smiled too, and said :

"Yes. You thought me very ugly just now, did you not?"

Tom hung down his head, and got very red about the ears.

"And I am very ugly. I am the ugliest fairy in the world; and I shall be, till people behave themselves as they ought to do. And then I shall grow as handsome as my sister, who is the loveliest fairy in the world; and her name is Mrs. Doasyouwouldbedoneby. So she begins where I end, and I begin where she ends; and those who will not listen to her must listen to me, as you will see. Now, all of you run away, except Tom; and he may stay and see what I am going to do. It will be a very good warning for him to begin with, before he goes to school.

"Now, Tom, every Friday I come down here and call up all who have ill-used little children, and serve them as they served the children."

And at that Tom was frightened, and crept under a stone; which made the two crabs who lived there very angry, and frightened their friend the butter-fish into flapping hysterics: but he would not move for them.

And first she called up all the doctors who give little children so much physic (they were most of them old ones; for the young ones have learnt better, all but a few army surgeons, who still fancy that a baby's inside is much like a Scotch grenadier's), and she set them all in a row; and very rueful they looked; for they knew what was coming.

And first she pulled all their teeth out; and then she bled them all round; and then she dosed them with calomel, and jalap, and salts and senna, and brimstone and treacle; and horrible faces they made; and then she gave them a great emetic of mustard and water, and no basons; and began all over again; and that was the way she spent the morning.

And then she called up a whole troop of foolish ladies, who pinch up their children's waists and toes;

and she laced them all up in tight stays, so that they were choked and sick, and their noses grew red, and their hands and feet swelled; and then she crammed their poor feet into the most dreadfully tight boots, and made them all dance, which they did most clumsily indeed; and then she asked them how they liked it; and when they said not at all, she let them go: because they had only done it out of foolish fashion, fancying it was for their children's good, as if wasps' waists and pigs' toes could be pretty, or wholesome, or of any use to anybody.

Then she called up all the careless nurserymaids, and stuck pins into them all over, and wheeled them about in perambulators with tight straps across their stomachs and their heads and arms hanging over the side, till they were quite sick and stupid, and would have had sun-strokes: but, being under the water, they could only have water-strokes; which, I assure you, are nearly as bad, as you will find if you try to sit under a mill wheel. And mind—when you hear a rumbling at the bottom of the sea, sailors will tell you that it is a ground-swell: but now you know better. It is the old lady wheeling the maids about in perambulators.

And by that time she was so tired, she had to go to luncheon.

And after luncheon she set to work again, and called up all the cruel schoolmasters—whole regiments and brigades of them; and, when she saw them, she frowned most terribly, and set to work in earnest, as if the best part of the day's work was to come. More than half of them were nasty, dirty, frowzy, grubby, smelly old monks, who, because they dare not hit a man of their own size, amused themselves with beating little children instead; as you may see in the picture of old Pope Gregory (good man and true though he was, when he meddled with things which he did understand), teaching children to sing their fa-fa-mi-fa with a cat-o'-nine tails under his chair; but, because they never had any children of their own, they took into their heads (as some folks do still) that they were the only people in the world who knew how to manage children; and they first brought into England, in the old Anglo-Saxon times, the fashion of treating free boys, and girls too, worse than you would treat a dog or a horse: but Mrs. Bedonebyasyoudid has caught them all long ago; and given them many a taste of their own rods; and much good may it do them.

And she boxed their ears, and thumped them over the head with rulers, and pandied their hands with canes, and told them that they told stories, and were this and that bad sort of people; and the more they were very indignant, and stood upon their honour, and declared they told the truth, the more she declared they were not, and that they were only telling lies; and at last she birched them all round soundly with her great birch-rod, and set them each an imposition of three hundred thousand lines of Hebrew to learn by heart before she came back next Friday. And at that they all cried and howled so, that their breaths came all up through the sea like bubbles out of soda-water; and that is one reason of the bubbles in the sea. There are others: but that is the one which principally concerns little boys. And by that time she was so tired that she was glad to stop; and, indeed, she had done a very good day's work.

Tom did not quite dislike the old lady: but he could not help thinking her a little spiteful—and no wonder if she was, poor old soul; for, if she has to wait to grow handsome till people do as they would be done by, she will have to wait a very long time.

Poor old Mrs. Bedonebyasyoudid! she has a great deal of hard work before her, and had better have been born a washerwoman, and stood over a tub all day: but, you see, people cannot always choose their own profession.

But Tom longed to ask her one question; and after all, whenever she looked at him, she did not look cross at all; and now and then there was a funny smile in her face, and she chuckled to herself in a way which gave Tom courage, and at last he said:

"Pray, ma'am, may I ask you a question?"

" Certainly, my little dear."

" Why don't you bring all the bad masters here, and serve them out too ?   The butties that knock about the poor collier-boys ; and the nailers that file off their lads' noses and hammer their fingers ; and all the master sweeps, like my master Grimes ?   I saw him fall into the water long ago ; so I surely expected he would have been here.   I'm sure he was bad enough to me."

Then the old lady looked so very stern that Tom was quite frightened, and sorry that he had been so bold. But she was not angry with him.   She only answered, " I look after them all the week round ; and they are in a very different place from this, because they knew that they were doing wrong."

She spoke very quietly ; but there was something in her voice which made Tom tingle from head to foot, as if he had got into a shoal of sea-nettles.

" But these people," she went on, " did not know that they were doing wrong : they were only stupid and impatient ; and therefore I only punish them till they become patient, and learn to use their common sense like reasonable beings.   But as for chimney-sweeps, and collier-boys, and nailer lads, my sister has set good people to stop all that sort of thing ; and very much obliged to her I am ; for if she could only stop the cruel masters from ill-using poor children, I should grow handsome at least a thousand years sooner.   And now do you be a good boy, and do as you would be done by, which they did not ; and then, when my sister, Madame Doasyouwouldbedoneby, comes on Sunday, perhaps she will take notice of you, and teach you how to behave. She understands that better than I do."   And so she went.

Tom was very glad to hear that there was no chance of meeting Grimes again, though he was a little sorry for him, considering that he used sometimes to give him the leavings of the beer : but he determined to be a very good boy all Saturday ; and he was ; for he never frightened one crab, nor tickled any live corals, nor put stones into the sea-anemones' mouths, to make them fancy they had got a dinner ; and, when Sunday morning

came, sure enough, Mrs. Doasyouwouldbedoneby came
too. Whereat all the little children began dancing and
clapping their hands, and Tom danced too with all his
might.

And as for the pretty lady, I cannot tell you what the
colour of her hair was, or of her eyes : no more could Tom ;
for, when any one looks at her, all they can think of is,
that she has the sweetest, kindest, tenderest, funniest,
merriest face they ever saw, or want to see. But Tom
saw that she was a very tall woman, as tall as her sister :
but instead of being gnarly, and horny, and scaly, and
prickly, like her, she was the most nice, soft, fat, smooth,
pussy, cuddly, delicious creature who ever nursed a
baby ; and she understood babies thoroughly, for she
had plenty of her own, whole rows and regiments of them,
and has to this day. And all her delight was, whenever
she had a spare moment, to play with babies, in which
she showed herself a woman of sense ; for babies are the
best company, and the pleasantest playfellows, in the
world ; at least, so all the wise people in the world think.
And therefore when the children saw her, they naturally
all caught hold of her, and pulled her till she sat down
on a stone, and climbed into her lap, and clung round
her neck, and caught hold of her hands ; and then they
all put their thumbs into their mouths, and began cuddling and purring like so many kittens, as they ought to
have done. While those who could get nowhere else
sat down on the sand, and cuddled her feet—for no one,
you know, wears shoes in the water, except horrid old
bathing-women, who are afraid of the water-babies pinch-
ing their horny toes. And Tom stood staring at them ;
for he could not understand what it was all about.

" And who are you, you little darling ? " she said.

" Oh, that is the new baby ! " they all cried, pulling
their thumbs out of their mouths ; " and he never had
any mother," and they all put their thumbs back again,
for they did not wish to lose any time.

" Then I will be his mother, and he shall have the
very best place ; so get out all of you, this moment."

And she took up two great armfuls of babies—nine

hundred under one arm, and thirteen hundred under the other—and threw them away, right and left, into the water. But they minded it no more than the naughty boys in Struwelpeter minded when St. Nicholas dipped them in his inkstand; and did not even take their thumbs out of their mouths, but came paddling and wriggling back to her like so many tadpoles, till you could see nothing of her from head to foot for the swarm of little babies.

But she took Tom in her arms, and laid him in the softest place of all, and kissed him, and patted him, and talked to him, tenderly and low, such things as he had never heard before in his life; and Tom looked up into her eyes, and loved her, and loved, till he fell fast asleep from pure love.

And when he awoke, she was telling the children a story. And what story did she tell them? One story she told them, which begins every Christmas Eve, and yet never ends at all for ever and ever; and, as she went on, the children took their thumbs out of their mouths, and listened quite seriously; but not sadly at all; for she never told them anything sad; and Tom listened too, and never grew tired of listening. And he listened so long that he fell fast asleep again, and, when he woke, the lady was nursing him still.

"Don't go away," said little Tom. "This is so nice. I never had any one to cuddle me before."

"Don't go away," said all the children; "you have not sung us one song."

"Well, I have time for only one. So what shall it be?"

"The doll you lost! The doll you lost!" cried all the babies at once.

So the strange fairy sang:—

> "I once had a sweet little doll, dears,
>   The prettiest doll in the world;
> Her cheeks were so red and so white, dears,
>   And her hair was so charmingly curled.
> But I lost my poor little doll, dears,
>   As I played in the heath one day;
> And I cried for her more than a week, dears;
>   But I never could find where she lay.

> I found my poor little doll, dears,
>   As I played in the heath one day:
> Folks say she is terribly changed, dears,
>   For her paint is all washed away,
> And her arm trodden off by the cows, dears,
>   And her hair not the least bit curled:
> Yet for old sakes' sake she is still, dears,
>   The prettiest doll in the world."

What a silly song for a fairy to sing!

And what silly water-babies to be quite delighted at it!

Well, but you see they have not the advantage of Aunt Agitate's Arguments in the sea-land down below.

"Now," said the fairy to Tom, "will you be a good boy for my sake, and torment no more sea-beasts, till I come back?"

"And you will cuddle me again?" said poor little Tom.

"Of course I will, you little duck. I should like to take you with me, and cuddle you all the way, only I must not;" and away she went.

So Tom really tried to be a good boy, and tormented no sea-beasts after that, as long as he lived; and he is quite alive, I assure you, still.

Oh, how good little boys ought to be, who have kind pussy mammas to cuddle them and tell them stories; and how afraid they ought to be of growing naughty, and bringing tears into their mammas' pretty eyes!

CHAPTER VI

" Thou little child, yet glorious in the might
Of heaven-born freedom on thy Being's height,
Why with such earnest pains dost thou provoke
The Years to bring the inevitable yoke—
Thus blindly with thy blessedness at strife?
Full soon thy soul shall have her earthly freight,
And custom lie upon thee with a weight
Heavy as frost, and deep almost as life."

—WORDSWORTH.

CHAPTER VI

ERE I come to the very saddest part of all my story. I know some people who will only laugh at it, and call it much ado about nothing. But I know one man who would not; and he was an officer with a pair of grey moustaches as long as your arm, who said once in company, that two of the most heart-rending sights in the world, which moved him most to tears, which he would do anything to prevent or remedy, were a child over a broken toy, and a child stealing sweets.

The company did not laugh at him; his moustaches were too long and too grey for that: but, after he was gone, they called him sentimental, and so forth, all but one dear little old quaker lady with a soul as white as her cap, who was not, of course, generally partial to soldiers; and she said very quietly, like a quaker:

"Friends, it is borne upon my mind that that is a truly brave man."

Now you may fancy that Tom was quite good, when he had everything that he could want or wish: but you would be very much mistaken. Being quite comfortable is a very good thing; but it does not make people good. Indeed, it sometimes makes them naughty, as it has made the people in America; and as it made the people in the Bible, who waxed fat and kicked, like horses overfed and underworked. And I am very sorry to say that this happened to little Tom. For he grew so fond of the sea-bull's-eyes and sea-lollipops, that his foolish little head could think of nothing else : and he was always longing for more, and wondering when the strange lady would come again and give him some, and what she would give him, and how much, and whether she would give him more than the others. And he thought of nothing but lollipops by day, and dreamt of nothing else by night—and what happened then ?

That he began to watch the lady to see where she kept the sweet things ; and began hiding, and sneaking, and following her about, and pretending to be looking the other way, or going after something else, till he found out that she kept them in a beautiful mother-of-pearl cabinet, away in a deep crack of the rocks.

And he longed to go to the cabinet, and yet he was afraid ; and then he longed again, and was less afraid ; and at last, by continual thinking about it, he longed so violently, that he was not afraid at all. And one night, when all the other children were asleep, and he could not sleep for thinking of lollipops, he crept away among the rocks, and got to the cabinet, and behold ! it was open.

But, when he saw all the nice things inside, instead of being delighted, he was quite frightened, and wished he had never come there. And then he would only touch them, and he did ; and then he would only taste one, and he did ; and then he would only eat one, and he did ; and then he would only eat two, and then three, and so on ; and then he was terrified lest she should come and catch him, and began gobbling them down so fast that he did not taste them, or have any pleasure in them ; and then he felt sick, and would have only one more ; and then only one more again ; and so on till he had eaten them all up.

And all the while, close behind him, stood Mrs. Bedonebyasyoudid.

Some people may say, But why did she not keep her cupboard locked ? Well, I know.—It may seem a very strange thing, but she never does keep her cupboard locked; every one may go and taste for themselves, and fare accordingly. It is very odd, but so it is; and I am quite sure that she knows best. Perhaps she wishes people to keep their fingers out of the fire, by having them burnt.

She took off her spectacles, because she did not like to see too much; and in her pity she arched up her eyebrows into her very hair, and her eyes grew so wide that they would have taken in all the sorrows of the world, and filled with great big tears, as they too often do.

But all she said was:

"Ah, you poor little dear! you are just like all the rest."

But she said it to herself, and Tom neither heard nor saw her. Now, you must not fancy that she was sentimental at all. If you do, and think that she is going to let off you, or me, or any human being when we do wrong, because she is too tender-hearted to punish us, then you will find yourself very much mistaken, as many a man does every year and every day.

But what did the strange fairy do when she saw all her lollipops eaten?

Did she fly at Tom, catch him by the scruff of the neck, hold him, howk him, hump him, hurry him, hit him, poke him, pull him, pinch him, pound him, put him in the corner, shake him, slap him, set him on a cold stone to reconsider himself, and so forth?

Not a bit. You may watch her at work, if you know where to find her. But you will never see her do that. For, if she had, she knew quite well, Tom would have fought, and kicked, and bit, and said bad words, and turned again that moment into a naughty little heathen chimney-sweep, with his hand, like Ishmael's of old, against every man, and every man's hand against him.

Did she question him, hurry him, frighten him, threaten him, to make him confess? Not a bit. You may see her, as I said, at her work often enough, if you know where to look for her: but you will never see her do that. For if she had, she would have tempted him to tell lies in his fright; and that would have been worse for him, if possible, than even becoming a heathen chimney sweep again.

No.   She leaves that for anxious parents and teachers (lazy ones, some call them), who, instead of giving children a fair trial, such as they would expect and demand for themselves, force them by fright to confess their own faults—which is so cruel and unfair, that no judge on the bench dare do it to the wickedest thief or murderer, for the good British law forbids it—ay, and even punish them to make them confess, which is so detestable a crime, that it is never committed now, save by Inquisitors, and Kings of Naples, and a few other wretched people of whom the world is weary.   And then they say, " We have trained up the child in the way he should go, and when he grew up he has departed from it.   Why then did Solomon say that he would not depart from it ? " But perhaps the way of beating, and hurrying, and frightening, and questioning, was not the way that the child should go ; for it is not even the way in which a colt should go, if you want to break it in, and make it a quiet serviceable horse.

Some folks may say, " Ah ! but the fairy does not need to do that, if she knows everything already."   True. But if she did not know, she would not surely behave worse than a British judge and jury ; and no more should parents and teachers either.

So she just said nothing at all about the matter, not even when Tom came next day with the rest for sweet things.   He was horribly afraid of coming : but he was still more afraid of staying away, lest any one should suspect him.   He was dreadfully afraid, too, lest there should be no sweets—as was to be expected, he having eaten them all—and lest then the fairy should inquire who had taken them.   But, behold ! she pulled out just as many as ever, which astonished Tom, and frightened him still more.

And, when the fairy looked him full in the face, he shook from head to foot : however, she gave him his share like the rest, and he thought within himself that she could not have found him out.

But, when he put the sweets into his mouth, he hated the taste of them; and they made him so sick, that he had to get away as fast as he could; and terribly sick he was, and very cross and unhappy, all the week after.

Then, when next week came, he had his share again; and again the fairy looked him full in the face; but more sadly than she had ever looked. And he could not bear the sweets: but took them again in spite of himself.

And, when Mrs. Doasyouwouldbedoneby came, he wanted to be cuddled like the rest; but she said very seriously:

"I should like to cuddle you; but I cannot, you are so horny and prickly."

And Tom looked at himself: and he was all over prickles, just like a sea-egg.

Which was quite natural; for you must know and believe that people's souls make their bodies, just as a snail makes its shell (I am not joking, my little man; I am in serious, solemn earnest). And, therefore, when Tom's soul grew all prickly with naughty tempers, his body could not help growing prickly too, so that nobody would cuddle him, or play with him, or even like to look at him.

What could Tom do now, but go away and hide in a corner, and cry? For nobody would play with him, and he knew full well why.

And he was so miserable all that week that, when the ugly fairy came, and looked at him once more full in the face, more seriously and sadly than ever, he could stand it no longer, and thrust the sweetmeats away, saying, "No, I don't want any; I can't bear them now," and then burst out crying, poor little man, and told Mrs. Bedonebyasyoudid every word as it happened.

He was horribly frightened when he had done so; for he expected her to punish him very severely. But, instead, she only took him up and kissed him, which was not quite pleasant, for her chin was very bristly indeed; but he was so lonely-hearted, he thought that rough kissing was better than none.

"I will forgive you, little man," she said. "I always

forgive every one the moment they tell me the truth of their own accord."

"Then you will take away all these nasty prickles?"

"That is a very different matter. You put them there yourself, and only you can take them away."

"But how can I do that?" asked Tom, crying afresh.

"Well, I think it is time for you to go to school; so I shall fetch you a schoolmistress, who will teach you how to get rid of your prickles."   And so she went away.

Tom was frightened at the notion of a schoolmistress; for he thought she would certainly come with a birch-rod or a cane ; but he comforted himself, at last, that she might be something like the old woman in Vendale—which she was not in the least ; for, when the fairy brought her, she was the most beautiful little girl that ever was seen, with long curls floating behind her like a golden cloud, and long robes floating all round her like a silver one.

"There he is," said the fairy ; "and you must teach him to be good, whether you like or not."

"I know," said the little girl ; but she did not seem quite to like, for she put her finger in her mouth, and looked at Tom under her brows ; and Tom put his finger to his mouth, and looked at her under his brows, for he was horribly ashamed of himself.

The little girl seemed hardly to know how to begin ; and perhaps she would never have begun at all, if poor Tom had not burst out crying, and begged her to teach him to be good, and help him to cure his prickles ; and at that she grew so tender-hearted, that she began teaching him as prettily as ever child was taught in the world.

And what did the little girl teach Tom? She taught him, first, what you have been taught ever since you said your first prayers at your mother's knees ; but she taught him much more simply.   For the lessons in that world, my child, have no such hard words in them as the lessons in this, and therefore the water-babies like them better than you like your lessons, and long to learn them more and more ; and grown men cannot puzzle nor quarrel over their meaning, as they do here on land ; for those lessons all rise clear and pure, like the Test out of Overton Pool, out of the everlasting ground of all life and truth.

So she taught Tom every day in the week; only on Sundays she always went away home, and the kind fairy took her place. And, before she had taught Tom many Sundays, his prickles had vanished quite away, and his skin was smooth and clean again.

"Dear me!" said the little girl; "why, I know you now. You are the very same little chimney-sweep who came into my bedroom."

"Dear me!" cried Tom. "And I know you, too, now. You are the very little white lady whom I saw in bed." And he jumped at her, and longed to hug and kiss her; but did not, remembering that she was a lady born; so he only jumped round and round her, till he was quite tired.

And then they began telling each other all their story —how he had got into the water, and she had fallen over the rock; and how he had swam down to the sea, and how she had flown out of the window; and how this, that, and the other, till it was all talked out: and then they both began over again, and I can't say which of the two talked fastest.

And then they set to work at their lessons again, and both liked them so well, that they went on well till seven full years were past and gone.

You may fancy that Tom was quite content and happy all those seven years; but the truth is, he was not. He had always one thing on his mind, and that was—where little Ellie went, when she went home on Sundays.

To a very beautiful place, she said.

But what was the beautiful place like, and where was it?

Ah! that is just what she could not say. And it is strange, but true, that no one can say; and that those who have been oftenest in it, or even nearest to it, can say least about it, and make people understand least what it is like. There are a good many folks about the Other-end-of-Nowhere (where Tom went afterwards), who pretend to know it from north to south as well as if they had been penny postmen there; but, as they are safe at the Other-end-of-Nowhere, nine hundred and ninety-nine million miles away, what they say cannot concern us.

But the dear, sweet, loving, wise, good, self-sacrificing people, who really go there, can never tell you anything about it, save that it is the most beautiful place in all the world ; and, if you ask them more, they grow modest, and hold their peace, for fear of being laughed at ; and quite right they are.

So all that good little Ellie could say was, that it was worth all the rest of the world put together.   And of course that only made Tom the more anxious to go likewise.

" Miss Ellie," he said, at last, " I will know why I cannot go with you when you go home, on Sundays, or I shall have no peace, and give you none either."

" You must ask the fairies that."

So when the fairy, Mrs. Bedonebyasyoudid, came next, Tom asked her.

" Little boys who are only fit to play with sea-beasts cannot go there," she said.   " Those who go there must go first where they do not like, and do what they do not like, and help somebody they do not like."

" Why, did Ellie do that ? "

" Ask her."

And Ellie blushed, and said, " Yes, Tom ; I did not like coming here at first ; I was so much happier at home, where it is always Sunday.   And I was afraid of you, Tom, at first, because—because——"

" Because I was all over prickles?   But I am not prickly now, am I, Miss Ellie ? "

" No," said Ellie.   " I like you very much now ; and I like coming here, too."

" And perhaps," said the fairy, " you will learn to like going where you don't like, and helping some one that you don't like, as Ellie has."

But Tom put his finger in his mouth, and hung his head down ; for he did not see that at all.

So when Mrs. Doasyouwouldbedoneby came, Tom asked her ; for he thought in his little head, She is not so strict as her sister, and perhaps she may let me off more easily.

Ah, Tom, Tom, silly fellow! and yet I don't know why I should blame you, while so many grown people have got the very same notion in their heads.

But, when they try it, they get just the same answer as Tom did. For, when he asked the second fairy, she told him just what the first did, and in the very same words.

Tom was very unhappy at that. And, when Ellie went home on Sunday, he fretted and cried all day, and did not care to listen to the fairy's stories about good children, though they were prettier than ever. Indeed, the more he overheard of them, the less he liked to listen, because they were all about children who did what they did not like, and took trouble for other people, and worked to feed their little brothers and sisters, instead of caring only for their play. And, when she began to tell a story about a holy child in old times, who was martyred by the heathen because it would not worship idols, Tom could bear no more, and ran away and hid among the rocks.

And, when Ellie came back, he was shy with her, because he fancied she looked down on him, and thought him a coward. And then he grew quite cross with her, because she was superior to him, and did what he could not do. And poor Ellie was quite surprised and sad; and at last Tom burst out crying; but he would not tell her what was really in his mind.

And all the while he was eaten up with curiosity to know where Ellie went to; so that he began not to care for his playmates, or for the sea-palace, or anything else. But perhaps that made matters all the easier for him; for he grew so discontented with everything round him, that he did not care to stay, and did not care where he went.

"Well," he said, at last, "I am so miserable here, I'll go; if only you will go with me."

"Ah!" said Ellie, "I wish I might; but the worst of it is, that the fairy says, that you must go alone, if you go at all. Now don't poke that poor crab about, Tom" (for he was feeling very naughty and mischievous), "or the fairy will have to punish you."

Tom was very nearly saying, "I don't care if she does"; but he stopped himself in time.

"I know what she wants me to do," he said, whining most dolefully. "She wants me to go after that horrid old Grimes. I don't like him, that's certain. And if I find him, he will turn me into a chimney-sweep again, I know. That's what I have been afraid of all along."

"No, he won't—I know as much as that. Nobody can turn water-babies into sweeps, or hurt them at all, as long as they are good."

"Ah," said naughty Tom, "I see what you want; you are persuading me all along to go, because you are tired of me, and want to get rid of me."

Little Ellie opened her eyes very wide at that, and they were all brimming over with tears.

"Oh, Tom, Tom!" she said, very mournfully—and then she cried, "Oh, Tom! where are you?"

And Tom cried, "Oh, Ellie, where are you?"

For neither of them could see each other—not the least. Little Ellie vanished quite away, and Tom heard her voice calling him, and growing smaller and smaller, and fainter and fainter, till all was silent.

Who was frightened then but Tom? He swam up and down among the rocks, into all the halls and chambers, faster than ever he swam before, but could not find her. He shouted after her, but she did not answer; he asked all the other children, but they had not seen her; and at last he went up to the top of the water and began crying and screaming for Mrs. Doasyouwouldbedoneby, but she did not come. Then he began crying and screaming for Mrs. Bedonebyasyoudid—which perhaps was the best thing to do—for she came in a moment.

"Oh!" said Tom. "Oh dear, oh dear! I have been naughty to Ellie, and I have killed her—I know I have killed her."

"Not quite that," said the fairy; "but I have sent her away home, and she will not come back again for I do not know how long."

And at that Tom cried so bitterly, that the salt sea was swelled with his tears, and the tide was ˙3,954,620,819 of an inch higher than it had been the day before : but perhaps that was owing to the waxing of the moon. It may have been so; but it is considered right in the new philosophy, you know, to give spiritual causes for physical phenomena—especially in parlour-tables; and, of course, physical causes for spiritual ones, like thinking, and praying, and knowing right from wrong. And so they odds it till it comes even, as folks say down in Berkshire.

"How cruel of you to send Ellie away!" sobbed Tom. "However, I will find her again, if I go to the world's end to look for her."

The fairy did not slap Tom, and tell him to hold his tongue: but she took him on her lap very kindly, just as her sister would have done; and put him in mind how it was not her fault, because she was wound up inside, like watches, and could not help doing things whether she liked or not. And then she told him how he had been in the nursery long enough, and must go out now and see the world, if he intended ever to be a man; and how he must go all alone by himself, as every one else that ever was born has to go, and see with his own eyes, and smell with his own nose, and make his own bed and lie on it, and burn his own fingers if he put them into the fire. And then she told him how many fine things there were to be seen in the world, and what an odd, curious, pleasant, orderly, respectable, well-managed, and, on the whole, successful (as, indeed, might have been expected) sort of a place it was, if people would only be tolerably brave and honest and good in it; and then she told him not to be afraid of anything he met, for nothing would harm him if he remembered all his lessons, and did what he knew was right. And at last she comforted poor little Tom so much, that he was quite eager to go, and wanted to set out that minute. "Only," he said, "if I might see Ellie once before I went!"

"Why do you want that?"

"Because—because I should be so much happier if I thought she had forgiven me."

And in the twinkling of an eye there stood Ellie, smiling, and looking so happy that Tom longed to kiss her; but was still afraid it would not be respectful, because she was a lady born.

"I am going, Ellie!" said Tom. "I am going, if it is to the world's end. But I don't like going at all, and that's the truth."

"Pooh! pooh! pooh!" said the fairy. "You will like it very well indeed, you little rogue, and you know that at the bottom of your heart. But if you don't, I will make you like it. Come here, and see what happens to people who do only what is pleasant."

And she took out of one of her cupboards (she had all sorts of mysterious cupboards in the cracks of the rocks) the most wonderful waterproof book, full of such photographs as never were seen. For she had found out photography (and this is a fact) more than 13,598,000 years before anybody was born; and, what is more, her photographs did not merely represent light and shade, as ours do, but colour also, and all colours, as you may see if you look at a black cock's tail, or a butterfly's wing, or, indeed, most things that are or can be, so to speak. And, therefore, her photographs were very curious and famous, and the children looked with great delight for the opening of the book.

And on the title-page was written, "The History of the great and famous nation of the Doasyoulikes, who came away from the country of Hardwork, because they wanted to play on the Jews'-harp all day long."

In the first picture they saw these Doasyoulikes living in the land of Readymade, at the foot of the Happygo-lucky Mountains, where flapdoodle grows wild; and if you want to know what that is, you must read Peter Simple.

They lived very much such a life as those jolly old Greeks in Sicily, whom you may see painted on the ancient vases, and really there seemed to be great ex-cuses for them, for they had no need to work.

Instead of houses, they lived in the beautiful caves of tufa, and bathed in the warm springs three times a day; and, as for clothes, it was so warm there that the gentle-men walked about in little beside a cocked hat and a pair of straps, or some light summer tackle of that kind;

and the ladies all gathered gossamer in autumn (when they were not too lazy) to make their winter dresses.

They were very fond of music, but it was too much trouble to learn the piano or the violin; and, as for dancing, that would have been too great an exertion. So they sat on ant-hills all day long, and played on the Jews'-harp; and, if the ants bit them, why they just got up and went to the next ant-hill, till they were bitten there likewise.

And they sat under the flapdoodle-trees, and let the flapdoodle drop into their mouths; and under the vines, and squeezed the grape-juice down their throats; and, if any little pigs ran about ready roasted, crying, "Come and eat me," as was their fashion in that country, they waited till the pigs ran against their mouths, and then took a bite, and were content, just as so many oysters would have been.

They needed no weapons, for no enemies ever came near their land; and no tools, for everything was ready-made to their hand; and the stern old fairy Necessity never came near them to hunt them up, and make them use their wits, or die.

And so on, and so on, and so on, till there were never such comfortable, easy-going, happy-go-lucky people in the world.

"Well, that is a jolly life," said Tom.

"You think so?" said the fairy. "Do you see that great peaked mountain there behind," said the fairy, "with smoke coming out of its top?"

"Yes."

"And do you see all those ashes, and slag, and cinders, lying about?"

"Yes."

"Then turn over the next five hundred years, and you will see what happens next."

And behold the mountain had blown up like a barrel of gunpowder, and then boiled over like a kettle; whereby one-third of the Doasyoulikes were blown into the air, and another third were smothered in ashes; so that there was only one-third left.

"You see," said the fairy, "what comes of living on a burning mountain."

"Oh, why did you not warn them?" said little Ellie.

"I did warn them all that I could. I let the smoke come out of the mountain; and wherever there is smoke there is fire. And I laid the ashes and cinders all about; and wherever there are cinders, cinders may be again. But they did not like to face facts, my dears, as very few people do; and so they invented a cock-and-bull story, which, I am sure, I never told them, that the smoke was the breath of a giant, whom some gods or other had buried under the mountain; and that the cinders were what the dwarfs roasted the little pigs whole with; and other nonsense of that kind. And, when folks are in that humour, I cannot teach them, save by the good old birch-rod."

And then she turned over the next five hundred years: and there were the remnant of the Doasyoulikes, doing as they liked, as before. They were too lazy to move away from the mountain; so they said, If it has blown up once, that is all the more reason that it should not blow up again. And they were few in number: but they only said, The more the merrier, but the fewer the better fare. However, that was not quite true; for all the flapdoodle-trees were killed by the volcano, and they had eaten all the roast pigs, who, of course, could not be expected to have little ones. So they had to live very hard, on nuts and roots which they scratched out of the ground with sticks. Some of them talked of sowing corn, as their ancestors used to do, before they came into the land of Readymade; but they had forgotten how to make ploughs (they had forgotten even how to make Jews'-harps by this time), and had eaten all the seed-corn which they brought out of the land of Hardwork years since; and of course it was too much trouble to go away and find more. So they lived miserably on roots and nuts, and all the weakly little children had great stomachs, and then died.

"Why," said Tom, "they are growing no better than savages."

"And look how ugly they are all getting," said Ellie.

"Yes; when people live on poor vegetables instead of roast beef and plum-pudding, their jaws grow large, and their lips grow coarse, like the poor Paddies who eat potatoes."

And she turned over the next five hundred years. And there they were all living up in trees, and making nests to keep off the rain. And underneath the trees lions were prowling about.

"Why," said Ellie, "the lions seem to have eaten a good many of them, for there are very few left now."

"Yes," said the fairy; "you see it was only the strongest and most active ones who could climb the trees, and so escape."

"But what great, hulking, broad-shouldered chaps they are," said Tom; "they are a rough lot as ever I saw."

"Yes, they are getting very strong now; for the ladies will not marry any but the very strongest and fiercest gentlemen, who can help them up the trees out of the lions' way."

And she turned over the next five hundred years. And in that they were fewer still, and stronger, and fiercer; but their feet had changed shape very oddly, for they laid hold of the branches with their great toes, as if they had been thumbs, just as a Hindoo tailor uses his toes to thread his needle.

The children were very much surprised, and asked the fairy whether that was her doing.

"Yes, and no," she said, smiling. "It was only those who could use their feet as well as their hands who could get a good living: or, indeed, get married; so that they got the best of everything, and starved out all the rest; and those who are left keep up a regular breed of toe-thumb-men, as a breed of shorthorns, or skye-terriers, or fancy pigeons is kept up."

"But there is a hairy one among them," said Ellie.

"Ah!" said the fairy, "that will be a great man in his time, and chief of all the tribe."

And, when she turned over the next five hundred years, it was true.

For this hairy chief had had hairy children, and they hairier children still; and every one wished to marry hairy husbands, and have hairy children too; for the climate was growing so damp that none but the hairy ones could live : all the rest coughed and sneezed, and had sore throats, and went into consumptions, before they could grow up to be men and women.

Then the fairy turned over the next five hundred years.   And they were fewer still.

"Why, there is one on the ground picking up roots," said Ellie, "and he cannot walk upright."

No more he could; for in the same way that the shape of their feet had altered, the shape of their backs had altered also.

"Why," cried Tom, " I declare they are all apes."

"Something fearfully like it, poor foolish creatures," said the fairy. "They are grown so stupid now, that they can hardly think : for none of them have used their wits for many hundred years. They have almost forgotten, too, how to talk. For each stupid child forgot some of the words it heard from its stupid parents, and had not wits enough to make fresh words for itself. Beside, they are grown so fierce and suspicious and brutal that they keep out of each other's way, and mope and sulk in the dark forests, never hearing each other's voice, till they have forgotten almost what speech is like. I am afraid they will all be apes very soon, and all by doing only what they liked."

And in the next five hundred years they were all dead and gone, by bad food and wild beasts and hunters ; all except one tremendous old fellow with jaws like a jack, who stood full seven feet high ; and M. du Chaillu came up to him, and shot him, as he stood roaring and thumping his breast. And he remembered that his ancestors had once been men, and tried to say, " Am I not a man and a brother ? " but had forgotten how to use his tongue ; and then he had tried to call for a doctor, but he had forgotten the word for one. So all he said was, "Ubboboo!" and died.

And that was the end of the great and jolly nation of the Doasyoulikes. And, when Tom and Ellie came to the end of the book, they looked very sad and solemn ; and they had good reason so to do, for they really fancied that the men were apes, and never thought, in their simplicity, of asking whether the creatures had hippopotamus majors in their brains or not ; in which case, as you have been told already, they could not possibly have been apes, though they were more apish than the apes of all aperies.

"But could you not have saved them from becoming apes ?" said little Ellie, at last.

"At first, my dear ; if only they would have behaved like men, and set to work to do what they did not like. But the longer they waited, and behaved like the dumb beasts, who only do what they like, the stupider and clumsier they grew ; till at last they were past all cure, for they had thrown their own wits away. It is such things as this that help to make me so ugly, that I know not when I shall grow fair."

"And where are they all now ?" asked Ellie.

"Exactly where they ought to be, my dear."

"Yes !" said the fairy, solemnly, half to herself, as she closed the wonderful book. "Folks say now that I can make beasts into men, by circumstance, and selection, and competition, and so forth. Well, perhaps they are right ; and perhaps, again, they are wrong. That is one of the seven things which I am forbidden to tell, till the coming of the Cocqcigrues ; and, at all events, it is no concern of theirs. Whatever their ancestors were, men they are ; and I advise them to behave as such, and act accordingly. But let them recollect this, that there are two sides to every question, and a downhill as well as an uphill road ; and, if I can turn beasts into men, I can, by the same laws of circumstance, and selection, and competition, turn men into beasts. You were very near being turned into a beast once or twice, little Tom. In- deed, if you had not made up your mind to go on this journey, and see the world, like an Englishman, I am not sure but that you would have ended as an eft in a pond."

"Oh, dear me!" said Tom; "sooner than that, and be all over slime, I'll go this minute, if it is to the world's end."

CHAPTER VII

" *And Nature, the old Nurse, took*
   The child upon her knee,
Saying 'Here is a story book
   Thy father hath written for thee.

  ' Come wander with me.'' she said,
   ' Into regions yet untrod,
And read what is still unread
   In the Manuscripts of God.'

  And he wandered away and away
   With Nature, the dear old Nurse,
Who sang to him night and day
   The rhymes of the universe.''
                              —LONGFELLOW.

CHAPTER VII

"OW," said Tom, "I am ready to be off, if it's to the world's end."

"Ah!" said the fairy, "that is a brave, good boy. But you must go further than the world's end, if you want to find Mr. Grimes; for he is at the Other-end-of-Nowhere. You must go to Shiny Wall, and through the white gate that never was opened; and then you will come to Peacepool, and Mother Carey's Haven, where the good whales go when they die. And there Mother Carey will tell you the way to the Other-end-of-Nowhere, and there you will find Mr. Grimes."

"Oh, dear!" said Tom. "But I do not know my way to Shiny Wall, or where it is at all."

"Little boys must take the trouble to find out things for themselves, or they will never grow to be men; so that you must ask all the beasts in the sea and the birds in the air, and if you have been good to them, some of them will tell you the way to Shiny Wall."

"Well," said Tom, "it will be a long journey, so I had better start at once. Good-bye, Miss Ellie; you know I am getting a big boy, and I must go out and see the world."

"I know you must," said Ellie; "but you will not forget me, Tom. I shall wait here till you come."

And she shook hands with him, and bade him good-bye. Tom longed very much again to kiss her; but he thought it would not be respectful, considering she was a lady born; so he promised not to forget her: but his little whirl-about of a head was so full of the notion of going out to see the world, that it forgot her in five minutes: however, though his head forgot her, I am glad to say his heart did not.

So he asked all the beasts in the sea, and all the birds in the air, but none of them knew the way to Shiny Wall. For why? He was still too far down south.

Then he met a ship, far larger than he had ever seen —a gallant ocean-steamer, with a long cloud of smoke trailing behind; and he wondered how she went on without sails, and swam up to her to see. A school of dolphins were running races round and round her, going three feet for her one, and Tom asked them the way to Shiny Wall: but they did not know. Then he tried to find out how she moved, and at last he saw her screw, and was so delighted with it that he played under her quarter all day, till he nearly had his nose knocked off by the fans, and thought it time to move. Then he watched the sailors upon deck, and the ladies, with their bonnets and parasols: but none of them could see him, because their eyes were not opened—as, indeed, most people's eyes are not.

At last there came out into the quarter-gallery a very pretty lady, in deep black widow's weeds, and in her arms a baby. She leaned over the quarter-gallery, and looked back and back toward England far away; and as she looked she sang:

I.

"Soft soft wind, from out the sweet south sliding,
Waft thy silver cloud-webs athwart the summer sea;
Thin thin threads of mist on dewy fingers twining
Weave a veil of dappled gauze to shade my babe and me.

II.

"Deep deep Love, within thine own abyss abiding,
Pour Thyself abroad, O Lord, on earth and air and sea;
Worn weary hearts within Thy holy temple hiding,
Shield from sorrow, sin, and shame my helpless babe and me."

Her voice was so soft and low, and the music of the

air so sweet, that Tom could have listened to it all day. But as she held the baby over the gallery-rail, to show it the dolphins leaping and the water gurgling in the ship's wake, lo! and behold, the baby saw Tom.

He was quite sure of that; for when their eyes met, the baby smiled and held out its hands; and Tom smiled and held out his hands too; and the baby kicked and leaped, as if it wanted to jump overboard to him.

"What do you see, my darling?" said the lady; and her eyes followed the baby's till she too caught sight of Tom, swimming about among the foam-beads below.

She gave a little shriek and start; and then she said, quite quietly, "Babies in the sea? Well, perhaps it is the happiest place for them," and waved her hand to Tom, and cried, "Wait a little, darling, only a little: and perhaps we shall go with you and be at rest."

And at that an old nurse, all in black, came out and talked to her, and drew her in. And Tom turned away northward, sad and wondering; and watched the great steamer slide away into the dusk, and the lights on board peep out one by one, and die out again, and the long bar of smoke fade away into the evening mist, till all was out of sight.

And he swam northward again, day after day, till at last he met the King of the Herrings, with a currycomb growing out of his nose, and a sprat in his mouth for a cigar, and asked him the way to Shiny Wall; so he bolted his sprat head foremost, and said:

"If I were you, young gentleman, I should go to the Allalonestone, and ask the last of the Gairfowl. She is of a very ancient clan, very nearly as ancient as my own; and knows a good deal which these modern upstarts don't, as ladies of old houses are likely to do."

Tom asked his way to her, and the King of the Herrings told him very kindly; for he was a courteous old gentleman of the old school, though he was horribly ugly, and strangely bedizened too, like the old dandies who lounge in the club-house windows.

But just as Tom had thanked him and set off, he called after him: "Hi! I say, can you fly?"

"I never tried," says Tom.   "Why?"

"Because, if you can, I should advise you to say nothing to the old lady about it.   There; take a hint. Good-bye."

And away Tom went for seven days and seven nights due north-west, till he came to a great codbank, the like of which he never saw before.   The great cod lay below in tens of thousands, and gobbled shell-fish all day long; and the blue sharks roved above in hundreds, and gobbled them when they came up.   So they ate, and ate, and ate each other, as they had done since the making of the world; for no man had come here yet to catch them, and find out how rich old Mother Carey is.

And there he saw the last of the Gairfowl, standing up on the Allalonestone, all alone.   And a very grand old lady she was, full three feet high, and bolt upright, like some old Highland chieftainess.   She had on a black velvet gown, and a white pinner and apron, and a very high bridge to her nose (which is a sure mark of high breeding), and a large pair of white spectacles on it, which made her look rather odd: but it was the ancient fashion of her house.

And instead of wings, she had two little feathery arms, with which she fanned herself, and complained of the dreadful heat; and she kept on crooning an old song to herself, which she learnt when she was a little baby-bird, long ago—

> "Two little birds, they sat on a stone,
>   One swam away, and then there was one;
>   With a fal-lal-la-lady.
>
> The other swam after, and then there was none,
>   And so the poor stone was left all alone;
>   With a fal-lal-la-lady."

It was "flew" away, properly, and not "swam" away: but, as she could not fly, she had a right to alter it. However, it was a very fit song for her to sing, because she was a lady herself.

Tom came up to her very humbly, and made his bow; and the first thing she said was—

"Have you wings? Can you fly?"

"Oh dear, no, ma'am; I should not think of such a thing," said cunning little Tom.

"Then I shall have great pleasure in talking to you, my dear. It is quite refreshing nowadays to see anything without wings. They must all have wings, forsooth, now, every new upstart sort of bird, and fly. What can they want with flying, and raising themselves above their proper station in life? In the days of my ancestors no birds ever thought of having wings, and did very well without; and now they all laugh at me because I keep to the good old fashion. Why, the very marrocks and dovekies have got wings, the vulgar creatures, and poor little ones enough they are; and my own cousins too, the razor-bills, who are gentlefolk born, and ought to know better than to ape their inferiors."

And so she was running on, while Tom tried to get in a word edgeways; and at last he did, when the old lady got out of breath, and began fanning herself again; and then he asked if she knew the way to Shiny Wall.

"Shiny Wall? Who should know better than I? We all came from Shiny Wall, thousands of years ago, when it was decently cold, and the climate was fit for gentlefolk; but now, what with the heat, and what with these vulgar-winged things who fly up and down and eat everything, so that gentlepeople's hunting is all spoilt, and one really cannot get one's living, or hardly venture off the rock for fear of being flown against by some creature that would not have dared to come within a mile of one a thousand years ago—what was I saying? Why, we have quite gone down in the world, my dear, and have nothing left but our honour. And I am the last of my family. A friend of mine and I came and settled on this rock when we were young, to be out of the way of low people. Once we were a great nation, and spread over all the Northern Isles. But men shot us so, and knocked us on the head, and took our eggs— why, if you will believe it, they say that on the coast of Labrador the sailors used to lay a plank from the rock on board the thing they called their ship, and drive us

along the plank by hundreds, till we tumbled down into
the ship's waist in heaps; and then, I suppose, they ate
us, the nasty fellows! Well—but—what was I saying?
At last there were none of us left, except on the old
Gairfowlskerry, just off the Iceland coast, up which no
man could climb. Even there we had no peace; for
one day, when I was quite a young girl, the land rocked,
and the sea boiled, and the sky grew dark, and all the
air was filled with smoke and dust, and down tumbled
the old Gairfowlskerry into the sea. The dovekies and
marrocks, of course, all flew away; but we were too
proud to do that. Some of us were dashed to pieces,
and some drowned; and those who were left got away
to Eldey, and the dovekies tell me they are all dead now,
and that another Gairfowlskerry has risen out of the sea
close to the old one, but that it is such a poor flat place
that it is not safe to live on: and so here I am left
alone."

This was the Gairfowl's story, and, strange as it may
seem, it is every word of it true.

"If you only had had wings!" said Tom; "then you
might all have flown away too."

"Yes, young gentleman: and if people are not gentlemen and ladies, and forget that *noblesse oblige*, they will
find it as easy to get on in the world as other people who
don't care what they do. Why, if I had not recollected
that *noblesse oblige*, I should not have been all alone now."
And the poor old lady sighed.

"How was that, ma'am?"

"Why, my dear, a gentleman came hither with me,
and after we had been here some time, he wanted to
marry—in fact, he actually proposed to me. Well, I
can't blame him; I was young, and very handsome then,
I don't deny: but you see, I could not hear of such
a thing, because he was my deceased sister's husband,
you see?"

"Of course not, ma'am," said Tom; though, of course,
he knew nothing about it. "She was very much diseased,
I suppose?"

"You do not understand me, my dear. I mean, that

being a lady, and with right and honourable feelings, as
our house always has had, I felt it my duty to snub him,
and howk him, and peck him continually, to keep him at
his proper distance; and, to tell the truth, I once pecked
him a little too hard, poor fellow, and he tumbled backwards off the rock, and—really, it was very unfortunate,
but it was not my fault—a shark coming by saw him
flapping, and snapped him up. And since then I have
lived all alone—

> With a fal-lal-la-lady.

And soon I shall be gone, my little dear, and nobody will
miss me; and then the poor stone will be left all alone."

"But, please, which is the way to Shiny Wall?" said
Tom.

"Oh, you must go, my little dear—you must go. Let
me see—I am sure—that is—really, my poor old brains
are getting quite puzzled. Do you know, my little dear,
I am afraid, if you want to know, you must ask some of
these vulgar birds about, for I have quite forgotten."

And the poor old Gairfowl began to cry tears of pure
oil; and Tom was quite sorry for her; and for himself
too, for he was at his wit's end whom to ask.

But by there came a flock of petrels, who are Mother
Carey's own chickens; and Tom thought them much
prettier than Lady Gairfowl, and so perhaps they were;
for Mother Carey had had a great deal of fresh experience
between the time that she invented the Gairfowl and the
time that she invented them. They flitted along like a
flock of black swallows, and hopped and skipped from
wave to wave, lifting up their little feet behind them so
daintily, and whistling to each other so tenderly, that
Tom fell in love with them at once, and called them to
know the way to Shiny Wall.

"Shiny Wall? Do you want Shiny Wall? Then come
with us, and we will show you. We are Mother Carey's
own chickens, and she sends us out over all the seas, to
show the good birds the way home."

Tom was delighted, and swam off to them, after he had
made his bow to the Gairfowl. But she would not return

his bow : but held herself bolt upright, and wept tears of oil as she sang :

> "And so the poor stone was left all alone ;
> With a fal-lal-la-lady."

But she was wrong there ; for the stone was not left all alone : and the next time that Tom goes by it, he will see a sight worth seeing.

The old Gairfowl is gone already : but there are better things come in her place ; and when Tom comes he will see the fishing-smacks anchored there in hundreds, from Scotland, and from Ireland, and from the Orkneys, and the Shetlands, and from all the Northern ports, full of the children of the old Norse Vikings, the masters of the sea.   And the men will be hauling in the great cod by thousands, till their hands are sore from the lines ; and they will be making cod-liver oil and guano, and salting down the fish ; and there will be a man-of-war steamer there to protect them, and a lighthouse to show them the way ; and you and I, perhaps, shall go some day to the Allalonestone to the great summer sea-fair, and dredge strange creatures such as man never saw before ; and we shall hear the sailors boast that it is not the worst jewel in Queen Victoria's crown, for there are eighty miles of codbank, and food for all the poor folk in the land. That is what Tom will see, and perhaps you and I shall see it too.   And then we shall not be sorry because we cannot get a Gairfowl to stuff, much less find gairfowl enough to drive them into stone pens and slaughter them, as the old Norsemen did, or drive them on board along a plank till the ship was victualled with them, as the old English and French rovers used to do, of whom dear old Hakluyt tells : but we shall remember what Mr. Tennyson says, how

> " The old order changeth, giving place to the new,
> And God fulfils Himself in many ways."

And now Tom was all agog to start for Shiny Wall ; but the petrels said no.   They must go first to Allfowlsness, and wait there for the great gathering of all the seabirds, before they start for their summer breeding-places far away in the Northern isles ; and there they would be sure to find some birds which were going to Shiny Wall : but where Allfowlsness was, he must promise never to tell, lest men should go there and shoot the birds, and stuff them, and put them into stupid museums, instead of leaving them to play and breed and work in Mother Carey's water-garden, where they ought to be.

So where Allfowlsness is nobody must know ; and all that is to be said about it is, that Tom waited there many days ; and as he waited, he saw a very curious sight. On the rabbit burrows on the shore there gathered hundreds and hundreds of hoodiecrows, such as you see in Cambridgeshire. And they made such a noise, that Tom came on shore and went up to see what was the matter.

And there he found them holding their great caucus, which they hold every year in the North ; and all their stump-orators were speechifying ; and for a tribune, the speaker stood on an old sheep's skull.

And they cawed and cawed, and boasted of all the clever things they had done ; how many lambs' eyes they had picked out, and how many dead bullocks they had eaten, and how many young grouse they had swallowed whole, and how many grouse-eggs they had flown away with, stuck on the point of their bills, which is the hoodie-crow's particularly clever feat, of which he is as proud as a gipsy is of doing the hokany-baro ; and what that is, I won't tell you.

And at last they brought out the prettiest, neatest young lady-crow that ever was seen, and set her in the middle, and all began abusing and vilifying, and rating, and bullyragging at her, because she had stolen no grouse-eggs, and had actully dared to say that she would not steal any. So she was to be tried publicly by their laws (for the hoodies always try some offenders in their great yearly parliament). And there she stood in the middle, in her black gown and grey hood, looking as meek and as neat as a quakeress, and they all bawled at her at once—

And it was in vain that she pleaded

That she did not like grouse-eggs ;

That she could get her living very well without them ;

That she was afraid to eat them, for fear of the gamekeepers ;

That she had not the heart to eat them, because the grouse were such pretty, kind, jolly birds ;

And a dozen reasons more.

For all the other scaul-crows set upon her, and pecked her to death there and then, before Tom could come to help her ; and then flew away, very proud of what they had done.

Now, was not this a scandalous transaction ?

But they are true republicans, these hoodies, who do every one just what he likes, and make other people do so too, so that, for any freedom of speech, thought, or action, which is allowed among them, they might as well be American citizens of the new school.

But the fairies took the good crow, and gave her nine new sets of feathers running, and turned her at last into the most beautiful bird of paradise with a green velvet suit and a long tail, and sent her to eat fruit in the Spice Islands, where cloves and nutmegs grow.

And Mrs. Bedonebyasyoudid settled her account with the wicked hoodies. For, as they flew away, what should they find but a nasty dead dog ?—on which they all set to work, pecking and gobbling and cawing and quarrelling, to their hearts' content. But the moment afterwards, they all threw up their bills into the air, and gave one screech ; and then turned head over heels backward, and fell down dead, one hundred and twenty-three of them at once. For why ? The fairy had told the gamekeeper in a dream, to fill the dead dog full of strychnine ; and so he did.

And after a while the birds began to gather at All-fowlsness, in thousands and tens of thousands, blackening all the air ; swans and brant geese, harlequins and eiders, harelds and garganeys, smews and goosanders, divers and loons, grebes and dovekies, auks and razorbills, gannets and petrels, skuas and terns, with gulls beyond all naming or numbering ; and they paddled and

washed and splashed and combed and brushed themselves on the sand, till the shore was white with feathers;
and they quacked and clucked and gabbled and chattered
and screamed and whooped as they talked over matters
with their friends, and settled where they were to go and
breed that summer, till you might have heard them ten
miles off; and lucky it was for them that there was no one
to hear them but the old keeper, who lived all alone upon
the Ness, in a turf hut thatched with heather and fringed
round with great stones slung across the roof by bent-
ropes, lest the winter gales should blow the hut right away.
But he never minded the birds nor hurt them, because
they were not in season: indeed, he minded but two
things in the whole world, and those were, his Bible and
his grouse; for he was as good an old Scotchman as ever
knit stockings on a winter's night: only, when all the
birds were going, he toddled out, and took off his cap to
them, and wished them a merry journey and a safe
return; and then gathered up all the feathers which they
had left, and cleaned them to sell down south, and make
feather-beds for stuffy people to lie on.

Then the petrels asked this bird and that whether they
would take Tom to Shiny Wall: but one set was going to
Sutherland, and one to the Shetlands, and one to Norway,
and one to Spitzbergen, and one to Iceland, and one to
Greenland; but none would go to Shiny Wall. So the
good-natured petrels said that they would show him part
of the way themselves, but they were only going as far
as Jan Mayen's land; and after that he must shift for
himself.

And then all the birds rose up, and streamed away in
long black lines, north, and north-east, and north-west,
across the bright blue summer sky; and their cry was
like ten thousand packs of hounds, and ten thousand
peals of bells. Only the puffins stayed behind, and
killed the young rabbits, and laid their eggs in the
rabbit-burrows; which was rough practice, certainly:
but a man must see to his own family.

And, as Tom and the petrels went north-eastward, it
began to blow right hard; for the old gentleman in the

grey great-coat, who looks after the big copper boiler in the gulf of Mexico, had got behind-hand with his work ; so Mother Carey had sent an electric message to him for more steam ; and now the steam was coming, as much in an hour as ought to have come in a week, puffing and roaring and swishing and swirling, till you could not see where the sky ended and the sea began. But Tom and the petrels never cared, for the gale was right abaft, and away they went over the crests of the billows, as merry as so many flying-fish.

And at last they saw an ugly sight—the black side of a great ship, water-logged in the trough of the sea. Her funnel and her masts were overboard, and swayed and surged under her lee ; her decks were swept as clean as a barn floor, and there was no living soul on board.

The petrels flew up to her, and wailed round her ; for they were very sorry indeed, and also they expected to find some salt pork ; and Tom scrambled on board of her and looked round, frightened and sad.

And there, in a little cot, lashed tight under the bulwark, lay a baby fast asleep ; the very same baby, Tom saw at once, which he had seen in the singing lady's arms.

He went up to it, and wanted to wake it : but behold, from under the cot out jumped a little black and tan terrier dog, and began barking and snapping at Tom, and would not let him touch the cot.

Tom knew the dog's teeth could not hurt him : but at least it could shove him away, and did ; and he and the dog fought and struggled, for he wanted to help the baby, and did not want to throw the poor dog overboard : but, as they were struggling, there came a tall green sea, and walked in over the weather side of the ship, and swept them all into the waves.

" Oh, the baby, the baby ! " screamed Tom : but the next moment he did not scream at all ; for he saw the cot settling down through the green water, with the baby smiling in it, fast asleep ; and he saw the fairies come up from below, and carry baby and cradle gently down in their soft arms ; and then he knew it was all right, and that there would be a new water-baby in St. Brandan's Isle.

And the poor little dog?

Why, after he had kicked and coughed a little, he sneezed so hard, that he sneezed himself clean out of his skin, and turned into a water-dog, and jumped and danced round Tom, and ran over the crests of the waves, and snapped at the jelly-fish and the mackerel, and followed Tom the whole way to the Other-end-of-No-where.

Then they went on again, till they began to see the peak of Jan Mayen's Land, standing up like a white sugar-loaf, two miles above the clouds.

And there they fell in with a whole flock of molly-mocks, who were feeding on a dead whale.

" These are the fellows to show you the way," said Mother Carey's chickens; " we cannot help you further north. We don't like to get among the ice pack, for fear it should nip our toes; but the mollys dare fly anywhere."

So the petrels called to the mollys: but they were so busy and greedy, gobbling and pecking and spluttering and fighting over the blubber, that they did not take the least notice.

" Come, come," said the petrels, " you lazy greedy lubbers, this young gentleman is going to Mother Carey, and if you don't attend on him, you won't earn your discharge from her, you know."

" Greedy we are," says a great fat old molly, " but lazy we ain't; and, as for lubbers, we're no more lubbers than you. Let's have a look at the lad."

And he flapped right into Tom's face, and stared at him in the most impudent way (for the mollys are audacious fellows, as all whalers know), and then asked him where he hailed from, and what land he sighted last.

And, when Tom told him, he seemed pleased, and said he was a good plucked one to have got so far.

" Come along, lads," he said to the rest, " and give this little chap a cast over the pack, for Mother Carey's sake. We've eaten blubber enough for to-day, and we'll e'en work out a bit of our time by helping the lad."

So the mollys took Tom up on their backs, and flew off with him, laughing and joking—and oh, how they did smell of train oil !

"Who are you, you jolly birds ?" asked Tom.

" We are the spirits of the old Greenland skippers (as every sailor knows), who hunted here, right whales and horse-whales, full hundreds of years agone. But, because we were saucy and greedy, we were all turned into mollys, to eat whale's blubber all our days. But lubbers we are none, and could sail a ship now against any man in the North Seas, though we don't hold with this new-fangled steam. And it's a shame of those black imps of petrels to call us so ; but because they're her grace's pets, they think they may say anything they like."

" And who are you ?" asked Tom of him, for he saw that he was the king of all the birds.

" My name is Hendrick Hudson, and a right good skipper was I ; and my name will last to the world's end, in spite of all the wrong I did. For I discovered Hudson River, and I named Hudson's Bay ; and many have come in my wake that dared not have shown me the way. But I was a hard man in my time, that's truth, and stole the poor Indians off the coast of Maine, and sold them for slaves down in Virginia ; and at last I was so cruel to my sailors, here in these very seas, that they set me adrift in an open boat, and I never was heard of more. So now I'm the king of all the mollys, till I've worked out my time."

And now they came to the edge of the pack, and beyond it they could see Shiny Wall looming, through mist, and snow, and storm. But the pack rolled horribly upon the swell, and the ice giants fought and roared, and leapt upon each other's backs, and ground each other to powder, so that Tom was afraid to venture among them, lest he should be ground to powder too. And he was the more afraid, when he saw lying among the ice pack the wrecks of many a gallant ship ; some with masts and yards all standing, some with the seamen frozen fast on board. Alas, alas, for them! They were all true English hearts; and they came to their end like good knights-errant, in searching for the white gate that never was opened yet.

But the good mollys took Tom and his dog up, and flew with them safe over the pack and the roaring ice giants, and set them down at the foot of Shiny Wall.

"And where is the gate?" asked Tom.

"There is no gate," said the mollys.

"No gate?" cried Tom aghast.

"None; never a crack of one, and that's the whole of the secret, as better fellows, lad, than you have found to their cost; and if there had been, they'd have killed by now every right whale that swims the sea."

"What am I to do, then?"

"Dive under the floe, to be sure, if you have pluck."

"I've not come so far to turn now," said Tom; "so here goes for a header."

"A lucky voyage to you, lad," said the mollys; "we knew you were one of the right sort. So good-bye."

"Why don't you come too?" asked Tom.

But the mollys only wailed sadly, "We can't go yet, we can't go yet," and flew away over the pack.

So Tom dived under the great white gate which never was opened yet, and went on in black darkness, at the bottom of the sea, for seven days and seven nights. And yet he was not a bit frightened. Why should he be? He was a brave English lad, whose business is to go out and see all the world.

And at last he saw the light, and clear clear water overhead; and up he came a thousand fathoms, among clouds of sea-moths, which fluttered round his head. There were moths with pink heads and wings and opal bodies, that flapped about slowly; moths with brown wings that flapped about quickly; yellow shrimps that hopped and skipped most quickly of all; and jellies of all the colours in the world, that neither hopped nor skipped, but only dawdled and yawned, and would not get out of his way. The dog snapped at them till his jaws were tired: but Tom hardly minded them at all, he was so eager to get to the top of the water, and see the pool where the good whales go.

And a very large pool it was, miles and miles across, though the air was so clear that the ice cliffs on the opposite side looked as if they were close at hand. All round it the ice cliffs rose, in walls and spires and battlements, and caves and bridges, and stories and galleries, in which the ice-fairies live, and drive away the storms and clouds, that Mother Carey's pool may lie calm from year's end to year's end. And the sun acted policeman, and walked round outside every day, peeping just over the top of the ice wall, to see that all went right; and now and then he played conjuring tricks, or had an exhibition of fireworks, to amuse the ice-fairies. For he would make himself into four or five suns at once, or paint the sky with rings and crosses and crescents of white fire, and stick himself in the middle of them, and wink at the fairies; and I dare say they were very much amused; for anything's fun in the country.

And there the good whales lay, the happy sleepy beasts, upon the still oily sea. They were all right whales, you must know, and finners, and razor-backs, and bottle-noses, and spotted sea-unicorns with long ivory horns. But the sperm whales are such raging, ramping, roaring, rumbustious fellows, that, if Mother Carey let them in, there would be no more peace in Peacepool. So she packs them away in a great pond by themselves at the South Pole, two hundred and sixty-three miles south-south-east of Mount Erebus, the great volcano in the ice; and there they butt each other with their ugly noses, day and night from year's end to year's end. And if they think that sport—why, so do their American cousins.

But here there were only good quiet beasts, lying about like the black hulls of sloops, and blowing every now and then jets of white steam, or sculling round with their huge mouths open, for the sea-moths to swim down their throats. There were no threshers there to thresh their poor old backs, or sword-fish to stab their stomachs, or saw-fish to rip them up, or ice-sharks to bite lumps out of their sides, or whalers to harpoon and lance them. They were quite safe and happy there; and all they had to do was to wait quietly in Peacepool, till Mother Carey sent for them to make them out of old beasts into new.

Tom swam up to the nearest whale, and asked the way to Mother Carey.

"There she sits in the middle," said the whale.

Tom looked; but he could see nothing in the middle of the pool, but one peaked iceberg: and he said so.

"That's Mother Carey," said the whale, "as you will find when you get to her. There she sits making old beasts into new all the year round."

"How does she do that?"

"That's her concern, not mine," said the old whale; and yawned so wide (for he was very large) that there swam into his mouth 943 sea-moths, 13,846 jelly-fish no bigger than pins' heads, a string of salpæ nine yards long, and forty-three little ice-crabs, who gave each other a parting pinch all round, tucked their legs under their stomachs, and determined to die decently, like Julius Cæsar.

"I suppose," said Tom, "she cuts up a great whale like you into a whole shoal of porpoises?"

At which the old whale laughed so violently that he coughed up all the creatures; who swam away again very thankful at having escaped out of that terrible whalebone net of his, from which bourne no traveller returns; and Tom went on to the iceberg, wondering.

And, when he came near it, it took the form of the grandest old lady he had ever seen—a white marble lady, sitting on a white marble throne. And from the foot of the throne there swum away, out and out into the sea, millions of new-born creatures, of more shapes and colours than man ever dreamed. And they were Mother Carey's children, whom she makes out of the sea-water all day long.

He expected, of course—like some grown people who ought to know better—to find her snipping, piecing, fitting, stitching, cobbling, basting, filing, planing, hammering, turning, polishing, moulding, measuring, chiselling, clipping, and so forth, as men do when they go to work to make anything.

But, instead of that, she sat quite still with her chin upon her hand, looking down into the sea with two great grand blue eyes, as blue as the sea itself. Her hair was as white as the snow—for she was very very old—in fact, as old as anything which you are likely to come across, except the difference between right and wrong.

And, when she saw Tom, she looked at him very kindly.

"What do you want, my little man? It is long since I have seen a water-baby here."

Tom told her his errand, and asked the way to the Other-end-of-Nowhere.

"You ought to know yourself, for you have been there already."

"Have I, ma'am? I'm sure I forget all about it."

"Then look at me."

And, as Tom looked into her great blue eyes, he recollected the way perfectly.

Now, was not that strange?

"Thank you, ma'am," said Tom. "Then I won't trouble your ladyship any more; I hear you are very busy."

"I am never more busy than I am now," she said, without stirring a finger.

"I heard, ma'am, that you were always making new beasts out of old."

"So people fancy. But I am not going to trouble myself to make things, my little dear. I sit here and make them make themselves."

"You are a clever fairy, indeed," thought Tom. And he was quite right.

That is a grand trick of good old Mother Carey's, and a grand answer, which she has had occasion to make several times to impertinent people.

There was once, for instance, a fairy who was so clever that she found out how to make butterflies. I don't mean sham ones; no : but real live ones, which would fly, and eat, and lay eggs, and do everything that they ought; and she was so proud of her skill that she went flying straight off to the North Pole, to boast to Mother Carey how she could make butterflies.

But Mother Carey laughed.

"Know, silly child," she said, "that any one can make things, if they will take time and trouble enough: but it is not every one who, like me, can make things make themselves."

But people do not yet believe that Mother Carey is as clever as all that comes to; and they will not till they, too, go the journey to the Other-end-of-Nowhere.

"And now, my pretty little man," said Mother Carey, "you are sure you know the way to the Other-end-of-Nowhere?"

Tom thought; and behold, he had forgotten it utterly.

"That is because you took your eyes off me."

Tom looked at her again, and recollected; and then looked away, and forgot in an instant.

"But what am I to do, ma'am? For I can't keep looking at you when I am somewhere else."

"You must do without me, as most people have to do, for nine hundred and ninety-nine thousandths of their lives; and look at the dog instead; for he knows the way well enough, and will not forget it. Besides, you may meet some very queer-tempered people there, who will not let you pass without this passport of mine, which you must hang round your neck and take care of; and, of course, as the dog will always go behind you, you must go the whole way backward."

"Backward!" cried Tom. "Then I shall not be able to see my way."

"On the contrary, if you look forward, you will not see a step before you, and be certain to go wrong; but, if you look behind you, and watch carefully whatever you have passed, and especially keep your eye on the dog, who goes by instinct, and therefore can't go wrong, then you will know what is coming next as plainly as if you saw it in a looking-glass."

Tom was very much astonished: but he obeyed her, for he had learnt always to believe what the fairies told him.

"So it is, my dear child," said Mother Carey; "and I will tell you a story, which will show you that I am perfectly right, as it is my custom to be."

"Once on a time, there were two brothers. One was called Prometheus, because he always looked before him, and boasted that he was wise beforehand. The other was called Epimetheus, because he always looked behind him, and did not boast at all; but said humbly, like the Irishman, that he had sooner prophesy after the event.

"Well, Prometheus was a very clever fellow, of course, and invented all sorts of wonderful things. But, unfortunately, when they were set to work, to work was just what they would not do: wherefore very little has come of them, and very little is left of them; and now nobody knows what they were, save a few archæological old gentlemen who scratch in queer corners, and find little there save Ptinum Furem, Blaptem Mortisagam, Acarum Horridum, and Tineam Laciniarum.

"But Epimetheus was a very slow fellow, certainly, and went among men for a clod, and a muff, and a milksop, and a slowcoach, and a bloke, and a boodle, and so forth. And very little he did, for many years: but what he did, he never had to do over again.

"And what happened at last? There came to the two brothers the most beautiful creature that ever was seen, Pandora by name; which means, All the gifts of the Gods. But because she had a strange box in her hand, this fanciful, forecasting, suspicious, prudential, theoretical, deductive, prophesying Prometheus, who was always settling what was going to happen, would have nothing to do with pretty Pandora and her box.

"But Epimetheus took her and it, as he took everything that came; and married her for better for worse, as every man ought, whenever he has even the chance of a good wife. And they opened the box between them, of course, to see what was inside: for, else, of what possible use could it have been to them?

"And out flew all the ills which flesh is heir to; all the children of the four great bogies, Self-will, Ignorance, Fear, and Dirt—for instance :

Measles,	Famines,
Monks,	Quacks,
Scarlatina,	Unpaid bills,
Idols,	Tight stays,
Hooping-coughs,	Potatoes,
Popes,	Bad Wine,
Wars,	Despots,
Peacemongers,	Demagogues,

And, worst of all, Naughty Boys and Girls : But one thing remained at the bottom of the box, and that was, Hope.

"So Epimetheus got a great deal of trouble, as most men do in this world : but he got the three best things in the world into the bargain—a good wife, and experience, and hope : while Prometheus had just as much trouble, and a great deal more (as you will hear), of his own making ; with nothing beside, save fancies spun out of his own brain, as a spider spins her web out of her stomach.

"And Prometheus kept on looking before him so far ahead, that as he was running about with a box of lucifers (which were the only useful things he ever invented, and do as much harm as good), he trod on his own nose, and tumbled down (as most deductive philosophers do), whereby he set the Thames on fire; and they have hardly put it out again yet. So he had to be chained to the top of a mountain, with a vulture by him to give him a peck whenever he stirred, lest he should turn the whole world upside down with his prophecies and his theories.

"But stupid old Epimetheus went working and grubbing on, with the help of his wife Pandora, always looking behind him to see what had happened, till he really learnt to know now and then what would happen next ; and understood so well which side his bread was buttered, and which way the cat jumped, that he began to make things which would work, and go on working, too; to till and drain the ground, and to make looms, and ships, and railroads, and steam ploughs, and electric telegraphs, and all the things which you see in the Great Exhibition; and to foretell famine, and bad weather, and the price of stocks, and the end of President Lincoln's policy; till as last he grew as rich as a Jew, and as fat as a farmer; and people thought twice before they meddled with him, and only once before they asked him to help them; for, because he earned his money well, he could afford to spend it well likewise.

"And his children are the men of science, who get good lasting work done in the world: but the children of Prometheus are the fanatics, and the theorists, and the bigots, and the bores, and the noisy windy people, who go telling silly folk what will happen, instead of looking to see what has happened already."

Now, was not Mother Carey's a wonderful story? And, I am happy to say, Tom believed it every word.

For so it happened to Tom likewise. He was very sorely tried; for though, by keeping the dog to heels (or rather to toes, for he had to walk backward), he could see pretty well which way the dog was hunting, yet it was much slower work to go backwards than to go forwards. But, what was more trying still, no sooner had he got out of Peacepool, than there came running to him all the conjurors, fortune-tellers, astrologers, prophesiers, projectors, prestigiators, as many as were in those parts (and there are too many of them everywhere), Old Mother Shipton on her broomstick, with Merlin, Thomas the Rhymer, Gerbertus, Rabanus Maurus, Nostradamus, Zadkiel, Raphael Moore, Old Nixon, and a good many in black coats and white ties who might have known better, considering in what century they were born, all bawling and screaming at him, "Look a-head, only look a-head; and we will show you what man never saw before, and right away to the end of the world!"

But I am proud to say that, though Tom had not been at Cambridge—for, if he had, he would have certainly been senior wrangler—he was such a little dogged, hard, gnarly, foursquare brick of an English boy, that he never turned his head round once all the way from Peacepool to the Other-end-of-Nowhere: but kept his eye on the dog, and let him pick out the scent, hot or cold, straight or crooked, wet or dry, up hill or down dale; by which means he never made a single mistake, and saw all the wonderful and hitherto by-no-mortal-man-imagined things, which it is my duty to relate to you in the next chapter.

CHAPTER VIll AND LAST

" Come to me, O ye children !
For I hear you at your play ;
And the questions that perplexed me
Have vanished quite away.

Ye open the Eastern windows,
That look towards the sun,
Where thoughts are singing swallows,
And the brooks of morning run.

.   .   .   .   .

For what are all our contrivings
And the wisdom of our books,
When compared with your caresses,
And the gladness of your looks ?

Ye are better than all the ballads
That ever were sung or said ;
For ye are living poems,
*And **all** the rest are dead."*

—LONGFELLOW.

CHAPTER VIII AND LAST

ERE begins the never-to-be-too-much-studied account of the nine-hundred-and-ninety-ninth part of the wonderful things which Tom saw, on his journey to the Other-end-of-Nowhere; which all good little children are requested to read; that, if ever they get to the Other-end-of-Nowhere, as they may very probably do, they may not burst out laughing, or try to run away, or do any other silly vulgar thing which may offend Mrs. Bedonebyasyoudid.

Now, as soon as Tom had left Peacepool, he came to the white lap of the great sea-mother, ten thousand fathoms deep; where she makes world-pap all day long, for the steam-giants to knead, and the fire-giants to bake, till it has risen and hardened into mountain-loaves and island-cakes.

And there Tom was very near being kneaded up in the world-pap, and turned into a fossil water-baby; which would have astonished the Geological Society of New Zealand some hundreds of thousands of years hence.

For, as he walked along in the silence of the sea-twilight, on the soft white ocean floor, he was aware of a hissing, and a roaring, and a thumping, and a pumping, as of all the steam-engines in the world at once. And, when he came near, the water grew boiling hot; not that that hurt him in the least: but it also grew as foul as gruel; and every moment he stumbled over dead shells, and fish, and sharks, and seals, and whales, which had been killed by the hot water.

And at last he came to the great sea-serpent himself, lying dead at the bottom; and, as he was too thick to scramble over, Tom had to walk round him three quarters of a mile and more, which put him out of his path sadly; and, when he had got round, he came to the place called Stop. And there he stopped, and just in time.

For he was on the edge of a vast hole in the bottom of the sea, up which was rushing and roaring clear steam enough to work all the engines in the world at once; so clear, indeed, that it was quite light at moments; and Tom could see almost up to the top of the water above, and down below into the pit for nobody knows how far.

But, as soon as he bent his head over the edge, he got such a rap on the nose from pebbles, that he jumped back again; for the steam, as it rushed up, rasped away the sides of the hole, and hurled it up into the sea in a shower of mud and gravel and ashes; and then it spread all around, and sank again, and covered in the dead fish so fast, that before Tom had stood there five minutes he was buried in silt up to his ancles, and began to be afraid that he should have been buried alive.

And perhaps he would have been, but that while he was thinking, the whole piece of ground on which he stood was torn off and blown upwards, and away flew Tom a mile up through the sea, wondering what was coming next.

At last he stopped—thump! and found himself tight in the legs of the most wonderful bogy which he had ever seen.

It had I don't know how many wings, as big as the sails of a windmill, and spread out in a ring like them; and with them it hovered over the steam which rushed up, as a ball hovers over the top of a fountain. And for every wing above it had a leg below, with a claw like a comb at the tip, and a nostril at the root; and in the middle it had no stomach and one eye; and as for its mouth, that was all on one side, as the madreporiform tubercle in a star-fish is. Well, it was a very strange beast; but no stranger than some dozens which you may see.

"What do you want here," it cried quite peevishly, "getting in my way?" and it tried to drop Tom: but he held on tight to its claws, thinking himself safer where he was.

So Tom told him who he was, and what his errand was. And the thing winked its one eye, and sneered:

"I am too old to be taken in in that way. You are come after gold—I know you are."

"Gold! What is gold?" And really Tom did not know; but the suspicious old bogy would not believe him.

But after a while Tom began to understand a little. For, as the vapours came up out of the hole, the bogy smelt them with his nostrils, and combed them and sorted them with his combs; and then, when they steamed up through them against his wings, they were changed into showers and streams of metal. From one wing fell gold-dust, and from another silver, and from another copper, and from another tin, and from another lead, and so on, and sank into the soft mud, into veins and cracks, and hardened there. Whereby it comes to pass that the rocks are full of metal.

But, all of a sudden, somebody shut off the steam below, and the hole was left empty in an instant: and then down rushed the water into the hole, in such a whirlpool that the bogy spun round and round as fast as a tee-totum. But that was all in his day's work, like a fair fall with the hounds; so all he did was to say to Tom—

"Now is your time, youngster, to get down, if you are in earnest, which I don't believe."

"You'll soon see," said Tom; and away he went, as bold as Baron Munchausen, and shot down the rushing cataract like a salmon at Ballisodare.

And, when he got to the bottom, he swam till he was washed on shore safe upon the Other-end-of-Nowhere; and he found it, to his surprise, as most other people do, much more like This-End-of-Somewhere than he had been in the habit of expecting.

And first he went through Waste-paper-land, where all the stupid books lie in heaps, up hill and down dale, like leaves in a winter wood; and there he saw people digging and grubbing among them, to make worse books out of bad ones, and thrashing chaff to save the dust of it; and a very good trade they drove thereby, especially among children.

Then he went by the sea of slops, to the mountain of messes, and the territory of tuck, where the ground was very sticky, for it was all made of bad toffee (not Everton toffee, of course), and full of deep cracks and holes choked with wind-fallen fruit, and green gooseberries, and sloes, and crabs, and whinberries, and hips and haws, and all the nasty things which little children will eat if they can get them. But the fairies hide them out of the way in that country as fast as they can, and very hard work they have, and of very little use it is. For as fast as they hide away the old trash, foolish and wicked people make fresh trash full of lime and poisonous paints, and actually go and steal receipts out of old Madame Science's big book to invent poisons for little children, and sell them at wakes and fairs and tuck-shops. Very well. Let them go on. Dr. Letheby and Dr. Hassall cannot catch them, though they are setting traps for them all day long. But the Fairy with the birch-rod will catch them all in time, and make them begin at one corner of their shops, and eat their way out at the other: by which time they will have got such stomach-aches as will cure them of poisoning little children.

Next he saw all the little people in the world, writing all the little books in the world, about all the other little people in the world; probably because they had no great people to write about: and if the names of the books were not Squeeky, nor the Pumplighter, nor the Narrow Narrow World, nor the Hills of the Chattermuch, nor the Children's Twaddeday, why then they were something else. And all the rest of the little people in the world read the books, and thought themselves each as good as the President; and perhaps they were right, for every one knows his own business best. But Tom thought he would sooner have a jolly good fairy tale, about Jack the Giant-killer or Beauty and the Beast, which taught him something that he didn't know already.

And next he came to the centre of Creation (the hub, they call it there), which lies in latitude 42.21 south, and longitude 108.56 east.

And there he found all the wise people instructing mankind in the science of spirit-rapping, while their house was burning over their heads : and when Tom told them of the fire, they held an indignation meeting forthwith, and unanimously determined to hang Tom's dog for coming into their country with gunpowder in his mouth. Tom couldn't help saying that though they did fancy they had carried all the wit away with them out of Lincolnshire two hundred years ago, yet if they had had one such Lincolnshire nobleman among them as good old Lord Yarborough, he would have called for the fire-engines before he hanged other people's dogs. But it was of no use, and the dog was hanged : and Tom couldn't even have his carcase ; for they had abolished the have-his-carcase act in that country, for fear lest when rogues fell out, honest men should come by their own. And so they would have succeeded perfectly, as they always do, only that (as they also always do) they failed in one little particular, viz. that the dog would not die, being a water-dog, but bit their fingers so abominably that they were forced to let him go, and Tom likewise, as British subjects. Whereon they recommenced rapping for the spirits of their fathers ; and very much astonished the poor old spirits were when they came, and saw how, according to the laws of Mrs. Bedonebyasyoudid, their descendants had weakened their constitution by hard living.

Then came Tom to the Island of Polupragmosyne, which some call Rogues' Harbour (but they are wrong ; for that is in the middle of Bramshill Bushes, and the county police have cleared it out long ago). There every one knows his neighbour's business better than his own ; and a very noisy place it is, as might be expected, considering that all the inhabitants are ex-officio on the wrong side of the house in the " Parliament of Man, and the Federation of the World"; and are always making wry mouths, and crying that the fairies' grapes were sour.

There Tom saw ploughs drawing horses, nails driving hammers, birds' nests taking boys, books making authors, bulls keeping china-shops, monkeys shaving cats, dead dogs drilling live lions, blind brigadiers shelfed as principals of colleges, play-actors not in the least shelfed as popular preachers; and, in short, every one set to do something which he had not learnt, because in what he had learnt, or pretended to learn, he had failed.

There stands the Pantheon of the great Unsuccessful, from the builders of the Tower of Babel to those of the Trafalgar Fountains; in which politicians lecture on the constitutions which ought to have marched, conspirators on the revolutions which ought to have succeeded, economists on the schemes which ought to have made every one's fortune, projectors on the discoveries which ought to have set the Thames on fire; and (in due time) presidents on the union which ought to have re-united, and secretaries of state on the greenbacks which ought to have done just as well as hard money. There cobblers lecture on orthopedy (whatsoever that may be) because they cannot sell their shoes; and poets on Æsthetics (whatsoever that may be) because they cannot sell their poetry. There philosophers demonstrate that England would be the freest and richest country in the world, if she would only turn Papist again; penny-a-liners abuse the *Times*, because they have not wit enough to get on its staff; and young ladies walk about with lockets of Charles the First's hair (or of somebody else's, when the Jews' genuine stock is used up), inscribed with the neat and appropriate legend—which indeed is popular through all that land, and which, I hope, you will learn to translate in due time and perpend likewise :—

" Victrix causa diis placuit, sed victa puellis."

When he got into the middle of the town, they all set on him at once, to show him his way; or rather, to show him that he did not know his way; for as for asking him what way he wanted to go, no one ever thought of that.

But one pulled him hither, and another poked him thither, and a third cried—

"You mustn't go west, I tell you; it is destruction to go west."

"But I am not going west, as you may see," said Tom.

And another, "The east lies here, my dear; I assure you this is the east."

"But I don't want to go east," said Tom.

"Well then at all events, whichever way you are going, you are going wrong," cried they all with one voice—which was the only thing which they ever agreed about; and all pointed at once to all the thirty-and-two points of the compass, till Tom thought all the signposts in England had got together, and fallen fighting.

And whether he would have ever escaped out of the town, it is hard to say, if the dog had not taken it into his head that they were going to pull his master in pieces, and tackled them so sharply about the gastrocnemius muscle, that he gave them some business of their own to think of at last; and while they were rubbing their bitten calves, Tom and the dog got safe away.

On the borders of that island he found Gotham, where the wise men live; the same who dragged the pond because the moon had fallen into it, and planted a hedge round the cuckoo, to keep spring all the year. And he found them bricking up the town gate, because it was so wide that little folks could not get through. And, when he asked why, they told him they were expanding their liturgy. So he went on; for it was no business of his: only he could not help saying that in his country, if the kitten could not get in at the same hole as the cat, she might stay outside and mew.

But he saw the end of such fellows, when he came to the island of the Golden Asses, where nothing but thistles grow. For there they were all turned into mokes with ears a yard long, for meddling with matters which they do not understand, as Lucius did in the story. And like him, mokes they must remain, till, by the laws of development, the thistles develop into roses. Till then, they must comfort themselves with the thought, that the longer their ears are, the thicker their hides; and so a good beating don't hurt them.

Then came Tom to the great land of Hearsay, in which are no less than thirty and odd kings, beside half-a-dozen Republics, and perhaps more by next mail.

And there he fell in with a deep, dark, deadly, and destructive war, waged by the princes and potentates of those parts, both spiritual and temporal, against what do you think? One thing I am sure of. That unless I told you, you would never know; nor how they waged that war either; for all their strategy and art military consisted in the safe and easy process of stopping their ears and screaming, "Oh, don't tell us!" and then running away.

So when Tom came into that land, he found them all, high and low, man, woman, and child, running for their lives day and night continually, and entreating not to be told they didn't know what: only the land being an island, and they having a dislike to the water (being a musty lot for the most part) they ran round and round the shore for ever, which (as the island was exactly of the same circumference as the planet on which we have the honour of living) was hard work, especially to those who had business to look after. But before them, as bandmaster and fugleman, ran a gentleman shearing a pig; the melodious strains of which animal led them for ever, if not to conquest, still to flight; and kept up their spirits mightily with the thought that they would at least have the pig's wool for their pains.

And running after them, day and night, came such a poor, lean, seedy, hard-worked old giant, as ought to have been cockered up, and had a good dinner given him, and a good wife found him, and been set to play with little children; and then he would have been a very presentable old fellow after all; for he had a heart, though it was considerably overgrown with brains.

He was made up principally of fish bones and parchment, put together with wire and Canada balsam; and smelt strongly of spirits, though he never drank any-thing but water: but spirits he used somehow, there was no denying. He had a great pair of spectacles on his nose, and a butterfly-net in one hand, and a geological hammer in the other; and was hung all over with pockets, full of collecting boxes, bottles, microscopes, telescopes, barometers, ordnance maps, scalpels, forceps, photographic apparatus, and all other tackle for finding out everything about everything, and a little more too. And, most strange of all, he was running not forwards but backwards, as fast as he could.

Away all the good folks ran from him, except Tom, who stood his ground and dodged between his legs; and the giant, when he had passed him, looked down, and cried, as if he was quite pleased and comforted,—

"What? who are you? And you actually don't run away, like all the rest?" But he had to take his spec-tacles off, Tom remarked, in order to see him plainly.

Tom told him who he was; and the giant pulled out a bottle and a cork instantly, to collect him with.

But Tom was too sharp for that, and dodged between his legs and in front of him; and then the giant could not see him at all.

"No, no, no!" said Tom, "I've not been round the world, and through the world, and up to Mother Carey's haven, beside being caught in a net and called a Holo-thurian and a Cephalopod, to be bottled up by any old giant like you."

And when the giant understood what a great traveller Tom had been, he made a truce with him at once, and would have kept him there to this day to pick his brains, so delighted was he at finding any one to tell him what he did not know before.

"Ah, you lucky little dog!" said he at last, quite simply—for he was the simplest, pleasantest, honestest, kindliest old Dominie Sampson of a giant that ever turned the world upside down without intending it— "Ah, you lucky little dog! If I had only been where you have been, to see what you have seen!"

"Well," said Tom, "if you want to do that, you had

best put your head under water for a few hours, as I did, and turn into a water-baby, or some other baby, and then you might have a chance."

"Turn into a baby, eh? If I could do that, and know what was happening to me for but one hour, I should know everything then, and be at rest. But I can't; I can't be a little child again; and I suppose if I could, it would be no use, because then I should know nothing about what was happening to me. Ah, you lucky little dog!" said the poor old giant.

"But why do you run after all these poor people?" said Tom, who liked the giant very much.

"My dear, it's they that have been running after me, father and son, for hundreds and hundreds of years, throwing stones at me till they have knocked off my spectacles fifty times, and calling me a malignant and a turbaned Turk, who beat a Venetian and traduced the state—goodness only knows what they mean, for I never read poetry—and hunting me round and round—though catch me they can't, for every time I go over the same ground, I go the faster, and grow the bigger. While all I want is to be friends with them, and to tell them something to their advantage, like Mr. Joseph Ady: only somehow they are so strangely afraid of hearing it. But, I suppose I am not a man of the world, and have no tact."

"But why don't you turn round and tell them so?"

"Because I can't. You see, I am one of the sons of Epimetheus, and must go backwards, if I am to go at all."

"But why don't you stop, and let them come up to you?"

"Why, my dear, only think. If I did, all the butter-flies and cockyolybirds would fly past me, and then I could catch no more new species, and should grow rusty and mouldy, and die. And I don't intend to do that, my dear; for I have a destiny before me, they say: though what it is I don't know, and don't care."

"Don't care?" said Tom.

"No. Do the duty which lies nearest you, and catch

the first beetle you come across, is my motto; and I have thriven by it for some hundred years. Now I must go on. Dear me, while I have been talking to you, at least nine new species have escaped me."

And on went the giant, behind before, like a bull in a china shop, till he ran into the steeple of the great idol temple (for they are all idolaters in those parts, of course, else they would never be afraid of giants), and knocked the upper half clean off, hurting himself horribly about the small of the back.

But little he cared; for as soon as the ruins of the steeple were well between his legs, he poked and peered among the falling stones, and shifted his spectacles, and pulled out his pocket-magnifier, and cried—

"An entirely new Oniscus, and three obscure Podurellæ! Beside a moth which M. le Roi des Papillons (though he, like all Frenchmen, is given to hasty inductions) says is confined to the limits of the Glacial Drift. This is most important!"

And down he sat on the nave of the temple (not being a man of the world) to examine his Podurellæ. Whereon (as was to be expected) the roof caved in bodily, smashing the idols, and sending the priests flying out of doors and windows, like rabbits out of a burrow when a ferret goes in.

But he never heeded; for out of the dust flew a bat, and the giant had him in a moment.

"Dear me! This is even more important! Here is a cognate species to that which Macgilliwaukie Brown insists is confined to the Buddhist Temples of Little Thibet; and now when I look at it, it may be only a variety produced by difference of climate!"

And having bagged his bat, up he got, and on he went; while all the people ran, being in none the better humour for having their temple smashed for the sake of three obscure species of Podurella, and a Buddhist bat.

"Well," thought Tom; "this is a very pretty quarrel, with a good deal to be said on both sides. But it is no business of mine."

And no more it was; because he was a water-baby,

and had the original sow by the right ear; which you will never have, unless you be a baby, whether of the water, the land, or the air, matters not, provided you can only keep on continually being a baby.

So the giant ran round after the people, and the people ran round after the giant, and they are running unto this day for aught I know, or do not know; and will run till either he, or they, or both, turn into little children.   And then, as Shakespeare says (and therefore it must be true)—

> "Jack shall have Gill
> Nought shall go ill
> The man shall have his mare again, and all go well."

Then Tom came to a very famous island, which was called, in the days of the great traveller Captain Gulliver, the Isle of Laputa.   But Mrs. Bedonebyasyoudid has named it over again, the Isle of Tomtoddies, all heads and no bodies.

And when Tom came near it, he heard such a grumbling and grunting and growling and wailing and weeping and whining that he thought people must be ringing little pigs, or cropping puppies' ears, or drowning kittens: but when he came nearer still, he began to hear words among the noise; which was the Tomtoddies' song which they sing morning and evening, and all night too, to their great idol Examination—

> "I can't learn my lesson: the examiner's coming !"

And that was the only song which they knew.

And when Tom got on shore the first thing he saw was a great pillar, on one side of which was inscribed, "Playthings not allowed here"; at which he was so shocked that he would not stay to see what was written on the other side.   Then he looked round for the people of the island: but instead of men, women, and children, he found nothing but turnips and radishes, beet and mangold wurzel, without a single green leaf among them, and half of them burst and decayed, with toadstools growing out of them. Those which were left began crying to Tom, in half-a-dozen different languages at once, and all of them badly spoken, "I can't learn my lesson; do come and help me!" And one cried, "Can you show me how to extract this square-root?"

And another, "Can you tell me the distance between α Lyræ and β Camelopardalis?"

And another, "What is the latitude and longitude of Snooksville, in Noman's County, Oregon, U.S.?"

And another, "What was the name of Mutius Scævola's thirteenth cousin's grandmother's maid's cat?"

And another, "How long would it take a school-inspector of average activity to tumble head over heels from London to York?"

And another, "Can you tell me the name of a place that nobody ever heard of, where nothing ever happened, in a country which has not been discovered yet?"

And another, "Can you show me how to correct this hopelessly corrupt passage of Graidiocolosyrtus Tabenniticus, on the cause why crocodiles have no tongues?"

And so on, and so on, and so on, till one would have thought they were all trying for tide-waiters' places, or cornetcies in the heavy dragoons.

"And what good on earth will it do you if I did tell you?" quoth Tom.

Well, they didn't know that: all they knew was the examiner was coming.

Then Tom stumbled on the hugest and softest nimble-comequick turnip you ever saw filling a hole in a crop of swedes, and it cried to him, "Can you tell me anything at all about anything you like?"

"About what?" says Tom.

"About anything you like; for as fast as I learn things I forget them again. So my mamma says that my intellect is not adapted for methodic science, and says that I must go in for general information."

Tom told him that he did not know general information, nor any officers in the army; only he had a friend once that went for a drummer: but he could tell him a great many strange things which he had seen in his travels.

So he told him prettily enough, while the poor turnip listened very carefully ; and the more he listened, the more he forgot, and the more water ran out of him.

Tom thought he was crying : but it was only his poor brains running away, from being worked so hard ; and as Tom talked, the unhappy turnip streamed down all over with juice, and split and shrank till nothing was left of him but rind and water ; whereat Tom ran away in a fright, for he thought he might be taken up for killing the turnip.

But, on the contrary, the turnip's parents were highly delighted, and considered him a saint and a martyr, and put up a long inscription over his tomb about his wonderful talents, early development, and unparalleled precocity. Were they not a foolish couple ? But there was a still more foolish couple next to them, who were beating a wretched little radish, no bigger than my thumb, for sullenness and obstinacy and wilful stupidity, and never knew that the reason why it couldn't learn or hardly even speak was, that there was a great worm inside it eating out all its brains. But even they are no foolisher than some hundred score of papas and mammas, who fetch the rod when they ought to fetch a new toy, and send to the dark cupboard instead of to the doctor.

Tom was so puzzled and frightened with all he saw, that he was longing to ask the meaning of it ; and at last he stumbled over a respectable old stick lying half covered with earth. But a very stout and worthy stick it was, for it belonged to good Roger Ascham in old time, and had carved on its head King Edward the Sixth, with the Bible in his hand.

"You see," said the stick, "there were as pretty little children once as you could wish to see, and might have been so still if they had been only left to grow up like human beings, and then handed over to me ; but their foolish fathers and mothers, instead of letting them pick flowers, and make dirt-pies, and get birds' nests, and dance round the gooseberry bush, as little children should, kept them always at lessons, working, working, working, learning weekday lessons all weekdays, and

Sunday lessons all Sunday, and weekly examinations every Saturday, and monthly examinations every month, and yearly examinations every year, everything seven times over, as if once was not enough, and enough as good as a feast—till their brains grew big, and their bodies grew small, and they were all changed into turnips, with little but water inside; and still their foolish parents actually pick the leaves off them as fast as they grow, lest they should have anything green about them."

"Ah!" said Tom, "if dear Mrs. Doasyouwouldbe-doneby knew of it she would send them a lot of tops, and balls, and marbles, and ninepins, and make them all as jolly as sand-boys."

"It would be no use," said the stick. "They can't play now, if they tried. Don't you see how their legs have turned to roots and grown into the ground, by never taking any exercise, but sapping and moping always in the same place? But here comes the Examiner-of-all-Examiners. So you had better get away, I warn you, or he will examine you and your dog into the bargain, and set him to examine all the other dogs, and you to examine all the other water-babies. There is no escaping out of his hands, for his nose is nine thousand miles long, and can go down chimneys and through keyholes, upstairs, downstairs, in my lady's chamber, examining all little boys, and the little boys' tutors likewise. But when he is thrashed—so Mrs. Bedonebyasyoudid has promised me —I shall have the thrashing of him : and if I don't lay it on with a will it's a pity."

Tom went off: but rather slowly and surlily; for he was somewhat minded to face this same Examiner-of-all-Examiners, who came striding among the poor turnips, binding heavy burdens and grievous to be borne, and laying them on little children's shoulders, like the Scribes and Pharisees of old, and not touching the same with one of his fingers ; for he had plenty of money, and a fine house to live in, and so forth ; which was more than the poor little turnips had.

But when he got near, he looked so big and burly and dictatorial, and shouted so loud to Tom to come and be examined, that Tom ran for his life, and the dog too. And really it was time; for the poor turnips, in their hurry and fright, crammed themselves so fast to be ready for the Examiner, that they burst and popped by dozens all round him, till the place sounded like Aldershot on a field-day, and Tom thought he should be blown into the air, dog and all.

As he went down to the shore he passed the poor turnip's new tomb. But Mrs. Bedonebyasyoudid had taken away the epitaph about talents and precocity and development, and put up one of her own instead which Tom thought much more sensible :—

> " Instruction sore long time I bore,
>   And cramming was in vain ;
> Till Heaven did please my woes to ease,
>   By water on the brain."

So Tom jumped into the sea, and swam on his way singing :—

> " Farewell, Tomtoddies all ; I thank my stars
> That nought I know save those three royal r's :
> Reading and riting sure, with rithmetick,
> Will help a lad of sense through thin and thick."

Whereby you may see that Tom was no poet : but no more was John Bunyan, though he was as wise a man as you will meet in a month of Sundays.

And next he came to Oldwivesfabledom, where the folks were all heathens, and worshipped a howling ape.

And there he found a little boy sitting in the middle of the road, and crying bitterly.

" What are you crying for ? " said Tom.

" Because I am not as frightened as I could wish to be."

" Not frightened ?   You are a queer little chap : but, if you want to be frightened, here goes—Boo ! "

" Ah," said the little boy, " that is very kind of you ; but I don't feel that it has made any impression."

Tom offered to upset him, punch him, stamp on him, fettle him over the head with a brick, or anything else whatsoever which would give him the slightest comfort.

But he only thanked Tom very civilly, in fine long words which he had heard other folk use, and which, therefore, he thought were fit and proper to use himself; and cried on till his papa and mamma came, and sent off for the Powwow man immediately. And a very good-natured gentleman and lady they were, though they were heathens; and talked quite pleasantly to Tom about his travels, till the Powwow man arrived, with his thunder-box under his arm.

And a well-fed, ill-favoured gentleman he was, as ever served her Majesty at Portland. Tom was a little frightened at first; for he thought it was Grimes. But he soon saw his mistake: for Grimes always looked a man in the face; and this fellow never did. And when he spoke, it was fire and smoke; and when he sneezed, it was squibs and crackers; and when he cried (which he did whenever it paid him), it was boiling pitch; and some of it was sure to stick.

"Here we are again!" cried he, like the clown in a pantomime. "So you can't feel frightened, my little dear —eh? I'll do that for you. I'll make an impression on you! Yah! Boo! Whirroo! Hullabaloo!"

And he rattled, thumped, brandished his thunderbox, yelled, shouted, raved, roared, stamped, and danced corrobory like any black fellow; and then he touched a spring in the thunderbox, and out popped turnip-ghosts and magic-lanthorns and pasteboard bogies and spring-heeled Jacks and sallabalas, with such a horrid din, clatter, clank, roll, rattle, and roar, that the little boy turned up the whites of his eyes, and fainted right away.

And at that his poor heathen papa and mamma were as much delighted as if they had found a gold mine; and fell down upon their knees before the Powwow man, and gave him a palanquin with a pole of solid silver and curtains of cloth of gold; and carried him about in it on their own backs: but as soon as they had taken him up, the pole stuck to their shoulders, and they could not set him down any more, but carried him on willy-nilly, as Sinbad carried the old man of the sea: which was a pitiable sight to see; for the father was a very brave officer, and wore two swords and a blue button ; and the mother was as pretty a lady as ever had pinched feet like a Chinese. But you see, they had chosen to do a foolish thing just once too often ; so by the laws of Mrs. Bedonebyasyoudid, they had to go on doing it whether they chose or not, till the coming of the Cocqcigrues.

Ah ! don't you wish that some one would go and convert those poor heathens, and teach them not to frighten their little children into fits ?

"Now, then," said the Powwow man to Tom, "wouldn't you like to be frightened, my little dear ? For I can see plainly that you are a very wicked, naughty, graceless, reprobate boy."

"You're another," quoth Tom, very sturdily. And when the man ran at him, and cried "Boo !" Tom ran at him in return, and cried "Boo !" likewise, right in his face, and set the little dog upon him ; and at his legs the dog went.

At which, if you will believe it, the fellow turned tail, thunderbox and all, with a "Woof !" like an old sow on the common ; and ran for his life, screaming, "Help ! thieves ! murder ! fire ! He is going to kill me ! I am a ruined man ! He will murder me ; and break, burn, and destroy my precious and invaluable thunderbox ; and then you will have no more thunder showers in the land. Help ! help ! help !"

At which the papa and mamma and all the people of Oldwivesfabledom, flew at Tom, shouting, "Oh, the wicked, impudent, hard-hearted, graceless boy ! Beat him, kick him, shoot him, drown him, hang him, burn him !" and so forth : but luckily they had nothing to shoot, hang, or burn him with, for the fairies had hid all the killing-tackle out of the way a little while before ; so they could only pelt him with stones ; and some of the stones went clean through him, and came out the other side. But he did not mind that a bit ; for the holes closed up again as fast as they were made, because he was a water-baby. However, he was very glad when he was safe out of the country, for the noise there made him all but deaf.

Then he came to a very quiet place, called Leave-heavenalone. And there the sun was drawing water out of the sea to make steam-threads, and the wind was twisting them up to make cloud-patterns, till they had worked between them the loveliest wedding veil of Chantilly lace, and hung it up in their own Crystal Palace for any one to buy who could afford it , while the good old sea never grudged, for she knew they would pay her back honestly. So the sun span, and the wind wove, and all went well with the great steam-loom ; as is likely, considering—and considering—and considering——

And at last, after innumerable adventures, each more wonderful than the last, he saw before him a huge building, much bigger, and—what is most surprising—a little uglier than a certain new lunatic asylum, but not built quite of the same materials. None of it, at least—or, indeed, for aught that I ever saw, any part of any other building whatsoever—is cased with nine-inch brick inside and out, and filled up with rubble between the walls, in order that any gentleman who has been confined during her Majesty's pleasure may be unconfined during his own pleasure, and take a walk in the neighbouring park to improve his spirits, after an hour's light and wholesome labour with his dinner-fork or one of the legs of his iron bedstead. No. The walls of this building were built on an entirely different principle, which need not be described, as it has not yet been discovered.

Tom walked towards this great building, wondering what it was, and having a strange fancy that he might find Mr. Grimes inside it, till he saw running toward him, and shouting "Stop!" three or four people, who, when they came nearer, were nothing else than policemen's truncheons, running along without legs or arms.

Tom was not astonished. He was long past that. Besides, he had seen the naviculæ in the water move nobody knows how, a hundred times, without arms, or legs, or anything to stand in their stead. Neither was he frightened ; for he had been doing no harm.

So he stopped ; and, when the foremost truncheon came up and asked his business, he showed Mother Carey's pass ; and the truncheon looked at it in the oddest fashion ; for he had one eye in the middle of his upper end, so that when he looked at anything, being quite stiff, he had to slope himself, and poke himself, till it was a wonder why he did not tumble over; but, being quite full of the spirit of justice (as all policemen, and their truncheons, ought to be), he was always in a position of stable equilibrium, whichever way he put himself.

"All right—pass on," said he at last. And then he added: "I had better go with you, young man." And Tom had no objection, for such company was both respectable and safe; so the truncheon coiled its thong neatly round its handle, to prevent tripping itself up—for the thong had got loose in running—and marched on by Tom's side.

"Why have you no policeman to carry you?" asked Tom, after a while.

"Because we are not like those clumsy-made truncheons in the land-world, which cannot go without having a whole man to carry them about. We do our own work for ourselves; and do it very well, though I say it who should not."

"Then why have you a thong to your handle?" asked Tom.

"To hang ourselves up by, of course, when we are off duty."

Tom had got his answer, and had no more to say, till they came up to the great iron door of the prison. And there the truncheon knocked twice, with its own head.

A wicket in the door opened, and out looked a tremendous old brass blunderbuss charged up to the muzzle with slugs, who was the porter; and Tom started back a little at the sight of him.

"What case is this?" he asked in a deep voice, out of his broad bell-mouth.

"If you please, sir, it is no case; only a young gentleman from her ladyship, who wants to see Grimes the master-sweep."

"Grimes?" said the blunderbuss. And he pulled in his muzzle, perhaps to look over his prison-lists.

"Grimes is up chimney No. 345," he said from inside. "So the young gentleman had better go on to the roof."

Tom looked up at the enormous wall, which seemed at least ninety miles high, and wondered how he should ever get up: but, when he hinted that to the truncheon, it settled the matter in a moment. For it whisked round, and gave him such a shove behind as sent him up to the roof in no time, with his little dog under his arm.

And there he walked along the leads, till he met another truncheon, and told him his errand.

"Very good," it said. "Come along: but it will be of no use. He is the most unremorseful, hard-hearted, foul-mouthed fellow I have in charge; and thinks about nothing but beer and pipes, which are not allowed here, of course."

So they walked along over the leads, and very sooty they were, and Tom thought the chimneys must want sweeping very much. But he was surprised to see that the soot did not stick to his feet, or dirty them in the least. Neither did the live coals, which were lying about in plenty, burn him; for, being a water-baby, his radical humours were of a moist and cold nature, as you may read at large in Lemnius, Cardan, Van Helmont, and other gentlemen, who knew as much as they could, and no man can know more.

And at last they came to chimney No. 345. Out of the top of it, his head and shoulders just showing, stuck poor Mr. Grimes; so sooty, and bleared, and ugly, that Tom could hardly bear to look at him. And in his mouth was a pipe: but it was not a-light, though he was pulling at it with all his might.

"Attention, Mr. Grimes," said the truncheon; "here is a gentleman come to see you."

But Mr. Grimes only said bad words; and kept grumbling, "My pipe won't draw. My pipe won't draw."

"Keep a civil tongue, and attend!" said the truncheon; and popped up just like Punch, hitting Grimes such a crack over the head with itself, that his brains rattled inside like a dried walnut in its shell. He tried to get his hands out, and rub the place: but he could not, for they were stuck fast in the chimney.

Now he was forced to attend.

"Hey!" he said, "why, it's Tom! I suppose you have come here to laugh at me, you spiteful little atomy?"

Tom assured him he had not, but only wanted to help him.

"I don't want anything except beer, and that I can't get; and a light to this bothering pipe, and that I can't get either."

"I'll get you one," said Tom; and he took up a live coal (there were plenty lying about) and put it to Grime's pipe: but it went out instantly.

"It's no use," said the truncheon, leaning itself up against the chimney, and looking on. "I tell you, it is no use. His heart is so cold that it freezes everything that comes near him. You will see that presently, plain enough."

"Oh, of course, it's my fault. Everything's always my fault," said Grimes. "Now don't go to hit me again" (for the truncheon started upright, and looked very wicked); "you know, if my arms were only free, you daren't hit me then."

The truncheon leant back against the chimney, and took no notice of the personal insult, like a well-trained policeman as it was, though he was ready enough to avenge any transgression against morality or order.

"But can't I help you in any other way? Can't I help you to get out of this chimney?" said Tom.

"No," interposed the truncheon; "he has come to the place where everybody must help themselves; and he will find it out, I hope, before he is done with me."

"Oh, yes," said Grimes, "of course it's me. Did I ask to be brought here into the prison? Did I ask to be set to sweep your foul chimneys? Did I ask to have lighted straw put under me to make me go up? Did I ask to stick fast in the very first chimney of all, because it was so shamefully clogged up with soot? Did I ask to stay here—I don't know how long—a hundred years, I do believe, and never get my pipe, nor my beer, nor nothing fit for a beast, let alone a man."

"No," answered a solemn voice behind. "No more

did Tom, when you behaved to him in the very same way."

It was Mrs. Bedonebyasyoudid. And, when the truncheon saw her, it started bolt upright—Attention!—and made such a low bow, that if it had not been full of the spirit of justice, it must have tumbled on its end, and probably hurt its one eye. And Tom made his bow too.

"Oh, ma'am," he said, "don't think about me; that's all past and gone, and good times and bad times and all times pass over. But may not I help poor Mr. Grimes? Mayn't I try and get some of these bricks away, that he may move his arms?"

"You may try, of course," she said.

So Tom pulled and tugged at the bricks: but he could not move one. And then he tried to wipe Mr. Grimes's face: but the soot would not come off.

"Oh, dear!" he said, "I have come all this way, through all these terrible places, to help you, and now I am of no use after all."

"You had best leave me alone," said Grimes; "you are a good-natured forgiving little chap, and that's truth; but you'd best be off. The hail's coming on soon, and it will beat the eyes out of your little head."

"What hail?"

"Why hail that falls every evening here; and, till it comes close to me, it's like so much warm rain: but then it turns to hail over my head, and knocks me about like small shot."

"That hail will never come any more," said the strange lady. "I have told you before what it was. It was your mother's tears, those which she shed when she prayed for you by her bedside; but your cold heart froze it into hail. But she is gone to heaven now, and will weep no more for her graceless son."

Then Grimes was silent a while; and then he looked very sad.

"So my old mother's gone, and I never there to speak to her! Ah! a good woman she was, and might have been a happy one, in her little school there in Vendale, if it hadn't been for me and my bad ways."

"Did she keep the school in Vendale?" asked Tom. And then he told Grimes all the story of his going to her house, and how she could not abide the sight of a chimney-sweep, and then how kind she was, and how he turned into a water-baby.

"Ah!" said Grimes, "good reason she had to hate the sight of a chimney-sweep. I ran away from her and took up with the sweeps, and never let her know where I was, nor sent her a penny to help her, and now it's too late—too late!" said Mr. Grimes.

And he began crying and blubbering like a great baby, till his pipe dropped out of his mouth, and broke all to bits.

"Oh dear, if I was but a little chap in Vendale again, to see the clear beck, and the apple-orchard, and the yew-hedge, how different I would go on! But it's too late now. So you go along, you kind little chap, and don't stand to look at a man crying, that's old enough to be your father, and never feared the face of man, nor of worse neither. But I'm beat now, and beat I must be. I've made my bed, and I must lie on it. Foul I would be, and foul I am, as an Irishwoman said to me once; and little I heeded it. It's all my own fault: but it's too late." And he cried so bitterly that Tom began crying too.

"Never too late," said the fairy, in such a strange soft new voice that Tom looked up at her; and she was so beautiful for the moment, that Tom half fancied she was her sister.

No more was it too late. For, as poor Grimes cried and blubbered on, his own tears did what his mother's could not do, and Tom's could not do, and nobody's on earth could do for him; for they washed the soot off his face and off his clothes; and then they washed the mortar away from between the bricks; and the chimney crumbled down; and Grimes began to get out of it.

Up jumped the truncheon, and was going to hit him on the crown a tremendous thump, and drive him down again like a cork into a bottle. But the strange lady put it aside.

"Will you obey me if I give you a chance?"

"As you please, ma'am. You're stronger than me, that I know too well, and wiser than me, I know too well also. And, as for being my own master, I've fared ill enough with that as yet. So whatever your ladyship pleases to order me ; for I'm beat, and that's the truth."

"Be it so then—you may come out. But remember, disobey me again, and into a worse place still you go."

"I beg pardon, ma'am, but I never disobeyed you that I know of. I never had the honour of setting eyes upon you till I came to these ugly quarters."

"Never saw me? Who said to you, Those that will be foul, foul they will be?"

Grimes looked up ; and Tom looked up too ; for the voice was that of the Irishwoman who met them the day that they went out together to Harthover. "I gave you your warning then: but you gave it yourself a thousand times before and since. Every bad word that you said—every cruel and mean thing that you did—every time that you got tipsy—every day that you went dirty—you were disobeying me, whether you knew it or not."

"If I'd only known, ma'am——"

"You knew well enough that you were disobeying something, though you did not know it was me. But come out and take your chance. Perhaps it may be your last."

So Grimes stept out of the chimney, and, really, if it had not been for the scars on his face, he looked as clean and respectable as a master-sweep need look.

"Take him away," said she to the truncheon, "and give him his ticket-of-leave."

"And what is he to do, ma'am?"

"Get him to sweep out the crater of Etna ; he will find some very steady men working out their time there, who will teach him his business : but mind, if that crater gets choked again, and there is an earthquake in consequence, bring them all to me, and I shall investigate the case very severely"

So the truncheon marched off Mr. Grimes, looking as meek as a drowned worm.

And for aught I know, or do not know, he is sweeping the crater of Etna to this very day.

" And now," said the fairy to Tom, " your work here is done.　You may as well go back again."

" I should be glad enough to go," said Tom, " but how am I to get up that great hole again, now the steam has stopped blowing ? "

" I will take you up the backstairs : but I must bandage your eyes first ; for I never allow anybody to see those backstairs of mine."

" I am sure I shall not tell anybody about them, ma'am, if you bid me not."

" Aha !　So you think, my little man.　But you would soon forget your promise if you got back into the land-world.　For, if people only once found out that you had been up my backstairs, you would have all the fine ladies kneeling to you, and the rich men emptying their purses before you, and statesmen offering you place and power ; and young and old, rich and poor, crying to you, ' Only tell us the great backstairs secret, and we will be your slaves ; we will make you lord, king, emperor, bishop, arch-bishop, pope, if you like—only tell us the secret of the backstairs.　For thousands of years we have been paying, and petting, and obeying, and worshipping quacks who told us they had the key of the backstairs, and could smuggle us up them ; and in spite of all our disappoint-ments, we will honour, and glorify, and adore, and beatify, and translate, and apotheotise you likewise, on the chance of your knowing something about the backstairs, that we may all go on pilgrimage to it ; and, even if we cannot get up it, lie at the foot of it, and cry—

" ' Oh backstairs,

precious backstairs,	aristocratic backstairs,
invaluable backstairs,	respectable backstairs,
requisite backstairs,	gentlemanlike backstairs,
necessary backstairs,	ladylike backstairs,
good-natured backstairs,	commercial backstairs,
cosmopolitan backstairs,	economical backstairs,

comprehensive backstairs,
accommodating backstairs,
well-bred backstairs,
comfortable backstairs,
humane backstairs,
reasonable backstairs,
long-sought backstairs,
coveted backstairs,

practical backstairs,
logical backstairs,
deductive backstairs,
orthodox backstairs,
probable backstairs,
credible backstairs,
demonstrable backstairs,
irrefragable backstairs,

potent backstairs,
all-but-omnipotent backstairs,
&c.

Save us from the consequences of our own actions, and from the cruel fairy, Mrs. Bedonebyasyoudid!' Do not you think that you would be a little tempted then to tell what you know, laddie?"

Tom thought so certainly. "But why do they want so to know about the backstairs?" asked he, being a little frightened at the long words, and not understanding them the least; as, indeed, he was not meant to do, or you either.

"That I shall not tell you. I never put things into little folks' heads which are but too likely to come there of themselves. So come—now I must bandage your eyes." So she tied the bandage on his eyes with one hand, and with the other she took it off.

"Now," she said, "you are safe up the stairs." Tom opened his eyes very wide, and his mouth too; for he had not, as he thought, moved a single step. But, when he looked round him, there could be no doubt that he was safe up the backstairs, whatsoever they may be, which no man is going to tell you, for the plain reason that no man knows.

The first thing which Tom saw was the black cedars, high and sharp against the rosy dawn; and St. Brandan's Isle reflected double in the still broad silver sea. The wind sang softly in the cedars, and the water sang among the caves; the sea-birds sang as they streamed out into the ocean, and the land-birds as they built among the boughs; and the air was so full of song that it stirred St. Brandan and his hermits, as they slumbered in the shade ; and they moved their good old lips, and sang their morning hymn amid their dreams.   But among all the songs one came across the water more sweet and clear than all ; for it was the song of a young girl's voice.

And what was the song which she sang ?   Ah, my little man, I am too old to sing that song, and you too young to understand it.   But have patience, and keep your eye single, and your hands clean, and you will learn some day to sing it yourself, without needing any man to teach you.

And as Tom neared the island, there sat upon a rock the most graceful creature that ever was seen, looking down, with her chin upon her hand, and paddling with her feet in the water.   And when they came to her she looked up, and behold it was Ellie.

" Oh, Miss Ellie," said he, " how you are grown ! "

" Oh, Tom," said she, " how you are grown, too ! "

And no wonder ; they were both quite grown up—he into a tall man, and she into a beautiful woman.

" Perhaps I may be grown," she said.   " I have had time enough ; for I have been sitting here waiting for you many a hundred years, till I thought you were never coming."

" Many a hundred years ? " thought Tom ; but he had seen so much in his travels that he had quite given up being astonished ; and, indeed, he could think of nothing but Ellie.   So he stood and looked at Ellie, and Ellie looked at him ; and they liked the employment so much that they stood and looked for seven years more, and neither spoke or stirred.

At last they heard the fairy say : " Attention, children ! Are you never going to look at me again ? "

" We have been looking at you all this while," they said.   And so they thought they had been.

" Then look at me once more," said she.

They looked—and both of them cried out at once, " Oh, who are you, after all ? "

" You are our dear Mrs. Doasyouwouldbedoneby."

" No, you are good Mrs. Bedonebyasyoudid ; but you are grown quite beautiful now ! "

" To you," said the fairy.   " But look again."

" You are Mother Carey," said Tom, in a very low, solemn voice; for he had found out something which made him very happy, and yet frightened him more than all that he had ever seen.

" But you are grown quite young again."

" To you," said the fairy.   " Look again."

" You are the Irishwoman who met me the day I went to Harthover ! "

And when they looked she was neither of them, and yet all of them at once.

" My name is written in my eyes, if you have eyes to see it there."

And they looked into her great, deep, soft eyes, and they changed again and again into every hue, as the light changes in a diamond.

" Now read my name," said she, at last.

And her eyes flashed, for one moment, clear, white, blazing light: but the children could not read her name; for they were dazzled, and hid their faces in their hands.

" Not yet, young things, not yet," said she, smiling; and then she turned to Ellie.

" You may take him home with you now on Sundays, Ellie.   He has won his spurs in the great battle, and become fit to go with you, and be a man; because he has done the thing he did not like."

So Tom went home with Ellie on Sundays, and sometimes on week-days, too ; and he is now a great man of science, and can plan railroads, and steam-engines, and electric telegraphs, and rifled guns, and so forth ; and knows everything about everything, except why a hen's egg don't turn into a crocodile, and two or three other little things which no one will know till the coming of the Cocqcigrues.   And all this from what he learnt when he was a water-baby, underneath the sea.

" And of course Tom married Ellie ? "

My dear child, what a silly notion !   Don't you know that no one ever marries in a fairy tale, under the rank of a prince or a princess ?

" And Tom's dog ? "

Oh, you may see him any clear night in July; for the old dog-star was so worn out by the last three hot summers that there have been no dog-days since; so that they had to take him down and put Tom's dog up in his place. Therefore, as new brooms sweep clean, we may hope for some warm weather this year. And that is the end of my story.

MORAL.

And now, my dear little man, what should we learn from this parable?

We should learn thirty-seven or thirty-nine things, I am not exactly sure which: but one thing, at least, we may learn, and that is this—when we see efts in the ponds, never to throw stones at them, or catch them with crooked pins, or put them into vivariums with sticklebacks, that the sticklebacks may prick them in their poor little stomachs, and make them jump out of the glass into somebody's workbox, and so come to a bad end. For these efts are nothing else but the water-babies who are stupid and dirty, and will not learn their lessons and keep themselves clean; and, therefore (as comparative anatomists will tell you fifty years hence, though they are not learned enough to tell you now), their skulls grow flat, their jaws grow out, and their brains grow small, and their tails grow long, and they lose all their ribs (which I am sure you would not like to do), and their skins grow dirty and spotted, and they never get into the clear rivers, much less into the great wide sea, but hang about in dirty ponds, and live in the mud, and eat worms, as they deserve to do.

But that is no reason why you should ill-use them: but only why you should pity them, and be kind to them, and hope that some day they will wake up, and be ashamed of their nasty, dirty, lazy, stupid life, and try to amend, and become something better once more. For, perhaps, if they do so, then after 379,423 years, nine months, thirteen days, two hours, and twenty-one minutes (for aught that appears to the contrary), if they work very hard and wash very hard all that time, their brains may grow bigger, and their jaws grow smaller, and their ribs come back, and their tails wither off, and they will turn into water-babies again, and, perhaps, after that into land-babies; and after that, perhaps, into grown men.

You know they won't? Very well, I dare say you know best. But, you see, some folks have a great liking for those poor little efts. They never did anybody any harm, or could if they tried; and their only fault is, that they do no good—any more than some thousands of their betters. But what with ducks, and what with pike, and what with sticklebacks, and what with water-beetles, and what with naughty boys, they are "sae sair haddened doun," as the Scotsmen say, that it is a wonder how they live; and some folks can't help hoping, with good Bishop Butler, that they may have another chance, to make things fair and even, somewhere, somewhen, somehow.

Meanwhile, do you learn your lessons, and thank God that you have plenty of cold water to wash in; and wash in it too, like a true English man. And then, if my story is not true, something better is; and if I am not quite right, still you will be, as long as you stick to hard work and cold water.

But remember always, as I told you at first, that this is all a fairy tale, and only fun and pretence; and, therefore, you are not to believe a word of it, even if it is true.

GLAUCUS

OR

THE WONDERS OF THE SHORE

DEDICATION

BEYOND the shadow of the ship
I watch'd the water snakes :
They moved in tracks of shining white,
And when they rear'd, the elfish light
Fell off in hoary flakes.

  . . . . .

O happy living things ! no tongue
Their beauty might declare :
A spring of love gush'd from my heart,
And I bless'd them unaware.
     —COLERIDGE'S " Ancient Mariner."

GLAUCUS;

OR,

THE WONDERS OF THE SHORE

You are going down, perhaps, by railway, to pass your usual six weeks at some watering-place along the coast, and as you roll along think more than once, and that not over cheerfully, of what you shall do when you get there. You are half-tired, half-ashamed, of making one more in the "ignoble army of idlers," who saunter about the cliffs, and sands, and quays; to whom every wharf is but a "wharf of Lethe," by which they rot "dull as the oozy weed." You foreknow your doom by sad experience. A great deal of dressing, a lounge in the club-room, a stare out of the window with the telescope, an attempt to take a bad sketch, a walk up one parade and down another, interminable reading of the silliest of novels, over which you fall asleep on a bench in the sun, and probably have your umbrella stolen; a purposeless fine-weather sail in a yacht, accompanied by ineffectual attempts to catch a mackerel, and the consumption of many cigars; while your boys deafen your ears, and endanger your personal safety, by blazing away at innocent gulls and willocks, who go off to die slowly, a sport which you feel in your heart to be wanton, and cowardly, and cruel, and yet cannot find in your heart to stop, because "the lads have nothing else to do, and at all events it keeps them out of the billiard-room"; and after all, and worst of all, at night a soulless *rechauffé* of third-rate London frivolity; this is the life-in-death in which thousands spend the golden weeks of summer, and in which you confess with a sigh that you are going to spend them.

Now I will not be so rude as to apply to you the old hymn-distich about one who

> " Finds some mischief still
> For idle hands to do : "

but does it not seem to you, that there must surely be many a thing worth looking at earnestly, and thinking over earnestly, in a world like this, about the making of the least part whereof God has employed ages and ages, further back than wisdom can guess or imagination picture, and upholds that least part every moment by laws and forces so complex and so wonderful, that science, when it tries to fathom them, can only learn how little it can learn ? And does it not seem to you that six weeks' rest, free from the cares of town business, and the whirlwind of town pleasure, could not be better spent than in examining those wonders a little, instead of wandering up and down like the many, still wrapt up each in their little world of vanity and self-interest, unconscious of what and where they really are, as they gaze lazily around at earth and sea and sky, and have

> " No speculation in those eyes
> Which they do glare withal ? "

Why not, then, try to discover a few of the Wonders of the Shore ? For wonders there are there around you at every step, stranger than ever opium-eater dreamed, and yet to be seen at no greater expense than a very little time and trouble.

Perhaps you smile in answer, at the notion of becoming a "Naturalist" : and yet you cannot deny that there must be a fascination in the study of natural history, though what it is is as yet unknown to you. Your daughters, perhaps, have been seized with the prevailing " Pteridomania," and are collecting and buying ferns, with Ward's cases wherein to keep them (for which you have to pay), and wrangling over unpronounceable names of species (which seem to be dif-

ferent in each new Fern-book that they buy), till the
Pteridomania seems to you somewhat of a bore: and
yet you cannot deny that they find an enjoyment in it,
and are more active, more cheerful, more self-forgetful
over it, than they would have been over novels and
gossip, crochet and Berlin-wool.   At least you will confess that the abomination of "Fancy work," that standing
cloak for dreamy idleness (not to mention the injury
which it does to poor starving needlewomen), has all
but vanished from your drawing-room since the "Lady-
ferns" and "Venus's hair" appeared; and that you
could not help yourself looking now and then at the
said "Venus's hair," and agreeing that nature's real
beauties were somewhat superior to the ghastly woollen
caricatures which they had superseded.

You cannot deny, I say, that there is a fascination in
this same Natural History.   For do not you, the London
merchant, recollect how but last summer your douce and
portly head-clerk was seized by two keepers in the act
of wandering in Epping Forest at dead of night, with a
dark lantern, a jar of strange sweet compound, and innumerable pocketsful of pill-boxes; and found it very
difficult to make either his captors or you believe that he
was neither going to burn wheat-ricks, or poison pheasants,
but was simply "sugaring the trees for moths," as a
blameless entomologist?   And when, in self-justification,
he took you to his house in Islington, and showed you
the glazed and corked drawers full of delicate insects,
which had evidently cost him in the collecting the spare
hours of many busy years, and many a pound too, out
of his small salary, were you not a little puzzled to make
out what spell there could be in those "useless" moths,
to draw out of his warm bed, twenty miles down the
Eastern Counties Railway, and into the damp forest
like a deer-stealer, a sober white-headed Tim Linkin-
water like him, your very best man of business, given
to the reading of Scotch political economy, and gifted
with peculiarly clear notions on the currency question?

It is puzzling, truly.   I shall be very glad if these
pages help you somewhat toward solving the puzzle.

We shall agree at least that the study of Natural History has become nowadays an honourable one. A Cromarty stonemason is now perhaps the most important man in the City of Edinburgh, by dint of a work on fossil fishes ; and the successful investigator of the minutest animals takes place unquestioned among men of genius, and, like the philosopher of old Greece, is considered, by virtue of his science, fit company for dukes and princes. Nay, the study is now more than honourable ; it is (what to many readers will be a far higher recommendation) even fashionable. Every well-educated person is eager to know something at least of the wonderful organic forms which surround him in every sunbeam and every pebble ; and books of Natural History are finding their way more and more into drawing-rooms and schoolrooms, and exciting greater thirst for a knowledge which, even twenty years ago, was considered superfluous for all but the professional student.

What a change from the temper of two generations since, when the naturalist was looked on as a harmless enthusiast, who went " bug-hunting," simply because he had not spirit to follow a fox ! There are those alive who can recollect an amiable man being literally bullied out of the New Forest, because he dared to make a collection (at this moment, we believe, in some unknown abyss of that great Avernus, the British Museum) of fossil shells from those very Hordle Cliffs, for exploring which there is now established a society of subscribers and correspondents. They can remember, too, when, on the first appearance of Bewick's " British Birds," the excellent sportsman who brought it down to the Forest, was asked, Why on earth he had bought a book about " cock-sparrows "? and had to justify himself again and again, simply by lending the book to his brother sportsmen, to convince them that there were rather more than a dozen sorts of birds (as they then held) indigenous to Hampshire. But the book, perhaps, which turned the tide in favour of Natural History, among the higher classes at least, in the south of England, was White's " History of Selbourne." A Hampshire gentleman and sportsman, whom everybody knew, had taken the trouble to write a book about the birds and the weeds in his own parish, and the everyday-things which went on under his eyes, and every one else's. And all gentlemen, from the Weald of Kent to the Vale of Blackmore, shrugged their shoulders mysteriously, and said, "Poor fellow!" till they opened the book itself, and discovered to their surprise that it read like any novel. And then came a burst of confused, but honest admiration; from the young squire's "Bless me! who would have thought that there were so many wonderful things to be seen in one's own park!" to the old squire's more morally valuable "Bless me! why I have seen that and that a hundred times, and never thought till now how wonderful they were!"

There were great excuses, though, of old, for the contempt in which the naturalist was held; great excuses for the pitying tone of banter with which the Spectator talks of "the ingenious" Don Saltero (as no doubt the Neapolitan gentlemen talked of Ferrante Imperato the apothecary, and his museum); great excuses for Voltaire, when he classes the collection of butterflies among the other "bigarrures de l'esprit humain." For, in the last generation, the needs of the world were different. It had no time for butterflies and fossils. While Buonaparte was hovering on the Boulogne coast, the pursuits and the education which were needed were such as would raise up men to fight him; so the coarse, fierce, hard-handed training of our grandfathers came when it was wanted, and did the work which was required of it, else we had not been here now. Let us be thankful that we have had leisure for science; and show now in war that our science has at least not unmanned us.

Moreover, Natural History, if not fifty years ago, certainly a hundred years ago, was hardly worthy of men of practical common-sense. After, indeed, Linné, by his invention of generic and specific names, had made classification possible, and by his own enormous labours had shown how much could be done when once a method was established, the science has grown rapidly enough. But before him little or nothing had been put into form definite enough to allure those who (as the many always will) prefer to profit by others' discoveries, than to discover for themselves ; and Natural History was attractive only to a few earnest seekers, who found too much trouble in disencumbering their own minds of the dreams of bygone generations (whether facts, like cockatrices, basilisks, and krakens, the breeding of bees out of a dead ox, and of geese from barnacles, or theories, like those of the four elements, the *vis plastrix* in Nature, animal spirits, and the other musty heirlooms of Aristotelism and Neo-platonism), to try to make a science popular, which as yet was not even a science at all. Honour to them, nevertheless. Honour to Ray and his illustrious contemporaries in Holland and France. Honour to Seba and Aldrovandus ; to Pomet, with his "Historie of Drugges" ; even to the ingenious Don Saltero, and his tavern-museum in Cheyne Walk. Where all was chaos, every man was useful who could contribute a single spot of organised standing ground in the shape of a fact or a specimen. But it is a question whether Natural History would have ever attained its present honours, had not Geology arisen, to connect every other branch of Natural History with problems as vast and awful as they are captivating to the imagination. Nay, the very opposition with which Geology met was of as great benefit to the sister sciences as to itself. For, when questions belonging to the most sacred hereditary beliefs of Christendom were supposed to be affected by the verification of a fossil shell, or the proving that the Maestricht "homo diluvii testis" was, after all, a monstrous eft, it became necessary to work upon Conchology, Botany, and Comparative Anatomy, with a care and a reverence, a caution and a severe induction, which had been never before applied to them ; and thus gradually, in the last half century, the whole choir of cosmical sciences have acquired a soundness, severity, and fulness, which render them, as mere intellectual exercises, as valuable to a manly mind as Mathematics and Metaphysics.

But how very lately have they attained that firm and honourable standing ground! It is a question, whether, even twenty years ago, Geology, as it then stood, was worth troubling one's head about, so little had been really proved. And heavy and uphill was the work, even within the last fifteen years, of those who steadfastly set themselves to the task of proving, and of asserting at all risks, that the Maker of the coal seam and the diluvial cave could not be a " Deus quidam deceptor," and that the facts which the rock and the silt revealed were sacred, not to be warped or trifled with for the sake of any cowardly and hasty notion that they contradicted His other messages. When a few more years are past, Buckland and Sedgwick, Lyell and Jamieson, and the group of brave men who accompanied and followed them, will be looked back to as moral benefactors to their race; and almost as martyrs, also, when it is remembered how much misunderstanding, obloquy, and plausible folly they had to endure from well-meaning fanatics like Fairholme or Granville Penn, and the respectable mob at their heels, who tried (as is the fashion in such cases) to make a hollow compromise between fact and the Bible, by twisting facts just enough to make them fit the fancied meaning of the Bible, and the Bible just enough to make it fit the fancied meaning of the facts. But there were a few who would have no compromise; who laboured on with a noble recklessness, determined to speak the thing which they had seen, and neither more nor less, sure that God could take better care than they of His own everlasting truth; and now they have conquered; the facts which were twenty years ago denounced as contrary to Revelation, are at last accepted not merely as consonant with, but as corroborative thereof; and sound practical geologists, like Hugh Miller, in his "Footprints of the Creator," and Professor Sedgwick, in the invaluable notes to his "Discourse on the Studies of Cambridge," are wielding in defence of Christianity the very science which was faithlessly and cowardly expected to subvert it.

But if you seek, reader, rather for pleasure than

for wisdom, you can find it in such studies, pure and undefiled.

Happy, truly, is the naturalist. He has no time for melancholy dreams. The earth becomes to him transparent; everywhere he sees significances, harmonies, laws, chains of cause and effect endlessly interlinked. which draw him out of the narrow sphere of self-interest and self-pleasing, into a pure and wholesome region of solemn joy and wonder. He goes up some Snowdon valley; to him it is a solemn spot (though unnoticed by his companions), where the stag's-horn clubmoss ceases to straggle across the turf, and the tufted alpine clubmoss takes its place; for he is now in a new world; a region whose climate is eternally influenced by some fresh law (after which he vainly guesses with a sigh at his own ignorance) which renders life impossible to one species, possible to another. And it is a still more solemn thought to him, that it was not always so; that æons and ages back, that rock which he passed a thousand feet below was fringed, not as now with fern, and blue bugle, and white bramble-flowers, but perhaps with the alp-rose and the "gemsen-kraut" of Mont Blanc, at least with Alpine Saxifrages which have now retreated fifteen hundred feet up the mountain side, and with the blue Snow-Gentian, and the Canadian Ledum, which have all but vanished out of the British Isles. And what is it which tells him that strange story? Yon smoothed and rounded surface of rock, polished, remark, across the strata, and against the grain; and furrowed here and there, as if by iron talons, with long parallel scratches. It was the crawling of a glacier which polished that rock-face; the stones fallen from Snowdon peak into the half-liquid lake of ice above, which ploughed those furrows. Æons and æons ago, before the time when Adam first

> "Embraced his Eve in happy hour,
>   And every bird of Eden burst
>   In carol, every bud in flower,"

those marks were there; the records of the "Age of ice";

slight truly; to be effaced by the next farmer who needs
to build a wall; but unmistakable, boundless in signi-
ficance, like Crusoe's one savage footprint on the sea-
shore: and the naturalist acknowledges the finger-mark
of God, and wonders, and worships.

Happy, especially, is the sportsman who is also a naturalist: for as he roves in pursuit of his game, over hills or
up the beds of streams where no one but a sportsman ever
thinks of going, he will be certain to see things noteworthy,
which the mere naturalist would never find, simply because
he could never guess that they were there to be found.   I
do not speak merely of the rare birds which may be shot,
the curious facts as to the habits of fish which may be
observed, great as these pleasures are.   I speak of the
scenery, the weather, the geological formation of the
country, its vegetation, and the living habits of its denizens.
A sportsman out in all weathers, and often dependent for
success on his knowledge of "what the sky is going to
do," has opportunities for becoming a meteorologist
which no one beside but a sailor possesses; and one has
often longed for a scientific gamekeeper or huntsman, who
by discovering a law for the mysterious and seemingly
capricious phenomena of "scent," might perhaps throw
light on a hundred dark passages of hygrometry.   The
fisherman, too,—what an inexhaustible treasury of wonders
lies at his feet, in the subaqueous world of the commonest
mountain burn!   All the laws which mould a world are
there busy, if he but knew it, fattening his trout for him,
and making them rise to the fly, by strange electric in-
fluences, at one hour rather than at another.   Many a
good geognostic lesson too, both as to the nature of a
country's rocks, and as to the laws by which strata are
deposited, may an observing man learn as he wades up
the bed of a trout-stream; not to mention the strange
forms and habits of the tribes of water-insects.   Moreover
no good fisherman but knows to his sorrow, that there are
plenty of minutes, ay hours, in each day's fishing, in which
he would be right glad of any employment better than
trying to

"Call spirits from the vasty deep,"

who will not

> "Come when you do call for them."

What to do then? You are sitting, perhaps, in your coracle, upon some mountain tarn, waiting for a wind, and waiting in vain.

> " Keine luft an keine seite,
>   Todes-stille fürchterlich ; "

As Göthe has it—

> " Und der schiffer sieht bekümmert
>   Glatte fläche rings umher."

You paddle to the shore on the side whence the wind ought to come, if it had any spirit in it ; tie the coracle to a stone, light your cigar, lie down on your back upon the grass, grumble, and finally fall asleep. In the meanwhile, probably, the breeze has come on, and there has been half-an-hour's lively fishing curl ; and you wake just in time to see the last ripple of it sneaking off at the other side of the lake, leaving all as dead-calm as before.

Now how much better, instead of falling asleep, to have walked quietly round the lake side, and asked of your own brains and of nature the question, " How did this lake come here? What does it mean?"

It is a hole in the earth. True, but how was the hole made? There must have been huge forces at work to form such a chasm. Probably the mountain was actually opened from within by an earthquake, and when the strata fell together again, the portion at either end of the chasm, being perhaps crushed together with greater force, re-mained higher than the centre, and so the water lodged between them. Perhaps it was formed thus. You will at least agree that its formation must have been a grand sight enough, and one during which a spectator would have had some difficulty in keeping his footing.

And when you learn that this convulsion probably took place at the bottom of an ocean, hundreds of thousands of years ago, you have at least a few thoughts over which to ruminate, which will make you at once too busy to grumble, and ashamed to grumble.

Yet after all, I hardly think the lake was formed in this way, and suspect that it may have been dry land for ages after it emerged from the primeval waves, and Snowdonia was a palm-fringed island in a tropic sea. Let us look the place over more carefully.

You see the lake is nearly circular; on the side where we stand, the pebbly beach is not six feet above the water, and slopes away steeply into the valley behind us, while before us it shelves gradually into the lake; forty yards out, as you know, there is not ten feet water; and then a steep bank, the edge whereof we and the big trout know well, sinks suddenly to unknown depths. On the opposite side, that vast flat-topped wall of rock towers up shoreless into the sky, seven hundred feet perpendicular; the deepest water of all, we know, is at its very foot. Right and left, two shoulders of down slope into the lake. Now turn round and look down the gorge. Remark that this pebble bank on which we stand reaches some fifty yards downward: you see the loose stones peeping out everywhere. We may fairly suppose that we stand on a dam of loose stones, a hundred feet deep.

But why loose stones?—and if so, what matter, and what wonder? There are rocks cropping out everywhere down the hill-side.

Because if you will take up one of these stones and crack it across, you will see that it is not of the same stuff as those said rocks. Step into the next field and see. That rock is the common Snowdon slate, which we see everywhere. The two shoulders of down, right and left, are slate too; you can see that at a glance. But the stones of the pebble bank are a close-grained, yellow-spotted rock. They are Syenite; and (you may believe me or not, as you will) they were once upon a time in the condition of hasty-pudding heated to some 800 degrees of Fahrenheit, and in that condition shoved their way up somewhere or other through these slates. But where? whence on earth did these Syenite pebbles come? Let us walk round to the cliff on the opposite side, and see.

It is worth while ; for even if my guess be wrong, there
is good spinning with a brass minnow round the angles of
the rocks.

Now see.   Between the cliff-foot and the sloping down
is a crack, ending in a gully ; the nearer side is of slate,
and the further side, the cliff itself, is—why, the whole
cliff is composed of the very same stone as the pebble
ridge !

Now, my good friend, how did those pebbles get three
hundred yards across the lake ?   Hundreds of tons, some
of them three feet long : who carried them across ?   The
old Cymry were not likely to amuse themselves by making
such a breakwater up here in No-man's-land, two thousand
feet above the sea : but somebody, or something, must
have carried them ; for stones do not fly, nor swim
either.

Shot out of a volcano ?   As you seem determined to
have a prodigy, it may as well be a sufficiently huge
one.

Well—these stones lie all together ; and a volcano
would have hardly made so compact a shot, not being in
the habit of using Ely's wire cartridges.   Our next hope
of a solution lies in John Jones, who carried up the
coracle.   Hail him, and ask him what is on the top of
that cliff . . . So ? " Plainshe and pogshe, and another
Llyn."   Very good.   Now, does it not strike you that
this whole cliff has a remarkably smooth and plastered
look, like a hare's run up an earth-bank ?   And do you
see that it is polished thus, only over the lake ? that as
soon as the cliff abuts on the downs right and left, it
forms pinnacles, caves, broken angular boulders ?   Syenite
usually does so in our damp climate, from the " weather-
ing " effect of frost and rain : why has it not done so
over the lake ?   On that part something (giants perhaps)
has been scrambling up or down on a very large scale,
and so rubbed off every corner which was inclined to
come away, till the solid core of the rock was bared.
And may not those mysterious giants have had a hand
in carrying the stones across the lake ? . . . Really I am
not altogether jesting.   Think awhile what agent could

possibly have produced either one, or both, of those effects?

There is but one; and that, if you have been an Alpine traveller, much more if you have been a Chamois hunter, you have seen many a time (whether you knew it or not) at the very same work.

Ice? Yes; ice; Hrymir the frost-giant, and no one else. And if you will look at the facts, you will see how ice may have done it. Our friend John Jones's report of plains and bogs and a lake above makes it quite possible that in the "Ice age" (Glacial Epoch, as the big-word-mongers call it) there was above that cliff a great nevé, or snowfield, such as you have seen often in the Alps at the head of each glacier. Over the face of this cliff a glacier has crawled down from that nevé, polishing the face of the rock in its descent: but the snow, having no large and deep outlet, has not slid down in a sufficient stream to reach the vale below, and form a glacier of the first order; and has therefore stopped short on the other side of the lake, as a glacier of the second order, which ends in an ice cliff hanging high upon the mountain-side, and kept from further progress by daily melting. If you have ever gone up the Mer de Glace to the Tacul, you saw a magnificent specimen of this sort on your right hand, just opposite the Tacul, in the glacier de Trela-porte, which comes down from the Aiguille de Charmoz.

This explains our pebble-ridge. The stones which the glacier rubbed off the cliff beneath it, it carried forward, slowly but surely, till they saw the light again in the face of the ice-cliff, and dropped out of it under the melting of the summer sun, to form a huge dam across the ravine; till the "Ice-age" past, a more genial climate succeeded, and nevé and glacier melted away: but the "moraine" of stones did not, and remain to this day, the dam which keeps up the waters of the lake.

There is my explanation. If you can find a better, do: but remember always that it must include an answer to—"How did the stones get across the lake?"

Now, reader, we have had no abstruse science here, no long words, not even a microscope or a book: and yet we, as two plain sportsmen, have gone back, or been led back by fact and common sense, into the most awful and sublime depths, into an epos of the destruction and re-creation of a former world.

This is but a single instance; I might give hundreds. This one, nevertheless, may have some effect in awakening you to the boundless world of wonders which is all around you, and make you ask yourself seriously, " What branch of Natural History shall I begin to investigate, if it be but for a few weeks, this summer?"

To which I answer, Try "the Wonders of the Shore." There are along every sea-beach more strange things to be seen, and those to be seen easily, than in any other field of observation which you will find in these islands. And on the shore only will you have the enjoyment of finding new species, of adding your mite to the treasures of science.

For not only the English ferns, but the natural history of all our land species, are now well-nigh exhausted. Our home botanists, entomologists, and ornithologists, are spending their time now, perforce, in verifying a few obscure species, and bemoaning themselves like Alexander, that there are no more worlds left to conquer. For the geologist, indeed, especially in the remoter districts, much remains to be done, but only at a heavy outlay of time, labour, and study ; and the dilettante (and it is for dilettanti, like myself, that I principally write) must be content to tread in the tracks of greater men who have preceded him, and accept at second and third hand their foregone conclusions.

But this is most unsatisfactory ; for in giving up discovery, one gives up one of the highest enjoyments of natural history. There is a mysterious delight in the discovery of a new species, akin to that of seeing for the first time in their native haunts, plants or animals of which one has till then only read. Some, surely, who read these pages, have experienced that latter delight ; and, though they might find it hard to define whence the pleasure arose, know well that it was a solid pleasure, the memory of which they would not give up for hard cash.

Some, surely, can recollect at their first sight of the Alpine
Soldanella, the Rhododendron, or the black Orchis,
growing upon the edge of the eternal snow, a thrill of
emotion, not unmixed with awe; a sense that they were,
as it were, brought face to face with the creatures of
another world; that nature was independent of them,
not merely they of her; that trees were not merely made
to build their houses, or herbs to feed their cattle; as
they looked on those wild gardens amid the wreaths of
the untrodden snow, which had lifted their gay flowers
to the sun year after year since the foundation of the
world, taking no heed of man, and all the coil which he
keeps in the valleys far below.

And even, to take a simpler instance, there are those
who will excuse, or even approve of a writer for saying
that, among the memories of a month's eventful tour,
those which stand out as beacon-points, those round
which all the others group themselves, are the first wolf-
track by the roadside in the Kyllwald; the first sight of
the blue and green Roller-birds, walking behind the
plough like rooks in the tobacco-fields of Wittlich; the
first ball of Olivine scraped out of the volcanic slag-heaps
of the Dreisser-Weiher; the first pair of the Lesser
Bustard which we flushed upon the downs of the Mosel-
kopf; the first sight of the cloud of white Ephemeræ,
fluttering in the dusk like a summer snowstorm between
us and the black cliffs of the Rheinstein, while the broad
Rhine beneath flashed blood-red in the blaze of the
lightning and the fires of the Mausenthurm, a lurid
Acheron above which seemed to hover ten thousand un-
buried ghosts; and last, but not least, on the lip of the
vast Mosel-kopf crater, just above the point where the
weight of the fiery lake has burst the side of the great
slag-cup, and rushed forth between two cliffs of clink-
stone across the downs, in a clanging stream of fire,
damming up rivulets, and blasting its path through
forests, far away toward the valley of the Moselle, the
sight of an object for which was forgotten for the
moment that battlefield of the Titans at our feet, and
all the glorious panorama, Hundsruck and Taunus,

Siebengebirge and Ardennes, and all the crater peaks around; and which was—smile not, reader—our first yellow foxglove.

But what is even this to the delight of finding a new species?—of rescuing (as it seems to you) one more thought of the divine mind from Hela, and the realms of the unknown, unclassified, uncomprehended? As it seems to you: though in reality it only seems so, in a world wherein not a sparrow falls to the ground un-noticed by our Father who is in heaven.

The truth is, the pleasure of finding new species is too great; it is morally dangerous; for it brings with it the temptation to look on the thing found as your own possession, all but your own creation; to pride yourself on it, as if God had not known it for ages since; even to squabble jealously for the right of having it named after you, and of being recorded in the Trans-actions of I-know-not-what Society as its first discoverer: —as if all the angels in heaven had not been admiring it, long before you were born or thought of.

But to be forewarned is to be forearmed; and I seriously counsel you to try if you cannot find some-thing new this summer along the coast to which you are going. There is no reason why you should not be as successful as a friend of mine, who, with a very slight smattering of science, and very desultory research, obtained last winter from the Torbay shores three entirely new species, beside several rare animals which had escaped all naturalists since the lynx-eye of Colonel Montagu discerned them forty years ago.

And do not despise the creatures because they are minute. No doubt we should both of us prefer helping Rajah Brooke to discover monstrous apes in the tropical forests of Borneo, or stumbling with Hooker upon herds of gigantic "Ammon sheep" amid the rhododendron thickets of the Himalaya: but it cannot be; and "he is a fool," says old Hesiod, "who knows not how much better half is than the whole." Let us be content with what is within our reach. And doubt not that in these tiny creatures are mysteries more than we shall ever fathom.

The zoophytes and microscopic animalcules which people every shore and every drop of water, have been now raised to a rank in the human mind, more important, perhaps, than even those gigantic monsters, whose models fill the lake at the New Crystal Palace. The research which has been bestowed, for the last century, upon these once unnoticed atomies, has well repaid itself; for from no branch of physical science has more been learnt of the *scientia scientiarum*, the priceless art of learning; no branch of science has more utterly confounded the wisdom of the wise, shattered to pieces systems and theories, and the idolatry of arbitrary names, and taught man to be silent while his Maker speaks, than this apparent pedantry of zoophytology, in which our old distinctions of "animal," "vegetable," and "mineral" are trembling in the balance, seemingly ready to vanish like their fellows, "the four elements" of fire, air, earth, and water. No branch of science has helped so much to sweep away that sensuous idolatry of mere size, which tempts man to admire and respect objects in proportion to the number of feet or inches which they occupy in space. No branch, moreover, has been more humbling to the boasted rapidity and omnipotence of the human reason, and taught those who have eyes to see, and hearts to understand, how weak and wayward, staggering and slow, are the steps of our fallen race (rapid and triumphant enough in that broad road of theories which leads to intellectual destruction) whensoever they tread the narrow path of true science, which leads (if I may be allowed to transfer our Lord's great parable from moral to intellectual matters) to Life; to the living and permanent knowledge of living things, and of the laws of their existence. Humbling, truly, to one who, in this summer of 1854, the centenary year of British zoophytology, looks back to the summer of 1754, when good Mr. Ellis, the wise and benevolent West Indian merchant, read before the Royal Society his famous paper proving the animal nature of corals, and followed it up the year after by that "Essay toward a Natural History of the Corallines, and other like marine productions of the British Coasts," which forms the groundwork of all our knowledge on the subject to this day. The chapter in Dr. G. Johnston's British Zoophytes, p. 407, or the excellent little résumé thereof in Dr. Landsborough's book on the same subject, is really a saddening one, as one sees how loth were not merely dreamers like Marsigli or Bonnet, but sound-headed men like Pallas and Linné, to give up the old sense-bound fancy, that these corals were vegetables, and their polypes some sort of living flowers. Yet after all there are excuses for them. Without our improved microscopes, and while the sciences of comparative anatomy and chemistry were yet infantile, it was difficult to believe what was the truth; and for this simple reason; that, as usual, the truth, when discovered, turned out far more startling and prodigious than the dreams which men had hastily substituted for it; more strange than Ovid's old story that the coral was soft under the sea, and hardened by exposure to air; than Marsigli's notion, that the coral-polypes were its flowers; than Dr. Parsons' contemptuous denial, that these complicated forms could be "the operations of little, poor, helpless, jelly-like animals, and not the work of more sure vegetation"; than Baker the microscopist's detailed theory of their being produced by the crystallisation of the mineral salts in the sea-water, just as he had seen "the particles of mercury and copper in aquafortis assume tree-like forms, or curious delineations of mosses and minute shrubs on slates and stones, owing to the shooting of salts intermixed with mineral particles":—one smiles at it now: yet these men were no less sensible than we of the year 1854; and if we know better, it is only because other men, and those few and far between, have laboured amid disbelief, ridicule, and error; needing again and again to retrace their steps, and to unlearn more than they learnt, seeming to go backwards when they were really progressing most; and now we have entered into their labours, and find them, as I have just said, more wondrous than all the poetic dreams of a Bonnet or

a Darwin. For who, after all, to take a few broad
instances (not to enlarge on the great root-wonder of a
number of distinct individuals connected by a common
life, and forming a seeming plant invariable in each
species), would have dreamed of the "bizarreries"
which these very zoophytes present in their classification? You go down to any shore after a gale of wind,
and pick up a few delicate little sea-ferns. You have
two in your hand, which probably look to you, even
under a good pocket magnifier, identical or nearly so.[1]
But you are told to your surprise, that however like
the dead horny polypidoms which you hold may be,
the two species of animal which have formed them
are at least as far apart in the scale of creation as a
quadruped is from a fish. You see in some Musselburgh
dredger's boat the phosphorescent sea-pen (unknown
in England), a living feather, of the look and con-
sistency of a cock's comb ; or the still stranger sea-rush
(*Virgularia mirabilis*), a spine two feet long, with
hundreds of rosy flowerets arranged in half-rings round
it from end to end ; and you are told that these are
the congeners of the great stony Venus's fan which
hangs in seamen's cottages, brought home from the
West Indies. And ere you have done wondering, you
hear that all three are congeners of the ugly shapeless
white "dead man's hand," which you may pick up after
a storm on any shore. You have a beautiful madrepore
or brainstone on your mantelpiece, brought home from
some Pacific coral-reef. You are to believe that it has
no more to do with the beautiful tubular corals among
which it was growing, than a bird has with a worm, and
that its first cousins are the soft slimy sea-anemones
which you see expanding their living flowers in every
rock-pool, bags of sea-water, without a trace of bone
or stone. You must believe it ; for in science, as in
higher matters, he who will walk surely, must "walk by
faith and not by sight."

---

[1] *Sertularia operculata* and *Gemellaria loriculata ;* or any of the
small *Sertulariæ*, compared with *Crisiæ* and *Cellulariæ*, are very
good examples.

These are but a few of the wonders which the classification of marine animals affords ; and only drawn from one
class of them, though almost as common among every other
family of that submarine world whereof Spenser sang—

> " Oh, what an endless work have I in hand,
>   To count the sea's abundant progeny !
> Whose fruitful seed far passeth those in land,
>   And also those which won in th' azure sky.
> For much more eath to tell the stars on high,
> Albe they endless seem in estimation,
>   Than to recount the sea's posterity ;
> So fertile be the flouds in generation,
> So huge their numbers, and so numberless their nation."

But these few examples will be sufficient to account
both for the slow pace at which the knowledge of sea-
animals has progressed, and for the allurement which
men of the highest attainments have found, and still find
in it. And when to this we add the marvels which meet
us at every step in the anatomy and the reproduction of
these creatures, and in the chemical and mechanical
functions which they fulfil in the great economy of our
planet, we cannot wonder at finding that books which treat
of them carry with them a certain charm of romance,
and feed the play of fancy, and that love of the marvellous which is inherent in man, at the same time that they
lead the reader to more solemn and lofty trains of thought,
which can find their full satisfaction only in self-forgetful
worship, and that hymn of praise which goes up ever
from land and sea, as well as from saints and martyrs
and the heavenly host, " Oh, all ye works of the Lord,
and ye, too, spirits and souls of the righteous, praise
Him, and magnify Him for ever ! "

I have said, that there were excuses for the old contempt of the study of Natural History. I have said too,
it may be hoped, enough to show that contempt to be
now ill-founded. But still, there are those who regard it
as a mere amusement, and that as a somewhat effeminate
one ; and think that it can at best help to while away a
leisure hour harmlessly, and perhaps usefully, as a substitute for coarser sports, or for the reading of novels.

Those, however, who have followed it out, especially on the sea-shore, know better. They can tell from experience, that over and above its accessory charms of pure sea-breezes, and wild rambles by cliff and loch, the study itself has had a weighty moral effect upon their hearts and spirits. There are those who can well understand how the good and wise John Ellis, amid all his philanthropic labours for the good of the West Indies, while he was spending his intellect and fortune in introducing into our tropic settlements the bread-fruit, the mangosteen, and every plant and seed which he hoped might be useful for medicine, agriculture, and commerce, could yet feel himself justified in devoting large portions of his ever well-spent time to the fighting the battle of the corallines against Parsons and the rest, and even in measuring pens with Linné, the prince of naturalists. There are those who can sympathise with the gallant old Scotch officer mentioned by some writer on sea-weeds, who, desperately wounded in the breach at Badajos, and a sharer in all the toils and triumphs of the Peninsular war, could in his old age show a rare sea-weed with as much triumph as his well-earned medals, and talk over a tiny spore-capsule with as much zest as the records of sieges and battles. Why not? That temper which made him a good soldier may very well have made him a good naturalist also. And certainly, the best naturalist, as far as logical acumen, as well as earnest research, is concerned, whom England has ever seen, was the Devonshire squire, Colonel George Montagu, of whom Mr. E. Forbes[1] well says, that "had ne been educated a physiologist" (and not, as he was, a soldier and a sportsman), "and made the study of nature his aim and not his amusement, his would have been one of the greatest names in the whole range of British science." I question, nevertheless, whether he would not have lost more than he would have gained by a different training. It might have made him a more learned

---

[1] "British Star-fishes." This delightful writer, and eager investigator, has just died, in the prime of life, from disease contracted (it is said) during a scientific journey in Asia Minor : one more martyr to the knight-errantry of science.

systematiser ; but would it have quickened in him that
"seeing eye" of the true soldier and sportsman, which
makes Montagu's descriptions indelible word-pictures,
instinct with life and truth ? "There is no question,"
says Mr. E. Forbes, after bewailing the vagueness of
most naturalists, "about the identity of any animal
Montagu described. . . . He was a forward-looking
philosopher ; he spoke of every creature as if one exceeding like it, yet different from it, would be washed up by
the waves next tide.   Consequently his descriptions are
permanent."   Scientific men will recognise in this the
highest praise which can be bestowed, because it attributes
to him that highest faculty—*The Art of Seeing* : but the
study and the book would not have given that.   It is
God's gift, wheresoever educated : but its true schoolroom
is the camp and the ocean, the prairie and the forest ;
active self-helping life, which can grapple with nature
herself : not merely with printed books about her.   Let
no one think that this same natural history is a pursuit
fitted only for effeminate or pedantic men.   We should
say rather, that the qualifications required for a perfect
naturalist are as many and as lofty as were required, by
old chivalrous writers, for the perfect knight-errant of the
middle ages ; for (to sketch an ideal, of which we are
happy to say our race now affords many a fair realisation)
our perfect naturalist should be strong in body ; able to
haul a dredge, climb a rock, turn a boulder, walk all day,
uncertain where he shall eat or rest ; ready to face sun
and rain, wind and frost, and to eat or drink thankfully
anything, however coarse or meagre ; he should know
how to swim for his life, to pull an oar, sail a boat, and
ride the first horse which comes to hand ; and, finally,
he should be a thoroughly good shot, and a skilful fisherman ; and if he go far abroad, be able on occasion to
fight for his life.

For his moral character, he must, like a knight of old,
be first of all gentle and courteous, ready and able
to ingratiate himself with the poor, the ignorant, and the
savage ; not only because foreign travel will be often
otherwise impossible, but because he knows how much

invaluable local information can be only obtained from fishermen, miners, hunters, and tillers of the soil. Next, he should be brave and enterprising, and withal patient and undaunted; not merely in travel, but in investigation; knowing (as Lord Bacon might have put it) that the kingdom of nature, like the kingdom of heaven, must be taken by violence, and that only to those who knock long and earnestly, does the great mother open the doors of her sanctuary. He must be of a reverent turn of mind also; not rashly discrediting any reports, however vague and fragmentary; giving man credit always for some germ of truth, and giving nature credit for an inexhaustible fertility and variety, which will keep him his life long always reverent, yet never superstitious; wondering at the commonest, but not surprised by the most strange; free from the idols of size and sensuous loveliness; able to see grandeur in the minutest objects, beauty in the most ungainly; estimating each thing not carnally, as the vulgar do, by its size or its pleasantness to the senses, but spiritually, by the amount of Divine thought revealed to him therein; holding every phenomenon worth the noting down; believing that every pebble holds a treasure, every bud a revelation; making it a point of conscience to pass over nothing through laziness or hastiness, lest the vision once offered and despised should be withdrawn; and looking at every object as if he were never to behold it again.

Moreover, he must keep himself free from all those perturbations of mind which not only weaken energy, but darken and confuse the inductive faculty; from haste and laziness, from melancholy, testiness, pride, and all the passions which make men see only what they wish to see. Of solemn and scrupulous reverence for truth; of the habit of mind which regards each fact and discovery not as our own possession, but as the possession of its Creator, independent of us, our tastes, our needs, or our vainglory, we hardly need to speak; for it is the very essence of a naturalist's faculty, the very tenure of his existence: and without truthfulness, science would be as impossible now as chivalry would have been of old.

And last, but not least, the perfect naturalist should have in him the very essence of true chivalry, namely, self-devotion ; the desire to advance, not himself and his own fame or wealth, but knowledge and mankind. He should have this great virtue ; and in spite of many shortcomings (for what man is there who liveth and sinneth not?), naturalists as a class have it, to a degree which makes them stand out most honourably in the midst of a self-seeking and mammonite generation, inclined to value everything by its money price, its private utility. The spirit which gives freely, because it knows that it has received freely ; which communicates knowledge without hope of reward, without jealousy and mean rivalry, to fellow-students and to the world ; which is content to delve and toil comparatively unknown, that from its obscure and seemingly worthless results others may derive pleasure, and even build up great fortunes, and change the very face of cities and lands, by the practical use of some stray talisman which the poor student has invented in his laboratory ;—this is the spirit which is abroad among our scientific men, to a greater degree than it ever has been among any body of men, for many a century past ; and might well be copied by those who profess deeper purposes and a more exalted calling, than the discovery of a new zoophyte, or the classification of a moorland crag.

And it is these qualities, however imperfectly they may be realised in any individual instance, which make our scientific men, as a class, the wholesomest and pleasantest of companions abroad, and at home the most blameless, simple, and cheerful, in all domestic relations ; men for the most part of manful heads, and yet of child-like hearts, who have turned to quiet study, in these late piping times of peace, an intellectual health and courage which might have made them, in more fierce and troublous times, capable of doing good service with very different instruments than the scalpel and the microscope.

I have been sketching an ideal : but one which I seriously recommend to the consideration of all parents ; for, though it may be impossible and absurd to wish that every young man should grow up a naturalist by profession, yet this age offers no more wholesome training, both moral and intellectual, than that which is given by instilling into the young an early taste for outdoor physical science. The education of our children is now more than ever a puzzling problem, if by education we mean the development of the whole humanity, not merely of some arbitrarily chosen part of it. How to feed the imagination with wholesome food, and teach it to despise French novels, and that sugared slough of sentimental poetry, in comparison with which the old fairy-tales and ballads were manful and rational; how to counteract the tendency to shallow and conceited sciolism, engendered by hearing popular lectures on all manner of subjects, which can only be really learnt by stern methodic study; how to give habits of enterprise, patience, accurate observation, which the counting-house or the library will never bestow; above all, how to develop the physical powers, without engendering brutality and coarseness,— are questions becoming daily more and more puzzling, while they need daily more and more to be solved, in an age of enterprise, travel, and emigration, like the present. For the truth must be told, that the great majority of men who are now distinguished by commercial success, have had a training the directly opposite to that which they are giving to their sons. They are for the most part men who have migrated from the country to the town, and had in their youth all the advantages of a sturdy and manful hill-side or sea-side training; men whose bodies were developed, and their lungs fed on pure breezes, long before they brought to work in the city the bodily and mental strength which they had gained by loch and moor. But it is not so with their sons. Their business habits are learnt in the counting-house; a good school, doubtless, as far as it goes : but one which will expand none but the lowest intellectual faculties; which will make them accurate accountants, shrewd computers and competitors, but never the originators of daring schemes, men able and willing to go forth to replenish the earth and subdue it. And in the hours of relaxation, how much of their time is thrown away, for want of anything better, on frivolity, not to say on secret profligacy, parents know too well; and often shut their eyes in very despair to evils which they know not how to cure. A frightful majority of our middle-class young men are growing up effeminate, empty of all knowledge but what tends directly to the making of a fortune; or rather, to speak correctly, to the keeping up the fortunes which their fathers have made for them; while of the minority, who are indeed thinkers and readers, how many women as well as men have we seen wearying their souls with study undirected, often mis-directed; craving to learn, yet not knowing how or what to learn; cultivating, with unwholesome energy, the head at the expense of the body and the heart; catching up with the most capricious self-will one mania after another, and tossing it away again for some new phantom; gorging the memory with facts which no one has taught them to arrange, and the reason with problems which they have no method for solving; till they fret themselves into a chronic fever of the brain, which too often urges them on to plunge, as it were to cool the inward fire, into the ever restless sea of doubt and disbelief. It is a sad picture. There are many who may read these pages whose hearts will tell them that it is a true one. What is wanted in these cases is a methodic and scientific habit of mind; and a class of objects on which to exer-cise that habit, which will fever neither the speculative intellect nor the moral sense; and those physical science will give, as nothing else can give it.

Moreover, to revert to another point which we touched just now, man has a body as well as a mind; and with the vast majority there will be no *mens sana* unless there be a *corpus sanum* for it to inhabit. And what outdoor training to give our youths, is, as we have already said, more than ever puzzling. This difficulty is felt, perhaps, less in Scotland than in England. The Scotch climate compels hardiness; the Scotch bodily strength makes it easy; and Scotland, with her mountain-tours in summer, and her frozen lochs in winter, her labyrinth of seashore, and, above all, that priceless boon which Providence has bestowed on her, in the contiguity of her great cities to the loveliest scenery, and hills where every breeze is health, affords facilities for healthy physical life unknown to the Englishman, who has no Arthur's Seat towering above his London, no Western Islands spotting the ocean firths beside his Manchester. Field sports, with the invaluable training which they give, if not

" The reason firm,"

yet still

" The temperate will,
Endurance, foresight, strength, and skill,"

have become impossible for the greater number; and athletic exercises are now, in England at least, so artificialised, so expensive, so mixed up with drinking, gambling, and other evils of which we need say nothing here, that one cannot wonder at any parents' shrinking from allowing their sons to meddle much with them. And yet the young man who has had no substitute for such amusements, will cut but a sorry figure in Australia, Canada, or India; and if he stays at home, will spend many a pound in doctors' bills, which could have been better employed elsewhere. " Taking a walk "—as one would take a pill or a draught—seems likely soon to become the only form of outdoor existence possible for us of the British Isles. But a walk without an object, unless in the most lovely and novel of scenery, is a poor exercise; and as a recreation, utterly nil. We never knew two young lads go out for a "constitutional," who did not, if they were commonplace youths, gossip the whole way about things better left unspoken; or, if they were clever ones, fall on arguing and brainsbeating on politics or metaphysics from the moment they left the door, and return with their wits even more heated and tired than they were when they set out. We cannot help fancying that Milton made a mistake in a certain celebrated passage; and that it was not "sitting on a hill apart," but tramping four miles out and four

miles in along a turnpike-road, that his hapless spirits
discoursed

> "Of fate, free-will, foreknowledge, absolute,
> And found no end, in wandering mazes lost."

Seriously, if we wish rural walks to do our children
any good, we must give them a love for rural sights, an
object in every walk; we must teach them—and we
can teach them—to find wonder in every insect, sub-
limity in every hedgerow, the records of past worlds in
every pebble, and boundless fertility upon the barren
shore; and so, by teaching them to make full use of
that limited sphere in which they now are, make them
faithful in a few things, that they may be fit hereafter to
be rulers over much.

I may seem to exaggerate the advantages of such
studies; but the question after all is one of experience;
and I have had experience enough and to spare that
what I say is true. I have seen the young man of fierce
passions, and uncontrollable daring, expend healthily
that energy which threatened daily to plunge him into
recklessness, if not into sin, upon hunting out and collecting, through rock and bog, snow and tempest, every
bird and egg of the neighbouring forest. I have seen
the cultivated man, craving for travel and for success in
life, pent up in the drudgery of London work, and yet
keeping his spirit calm, and perhaps his morals all the
more righteous, by spending over his microscope evenings which would too probably have gradually been
wasted at the theatre. I have seen the young London
beauty, amid all the excitement and temptation of luxury
and flattery, with her heart pure and her mind occupied
in a boudoir full of shells and fossils, flowers and sea-
weeds, and keeping herself unspotted from the world, by
considering the lilies of the field, how they grow. And
therefore it is that I hail with thankfulness every fresh
book of Natural History, as a fresh boon to the young,
a fresh help to those who have to educate them.

The greatest difficulty in the way of beginners is (as
in most things) how to "learn the art of learning." They

go out, search, find less than they expected, and give the subject up in disappointment. It is good to begin, therefore, if possible by playing the part of "jackal" to some practised naturalist, who will show the tyro where to look, what to look for, and, moreover, what it is that he has found; often no easy matter to discover. Five-and-twenty years ago, during an autumn's work of dead-leaf-searching in the Devon woods for poor old Dr. Turton, while he was writing his book on British land-shells, the present writer learnt more of the art of observing than he would have learnt in three years' desultory hunting on his own account: and he has often regretted that no naturalist has established shore-lectures at some watering place, like those up hill and down dale field-lectures which, in pleasant bygone Cambridge days, Professor Sedgwick used to give to young geologists, and Professor Henslow to young botanists.

This want, however, bids fair to be supplied at last. That most pious and most learned naturalist, Mr. Gosse, whose works will be so often quoted in these pages, purposes, it is understood, to establish this summer a regular shore-class, probably at Weymouth. And I advise any reader whose fancy such a project pleases, to apply to him for details of the scheme, either at his own house, 58 Huntingdon Street, Barnsbury Park, Islington, or at the Linnæan or Microscopic Society.

In the meanwhile, to show something of what such a class might be, let me put myself, in imagination, in Mr. Gosse's place, and do his work for him for half-an-hour, though in a far more shallow and clumsy way.

Leaving Weymouth to him, let me take you to a shore where I am more at home, and for whose richness I can vouch, and choose our season and our day to start forth, on some glorious morning of one of our Italian springs, to see what last night's easterly gale has swept from the populous shallows of Torbay, and cast up, high and dry, on Paignton sands.

Torbay is a place which should be as much endeared to the naturalist as to the patriot and to the artist. We cannot gaze on its blue ring of water, and the great limestone bluffs which bound it to the north and south, without a glow passing through our hearts, as we remember the terrible and glorious pageant which passed by in the glorious July days of 1588, when the Spanish Armada ventured slowly past Berry Head, with Elizabeth's gallant pack of Devon captains (for the London fleet had not yet joined) following fast in its wake, and dashing into the midst of the vast line, undismayed by size and numbers, while their kin and friends stood watching and praying on the cliffs, spectators of Britain's Salamis. The white line of houses, too, on the other side of the bay, is Brixham, famed as the landing-place of William of Orange; the stone on the pier-head, which marks his first footsteps on British ground, is sacred in the eyes of all true English Whigs; and close by stands the castle of the settler of Newfoundland, Sir Humphrey Gilbert, Raleigh's half-brother, most learned of all Elizabeth's admirals in life, most pious and heroic in death. And as for scenery, though it can boast of neither mountain peak or dark fiord, and would seem tame enough in the eyes of a western Scot or Irishman, yet Torbay surely has a soft beauty of its own. The rounded hills slope gently to the sea, spotted with squares of emerald grass, and rich red fallow fields, and parks full of stately timber trees. Long lines of tall elms, just flushing green in the spring hedges, run down to the very water's edge, their boughs unwarped by any blast; and here and there apple orchards are just bursting into flower in the soft sunshine, and narrow strips of water meadow line the glens, where the red cattle are already lounging knee-deep in richest grass, within ten yards of the rocky pebble beach. The shore is silent now, the tide far out: but six hours hence it will be hurling columns of rosy foam high into the sunlight, and sprinkling passengers, and cattle, and trim gardens which hardly know what frost and snow may be, but see the flowers of autumn meet the flowers of spring, and the old year linger smilingly to twine a garland for the new.

No wonder that such a spot as Torquay, with its delicious Italian climate, and endless variety of rich wood-

land, flowery lawn, fantastic rock-cavern, and broad bright
tide-sand, sheltered from every wind of heaven except
the soft south-east, should have become a favourite haunt,
not only for invalids, but for naturalists. Indeed, it may
well claim the honour of being the original home of marine
zoology and botany in England, as the Frith of Forth,
under the auspices of Sir John Dalzell, has been for
Scotland. For here worked Montagu, Turton, and Mrs.
Griffith, to whose masculine powers of research English
marine botany almost owes its existence, and who still
survives, at an age long beyond the natural term of man,
to see, in her cheerful and honoured old age, that knowledge become popular and general, which she pursued
for many a year unassisted and alone. And here too,
now, Dr. Battersby possesses a collection of shells,
inferior, perhaps, to hardly any in England. Torbay,
moreover, from the variety of its rocks, aspects, and sea-
floors, where limestones alternate with traps, and traps
with slates, while at the valley-mouths the soft sandstones
and hard conglomerates of the new red series slope down
into the tepid and shallow waves, affords an abundance
and variety of animal and vegetable life, unequalled,
perhaps, in any other part of Great Britain. It cannot
boast, certainly, of those strange deep-sea forms which
Messrs. Alder, Goodsir, and Laskey, dredge among the
lochs of the western Highlands, and the sub-marine
mountain glens of the Zetland sea ; but it has its own
varieties, its own ever fresh novelties ; and in spite of all
the research which has been lavished on its shores, a
naturalist cannot now work there for a winter without
discovering forms new to science, or meeting with
curiosities which have escaped all observers, since the
lynx eye of Montagu espied them full fifty years ago.

Follow us, then, reader, in imagination, out of the
gay watering place, with its London shops and London
equipages, along the broad road beneath the sunny limestone cliff, tufted with golden furze ; past the huge oaks
and green slopes of Tor Abbey ; and past the fantastic
rocks of Livermead, scooped by the waves into a labyrinth of double and triple caves, like Hindoo temples,

upborne on pillars banded with yellow and white and red, a week's study, in form and colour and chiaroscuro, for any artist; and a mile or so further along a pleasant road, with land-locked glimpses of the bay, to the broad sheet of sand which lies between the village of Paignton and the sea—sands trodden a hundred times by Montagu and Turton, perhaps, by Dillwyn and Gaertner, and many another pioneer of science. And once there, before we look at anything else, come down straight to the sea marge; for yonder lies, just left by the retiring tide, a mass of life such as you will seldom see again. It is somewhat ugly, perhaps, at first sight; for ankle-deep are spread, for some ten yards long by five broad, huge dirty shells, as large as the hand, each with its loathly grey and black tongue hanging out, a confused mass of slimy death. Let us walk on to some cleaner heap, and leave these, the great *Lutraria Elliptica*, which have been lying buried by thousands in the sandy mud, each with the point of its long siphon above the surface, sucking in and driving out again the salt water on which it feeds, till last night's ground-swell shifted the sea bottom, and drove them up hither to perish helpless, but not useless, on the beach.

See, close by is another shell bed, quite as large, but comely enough to please any eye. What a variety of forms and colours are there, amid the purple and olive wreaths of wrack, and bladder-weed, and tangle (oarweed, as they call it in the south), and the delicate green ribbons of the Zostera (the only English flowering plant which grows beneath the sea), surely contradicting, as do several other forms, that somewhat hasty assertion of Mr. Ruskin, that nature makes no ribbons, unless with a midrib, and I know not what other limitations, which seem to me to exist only in Mr. Ruskin's fertile, but fastidious fancy. What are they all? What are the long white razors? What are the delicate green-grey scimitars? What are the tapering brown spires? What the tufts of delicate yellow plants, like squirrels' tails, and lobsters' horns, and tamarisks, and fir-trees, and all other finely cut animal and vegetable forms? What are the groups of grey bladders, with something like a little bud at the tip? What are the hundreds of little pink-striped pears? What those tiny babies' heads, covered with grey prickles instead of hair? The great red star-fish, which Ulster children call "the bad man's hands"; and the great whelks, which the youth of Musselburgh know as roaring buckies, these we have seen; but what, oh what, are the red capsicums?—

Yes, what are the red capsicums? and why are they poking, snapping, starting, crawling, tumbling, wildly over each other, rattling about the huge mahogany cockles, as big as a man's two fists, out of which they are protruded? Mark them well, for you will perhaps never see them again. They are a Mediterranean species, or rather three species, left behind upon these extreme south-western coasts, probably at the vanishing of the same warmer ancient epoch, which clothed the Lizard point with the Cornish heath, and the Killarney moun-tains with Spanish saxifrages, and other relics of a flora whose home is now the Iberian peninsula, and the sunny cliffs of the Riviera. Rare in every other shore, even in the west, it abounds in Torbay to so prodigious an amount, that the dredge, after five minutes' scrape, will often come up choke full of this great cockle only. You will see tens of thousands of them in every cove for miles this day, and every heavy winter's tide brings up an equal multitude,—a seeming waste of life, which would be awful in our eyes, were not the Divine Ruler, as His custom is, making this destruction the means of fresh creation, by burying them in the sands, as soon as washed on shore, to fertilise the strata of some future world. It is but a shell-fish truly; but the great Cuvier thought it remarkable enough to devote to its anatomy elaborate descriptions and drawings, which have done more perhaps than any others to illustrate the curious economy of the whole class of bivalve, or double-shelled, mollusca. If you wish to know more about it than we can tell you, open Mr. Gosse's last book, the *Aquarium*, at p. 222.

"Many persons are aware that the common cockle can

perform gymnastic feats of no mean celebrity, but the
evolutions of Signor Tuberculato are worth seeing.   Some
of the troupe I had put into a pan of sea-water; others
I had turned out into a dish dry, as knowing that an
occasional exposure to the air is a contingency that they
are not unused to.   By-and-by, as we were quietly reading, our attention was attracted to the table, where the
dish was placed, by a rattling uproar, as if flint stones
were rolling one over the other about the dish.   'Oh,
look at the cockles!' was the exclamation; and they
were indeed displaying their agility, and their beauty too,
in fine style.   The valves of the largest were gaping to
the extent of three-quarters of an inch; but the inter-
mediate space was filled up by the spongy looking, fleshy
mantle, of a semipellucid orange hue.   At one end protruded the siphons, two thick short tubes, soldered, as it
were, into one, and enveloped on all sides in a shaggy
fringe of *cirri*, or tentacles.   The circular orifices of
these tubes—small holes, perfectly round, with a white
border—had a curious appearance, as we looked at the
heart-shaped end of the valves.   The discharging orifices,
however, were but rarely visible, being usually closed,
while the others remained constantly open.   But these
things were what we afterwards saw.   For some time we
could look at nothing but the magnificent foot, and the
curious manner in which it was used.

"The two lips of the mantle suddenly separate, and
gaping widely all along the front, recede nearly to the
valves ; while at the same moment a huge organ is thrust
out, somewhat like a tongue, nearly cylindrical, but a
little flattened and tapering to a point.   Its surface is
smooth, and brilliantly glossy, and its colour a fine rich
scarlet, approaching to orange ; but a better idea of it than
can be conveyed by any description, will be obtained by
supposing it to be made of polished cornelian."

Hardly that, most amiable and amusing of naturalists :
it is too opaque for cornelian ; and the true symbol is,
as I said before, in form, size, and colour, one of those
great red capsicums which hang drying in every Covent-
Garden seedsman's window.   Yet is your simile better than

the guess of a certain Countess, who, entering a room wherein a couple of *Cardium Tuberculatum* were waltzing about a plate, exclaimed, "Oh dear! I always heard that my pretty red coral came out of a fish, and here it is all alive!"

"This beautiful and versatile foot," continues Mr. Gosse, "is suddenly thrust out sideways, to the distance of four inches from the shell; then its point being curved backwards, the animal pushes it strongly against any opposing object by the resistance of which the whole animal, shell and all, makes a considerable step forwards. If the cockle were on its native sands, the leaps thus made would doubtless be more precise in their direction, and much more effective: but cooped up with its fellows, in a deep dish, all these Herculean efforts availed only to knock the massive shells against the sides, or roll them irregularly over each other.

"It was curious to notice the extent to which the interior of the cockle was revealed, when the mouth gaped, and the foot was thrust out. By the aid of a candle we could see the interior surfaces of both valves, as it seemed, almost to the very backs. I say, *as it seemed*, for so thin is the mantle where it lines the shell, and so closely does it adhere to it, that every character of the valves, whether as regards colour or irregularity of surface, was distinctly visible; and thus we were able to distinguish the species, not only by their external marks, but by one character drawn from the interior—the ribs in *tuberculatum* extending only half-way across the valves, while in *aculeatum* they reach back to the beaks. . . . The former is much the finer species; the valves are more globose and of a warmer colour; those that I have seen are even more spinous. The mantle is of a rich deep orange, with elevated ribs, corresponding to those of the valves, of a yellow hue. These ribs of the mantle are visible in *aculeatum* also, but in *tuberculatum* they are much more strongly marked, both in form and colour. The siphons display the same orange hue as the mantle-lips, and have a finer appearance than in the other species; the interior of the orifices in both is

covered with a layer of white pearly substance, almost
luminous. In the foot of *tuberculatum*, which agrees,
in the particulars already mentioned, with that of its
congener, I observed a beautiful opalescent gleam when
under water."

" *C. tuberculatum*," continues Mr. Gosse, "is far the
finest species. The valves are more globose and of a
warmer colour; those that I have are even more
spinous." Such may have been the case in his specimens; but it has occurred to the writer now and then to
dredge specimens of *C. aculeatum*, which had escaped
that rolling on the sand fatal in old age to its delicate
spines, and which equalled in colour, size, and perfect-
ness, the noble one figured in poor dear old Dr. Turton's
"British Bivalves." Besides, *aculeatum* is a far thinner
and more delicate shell. And a third species, *C. echinatum*, with curves more graceful and continuous, is to be
found now and then with the two former, in which each
point, instead of degenerating into a knot, as in *tuberculatum*, or developing from delicate, flat, briar-prickles,
into long, straight thorns, as in *aculeatum*, is close-set to
its fellow, and curved at the point transversely to the
shell, the whole being thus horrid with hundreds of
strong tenterhooks, making his castle impregnable to the
raveners of the deep. For we can hardly doubt that
these prickles are meant as weapons of defence, without
which so savoury a morsel as the mollusc within (cooked
and eaten largely on some parts of our south coast) would
be a staple article of food for sea-beasts of prey. And it
is noteworthy, first, that the defensive thorns which are
permanent on the two thinner species, *aculeatum* and
echinatum, disappear altogether on the thicker one,
tuberculatum, as old age gives him a solid and heavy
globose shell; and next, that he too, while young and
tender, and liable therefore to be bored through by
whelks and such murderous univalves, does actually
possess the same briar-prickles, which his thinner cousins
keep throughout life. Nevertheless (and this is a curious
fact, which makes, like most other facts, pretty strongly
against the transmutation of species, and the production of

organs by circumstances demanding them), prickles in all three species, are, as far as we can see, useless in Torbay, where no seal or wolf-fish (*Anarrhichas lupus*), or other shell-crushing pairs of jaws wander, terrible to lobster and to cockle.   Originally intended, as we suppose, to face the strong-toothed monsters of the Mediterranean, these foreigners have been left behind on shores where their armour is not now needed : and yet centuries of idleness and security have not been able to persuade them to lay it by ; as it is written, "They continue this day as at the beginning ; Thou hast given them a law which shall never be broken."

Enough of *Cardium tuberculatum*. What are the names of the other shells which you have gathered, any Introduction to Conchology will tell you ; and the Sea-side Book will give you many a curious fact as to their habits. If you wish to know more, you must consult that new collection of true fairy tales, Dr. Johnston's "Lectures on Conchology." But the little pink pears are rare, hundreds of them as there happen to be here to-day.   They are a delicate sea-anemone,[1] whose beautiful disc you may see well engraved in Gosse's "Naturalist in Devon."   They adhere by thousands to the under-side of loose stones among the sand, and some colony of them has been up-rooted by the pitiless roll of the ground-swell, and drifted in here, sick and sad, but not so far gone but that each, in a jar of salt-water, will expand again into a delicate compound flower, whose "snake-locked" arms are all marbled with pellucid greys and browns, till they look like a living mist, hovering above the pink-striped cylinder of the body.

There are a hundred more things to be talked of here : but we must defer the examination of them till our return ; for it wants an hour yet of the dead low spring-tide ; and ere we go home, we will spend a few minutes at least on the rocks at Livermead, where awaits us a strong-backed quarryman, with a strong-backed crowbar, as is to be hoped (for he snapped one right across there yesterday, falling miserably on his back into a pool thereby), and we will verify Mr. Gosse's observation, that—

[1] *Actinia anguicoma.*

" When once we have begun to look with curiosity on the strange things that ordinary people pass over without notice, our wonder is continually excited by the variety of phase, and often by the uncouthness of form, under which some of the meaner creatures are presented to us. And this is very specially the case with the inhabitants of the sea. We can scarcely poke or pry for an hour among the rocks, at low-water mark, or walk, with an observant downcast eye, along the beach after a gale, without finding some oddly fashioned, suspicious-looking being, unlike any form of life that we have seen before. The dark concealed interior of the sea becomes thus invested with a fresh mystery ; its vast recesses appear to be stored with all imaginable forms ; and we are tempted to think there must be multitudes of living creatures whose very figure and structure have never yet been suspected.

> " ' O sea ! old sea ! who yet knows half
>   Of thy wonders or thy pride ! ' "
>   —Gosse's "Aquarium," pp. 226, 227.

But first, as after descending the gap in the sea-wall we walk along the ribbed floor of hard yellow sand, be so kind as to keep a sharp look-out for a round grey disc, about as big as a penny-piece, peeping out on the surface. No ; that is not it, that little lump : open it, and you will find within one of the common little *Venus gallina.*—(They have given it some new name now, and no thanks to them : they are always changing the names, those closet collectors, instead of studying the live animals where Nature has put them, in which case they would have no time for word-inventing. And we verily suspect that the names grow, like other things ; at least, they get longer and longer and more jaw-breaking every year.) The little bivalve, however, finding itself left by the tide, has wisely shut up its siphons, and, by means of its foot and its edges, buried itself in a comfortable bath of cool wet sand, till the sea shall come back, and make it safe to crawl and lounge about on the surface, smoking the sea-water instead of tobacco. Neither is that lump what we seek. Touch it, and out poke a pair of astonished and inquiring horns and a little sharp muzzle : it is a long-armed crab, who saw us coming, and wisely shovelled himself into the sand by means of his nether-end. Neither is that; though it might be the hole down which what we seek has vanished : but that burrow contains one of the long white razors which you saw cast on shore at Paignton. The boys close by are boring for them with iron rods armed with a screw, and taking them in to sell in Torquay market, as excellent food. But there is one, at last !—a grey disc pouting up through the sand. Touch it, and it is gone down, quick as light. We must dig it out, and carefully, for it is a delicate monster. At last, after ten minutes' careful work, we have brought up, from a foot depth or more—what? A thick, dirty, slimy worm, without head or tail, form or colour. A slug has more artistic beauty about him. Be it so. At home in the aquarium (where, alas ! he will live but for a day or two, under the new irritation of light), he will make a very different figure. That is one of the rarest of British sea-animals, *Actinia chrysanthellum*, though really he is no *Actinia*,[1] and his value consists, not merely in his beauty (though that is not small), but in his belonging to what the long-word-makers call an "interos-culant" group,—a party of genera and species which connect families scientifically far apart, filling up a fresh link in the great chain, or rather the great net-work, of zoo-logical classification. And here we have a simple, and, as it were, crude form ; of which, if we dared to indulge in reveries, we might say, that the Divine Word realised it before either sea-anemones or holothurians, and then went on to perfect the idea contained in it in two different directions ; dividing it into two different families, and making on its model, by adding new organs, and taking away old ones, in one direction the whole family of *Actiniæ* (sea-anemones), and in a quite opposite one the *Holothuriæ*, those strange sea-cucumbers, with their mouth-fringe of feathery gills, of which you shall see some anon. Not (understand well) that there has been any "transmutation" or "development of species" (of in-

[1] Now "Peachia," of Mr. Gosse.

dividuals, as it ought honestly to be called, if the notion
is intended to represent a supposed fact)—a theory as
unsupported by experiment and induction, as it is by *à
priori* reason : but that there has been, in the Creative
Mind, as it gave life to new species, a development of the
idea on which older species were created, in order that
every mesh of the great net might gradually be supplied,
and there should be no gaps in the perfect variety of
Nature's forms. This development is the only one of which
we can conceive, if we allow that a Mind presides over the
universe, and not a mere brute necessity, a Law (absurd
misnomer) without a Lawgiver ; and to it (strangely
enough coinciding here and there with the Platonic
doctrine of Eternal Ideas existing in the Divine Mind),
all fresh inductive discovery seems to point more and
more ; and especially Professor Owen's invaluable tracts
on the Homology of the Vertebrate Skeleton.

Let us speak freely a few words on this important matter.   Geology has disproved the old popular
belief that the universe was brought into being as it now
exists, by a single fiat.   We know that the work has been
gradual ; that the earth

> " In tracts of fluent heat began,
> The seeming prey of cyclic storms,
> The home of seeming random forms,
> Till, at the last, arose the man."

And we know, also, that these forms, seeming random as
they are, have appeared according to a law, which, as far
as we can judge, has been only the whole one of progress,
—lower animals (though we cannot say, the lowest)
appearing first, and man, the highest mammal, " the roof
and crown of things," one of the latest in the series.
We have no more right, let it be observed, to say
that man, the highest, appeared last, than that the lowest
appeared first.   Both may have been the case ; but there
is utterly no proof of either ; and as we know that species
of animals lower than those which already existed
appeared again and again during the various eras, so it is
quite possible that they may be appearing now, and may

appear hereafter: and that for every extinct Dodo or Moa, a new species may be created, to keep up the equilibrium of the whole. This is but a surmise: but it may be wise, perhaps, just now, to confess boldly, even to insist on, its possibility, lest the advocates of the " Vestiges of Creation " theory should claim the notion as making for them, and fancy, from our unwillingness to allow it, that there would be aught in it, if proved, contrary to Christianity.

Let us, therefore, say boldly, that there has been a "progress of species," and that there may be again, in the true sense of that term; but say, as boldly, that the Transmutation theory is not one of a progress of *species* at all, which would be a change in the idea of the species, taking place in the Divine Mind,—in plain words, the creation of a new species. What the Transmutationists really mean, if they would express themselves clearly, or carefully analyse their own notions, is, a physical and actual change, not of species, but of *individuals*, of already existing living beings created according to one idea, into other living beings created according to another idea. And of this, in spite of the apparent change of species in the marvellous metamorphoses of lower animals, Nature has as yet given us no instance among all the facts which have been observed; and there is, therefore, an almost infinite inductive probability against it. As far as we know yet, though all the dreams of the Transmutationists are outdone by the transformations of many a polype, yet the species remain as permanent and strongly marked as in the highest mammal. Such progress as experimental science actually shows us, is quite awful and beautiful enough to keep us our lives long in wonder; but it is one which perfectly agrees with, and may be perfectly explained by, the simple old belief which the Bible sets before us, of a LIVING GOD : not a mere past will, such as the Koran sets forth, creating once and for all, and then leaving the universe, to use Goethe's simile, " to spin round his finger "; nor again, an " all-pervading spirit," words which are mere contradictory jargon, concealing, from those who utter them, blank Materialism : but One who works in all things which have obeyed Him to will and to do of His good pleasure, keeping His abysmal and self-perfect purpose, yet altering the methods by which that purpose is attained, from æon to æon, ay, from moment to moment, for ever various, yet for ever the same.   This great and yet most blessed paradox of the Changeless God, who yet can say, "It repenteth me," and "Behold, I work a new thing on the earth," is revealed no less by nature than by Scripture ; the changeableness, not of caprice or imper- fection, but of an Infinite Maker and "Poietes," draw- ing ever fresh forms out of the inexhaustible treasury of the primeval mind ; and yet never throwing away a conception to which He has once given actual birth in time and space, but (to compare reverently small things and great) lovingly repeating it, reapplying it ; producing the same effects by endlessly different methods ; or so delicately modifying the method that, as by the turn of a hair, it shall produce endlessly diverse effects ; looking back, as it were, ever and anon over the great work of all the ages, to retouch it, and fill up each chasm in the scheme, which for some good purpose had been left open in earlier worlds ; or leaving some open (the forms, for instance, necessary to connect the bimana and the quadrumana) to be filled up perhaps hereafter when the world needs them ; the handiwork, in short, of a living and loving MIND, perfect in His own eternity, but stoop- ing to work in time and space, and there rejoicing Him- self in the work of His own hands, and in His eternal Sabbaths ceasing in rest ineffable, that He may look on that which He hath made, and behold it is very good.

We speak, of course, under correction ; for this con- clusion is emphatically matter of induction, and must be verified or modified by ever-fresh facts : but we meet with many a Christian passage in scientific books, which seems to us to go, not too far, but rather not far enough, in asserting the God of the Bible, as Saint Paul says, "not to have left Himself without witness," in nature itself, that He is the God of grace.   Why speak of the God

of nature and the God of grace as two antithetical terms?
The Bible never, in a single instance, makes the distinction; and, surely, if God be (as He is) the Eternal
and Unchangeable One, and if (as we all confess)
the universe bears the impress of His signet, we have
no right, in the present infantile state of science, to put
arbitrary limits of our own to the revelation which He
may have thought good to make of Himself in nature.
Nay rather, let us believe that, if our eyes were opened,
we should fulfil the requirement of Genius, to "see the
universal in the particular," by seeing God's whole
likeness, His whole glory, reflected as in a mirror even in
the meanest flower; and that nothing but the dulness of
our own sinful souls prevents them from seeing day and
night in all things, however small or trivial to human
eclecticism, the Lord Jesus Christ Himself fulfilling His
own saying, "My Father worketh hitherto, and I work."

And therefore, when we meet with such an excellent
passage as this :—[1]

"Thus it is that Nature advances step by step,
gradually bringing out, through successive stages of being,
new organs and new faculties; and leaving, as she
moves along, at every step, some animals which rise
no higher, as if to serve for landmarks of her progress through all succeeding time.   And this it is which
makes the study of comparative anatomy so fascinating.
Not that I mean to favour a theory of '*development*,'
which would obliterate all idea of species, by supposing
that the more compound animal forms were developments of their simple ancestors.   For such an hypothesis,
Nature gives us no evidence : but she gives us, through
all her domains, the most beautiful and diversified
proofs of an adherence to a settled order, by which new
combinations are continually brought out.   In this
order, the lowest grades of being have certain characters,
above which they do not rise, but propagate beings as
simple as themselves.   Above them are others which,
passing through stages in their infancy equal to the adult

[1] Harvey's Sea-side Book, p. 166.

condition of those below them, acquire, when at maturity. a perfection of organs peculiarly their own. Others again rise above these, and their structures become more gradually compound ; till, at last, it may be said that the simpler animals represent, as in a glass, the scattered organs of the higher races."

——When we read such a passage as this, and confess, as we must, its truth, we cannot help sighing over certain expressions in it, which do unintentionally coincide with the very theory which Professor Harvey denies. Is this progress supposed to take place in time and space ?—or in the mind of a Being above time and space, who afterwards reduces to act and fact, in time and space, just so much and no more of that progress as shall seem good to Him, some here, some there; not binding Himself to begin at the lowest, and end with the highest, but compensating and balancing the lower with the higher in each successive stage of our planet? This last is what the Professor really means, we doubt not : but then, would that he had said boldly, that "God," and not "Nature," is the agent. So would he have raised at once the whole matter from the ground of destiny to that of will, from the material and logical ground to the moral and spiritual, from time and space into ever-present eternity. To us it seems (to sum up, in a few words, what we have tried to say) that such development and progress as have as yet been actually discovered in nature, have been proved, especially by Professor Sedgwick and Mr. Hugh Miller, to bear every trace of having been produced by successive acts of thought and will in some personal mind ; which, however boundlessly rich and powerful, is still *the Archetype of the human mind;* and therefore (for to this we boldly confess we have been all along tending), probably capable, without violence to its properties, of becoming, like the human mind, INCARNATE.

This progress, then, in the divine works, though tending ever to perfection in the very highest sense, need not be always forward and upward, according to the laws of comparative anatomy. It is possible, therefore, on the one hand, that the idea of the Chrysanthellum, and its congeners Scolanthus and Chirodota, has been developed downwards into the far lower Actinia, as well as upwards into the higher Holothurians; just as the idea of a fish was first realised in the highest type of that class, and not, as has been too hastily supposed, in the lowest; for it is now discovered that the sharks, the earliest of fish, are really higher, not lower, in the scale of creation, than those salmons and perches, which we from habit consider the archetypes and lords of the finny tribes. And it is equally possible that all our dream (though right in many another case, as in that of the shark just quoted) is here altogether wrong, and that these Chrysanthella are merely meant to fill up, for the sake of logical perfection, the space between the rooted Polypes and the free Echinoderms. Be this as it may, there is another, and more human, source of interest about this quaint animal who is wriggling himself clean in the glass jar of salt water; for he is one of the many curiosities which has been added to our fauna by that humble hero Mr. Charles Peach, the self-taught naturalist of Cornwall, of whom, as we walk on toward the rocks, something should be said, or rather read; for Mr. Chambers, in an often quoted passage from his *Edinburgh Journal*, which we must have the pleasure of quoting once again, has told the story better than we can tell it :—

"But who is that little intelligent looking man in a faded naval uniform, who is so invariably to be seen in a particular central seat in this section? That, gentle reader, is perhaps one of the most interesting men who attend the British Association. He is only a private in the mounted guard (preventive service) at an obscure part of the Cornwall coast, with four shillings a-day, and a wife and nine children, most of whose education he has himself to conduct. He never tastes the luxuries which are so common in the middle ranks of life, and even amongst a large portion of working-classes. He has to mend with his own hands every sort of thing that can break or wear in his house. Yet Mr. Peach is a votary of Natural History; not a student of the science in books, for he cannot afford books; but an investigator by sea and shore, a collector of zoophytes and echinodermata, strange creatures many of which are as yet hardly known to man. These he collects, preserves, and describes; and every year does he come up to the British Association with a few novelties of this kind, accompanied by illustrative papers and drawings : thus, under circumstances the very opposite of those of such men as Lord Enniskillen, adding, in like manner, to the general stock of knowledge.   On the present occasion he is unusually elated, for he has made the discovery of a holothuria with twenty tentacula, a species of the echinodermata which Professor Forbes, in his book on Star-Fishes, has said was never yet observed in the British seas.   It may be of small moment to you, who, mayhap, know nothing of Holothurias : but it is a considerable thing to the Fauna of Britian, and a vast matter to a poor private of the Cornwall mounted guard.   And accordingly he will go home in a few days, full of the glory of his exhibition, and strung anew by the kind notice taken of him by the masters of the science to similar inquiries, difficult as it may be to prosecute them under such a complication of duties, professional and domestic.   But he has still another subject of congratulation, for Dr. Carpenter has kindly given him a microscope, wherewith to observe the structure of his favourite animals, an instrument for which he has sighed for many years in vain.   Honest Peach ! humble as is thy home, and simple thy bearing, thou art an honour even to this assemblage of nobles and doctors : nay, more, when we consider everything, thou art an honour to human nature itself ; for where is the heroism like that of virtuous, intelligent, independent poverty ?   And such heroism is thine!"—Chambers's *Edinburgh Journal*, Nov. 23, 1844.

Mr. Peach is now, we are glad to say, rewarded in part for his long labours in the cause of science, by having been removed to a more lucrative post on the north coast of England ; the earnest, it is to be hoped, of still further promotion.

But here we are at the old bank of boulders, the ruins of an antique pier which the monks of Tor Abbey built for their convenience, while Torquay was but a knot of fishing huts within a lonely limestone cove. To get to it, though, we have passed many a hidden treasure; for every ledge of these flat New-red-sandstone-rocks, if torn up with the crowbar, discloses in its cracks and crannies nests of strange forms which shun the light of day; beautiful Actiniæ fill the tiny caverns with living flowers; great Pholades bore by hundreds in the softer strata; and wherever a thin layer of muddy sand intervenes between two slabs, long Annelid worms of quaintest forms and colours have their horizontal burrows, among those of that curious and rare radiate animal, the Spoonworm,[1] an eyeless bag about an inch long, half bluish grey, half pink, with a strange scalloped and wrinkled proboscis of saffron colour, which serves, in some mysterious way, soft as it is, to collect food, and clear its dark passage through the rock.

See, at the extreme low-water mark, where the broad olive fronds of the Laminariæ, like fan-palms, droop and wave gracefully in the retiring ripples, a great boulder which will serve our purpose. Its upper side is a whole forest of sea-weeds, large and small; and that forest, if you examined it closely, as full of inhabitants as those of the Amazon or the Gambia. To "beat" that dense cover would be an endless task; but on the under side, where no sea-weeds grow, we shall find full in view enough to occupy us till the tide returns. For the slab, see, is such a one as sea-beasts love to haunt. Its weed-covered surface shows that the surge has not shifted it for years past. It lies on other boulders clear of sand and mud, so that there is no fear of dead sea-weed having lodged and decayed under it, destructive to animal life. We can see dark crannies and caves beneath; yet too narrow to allow the surge to wash in, and keep the surface clean. It will be a fine menagerie of Nereus, if we can but turn it.

Now, the crowbar is well under it; heave, and with a will; and so, after five minutes' tugging, propping, slip-

[1] *Thalassema neptuni* (Forbes' British Star-Fishes, p. 259).

ping, and splashing, the boulder gradually tips over, and
we rush greedily upon the spoil.

A muddy dripping surface it is, truly, full of cracks
and hollows, uninviting enough at first sight : let us look
it round leisurely, to see if there are not materials enough
there for an hour's lecture.

The first object which strikes the eye is probably a
group of milk-white slugs, from two to six inches long,
cuddling snugly together.   You try to pull them off,
and find that they give you some trouble, such a firm
hold have the delicate white sucking arms, which fringe
each of their five edges.   You see at the head nothing
but a yellow dimple ; for eating and breathing are sus-
pended till the return of tide : but once settled in a jar
of salt-water, each will protrude a large chocolate-
coloured head, tipped with a ring of ten feathery gills,
looking very much like a head of " curled kale," but of
the loveliest white and primrose ; in the centre whereof
lies *perdu* a mouth with sturdy teeth—if indeed they, as
well as the whole inside of the worthy fellow, have not
been lately got rid of, and what you see be not a mere
bag, without intestine or other organ : but only for the
time being.   For hear it, worn-out epicures, and old
Indians who bemoan your livers, this little Holothuria
knows a secret which, if he could tell it, you would be
glad to buy of him for thousands sterling.   To him blue-
pill and muriatic acid are superfluous, and travels to
German Brunnen a waste of time.   Happy Holothuria !
who possesses really that secret of everlasting youth, which
ancient fable bestowed on the serpent and the eagle.
For when his teeth ache, or his digestive organs trouble
him, all he has to do is just to cast up forthwith his entire
inside, and *faisant maigre* for a month or so, grow a
fresh set, and then eat away as merrily as ever.   His
name, if you wish to consult so triumphant a hygieist,
is *Cucumaria Hyndmanni*, named after Mr. Hyndmann
of Belfast, his first discoverer : but he has many a stout
cousin round the Scotch coast, who knows the antibilious
panacea as well as he, and submits, among the northern
fishermen, to the rather rude and undeserved name of

sea-puddings; one of which grows in Shetland to the enormous length of three feet, rivalling there his huge congeners, who display their exquisite plumes on every tropic coral reef.

Next, what are those bright little buds, like salmon-coloured Banksia roses half expanded, sitting closely on the stone? Touch them; the soft part is retracted, and the orange flower of flesh is transformed into a pale pink flower of stone. That is the Madrepore, *Caryophyllia Smithii*, one of our south coast rarities; and see, on the lip of the last one, which we have carefully scooped off with the chisel, two little pink towers of stone, delicately striated; drop them into this small bottle of sea-water, and from the top of each tower issues every half second —what shall we call it?—a hand or a net of finest hairs, clutching at something invisible to our grosser sense. That is the *Pyrgoma*, parasitic only (as far as we know) on the lip of this same rare Madrepore; a little "cirrhi-pod," the cousin of those tiny barnacles which roughen every rock, and of those larger ones also, who burrow in the thick hide of the whale, and, borne about upon his mighty sides, throw out their tiny casting nets, as this *Pyrgoma* does, to catch every passing animalcule, and sweep them into the jaws concealed within its shell. And this creature, rooted to one spot through life and death, was in its infancy a free swimming animal, hovering from place to place upon delicate ciliæ, till, having sown its wild oats, it settled down in life, built itself a good stone house, and became a land-owner, or rather a *glebæ adscriptus*, for ever and a day. Mysterious destiny!—yet not so mysterious as that of the free medusoid young of every polype and coral, which ends as a rooted tree of horn or stone, and seems to the eye of sensuous fancy to have literally degenerated into a vegetable. Of them you must read for yourselves in Mr. Gosse's book; in the meanwhile he shall tell you something of the beautiful Madrepores themselves. His description,[1] by far the best yet published, should be read in full: we must content ourselves with extracts.

[1] "A Naturalist's Rambles on the Devonshire Coast," p. 110.

" Doubtless you are familiar with the stony skeleton of our Madrepore, as it appears in museums. It consists of a number of thin calcareous plates standing up edge-wise, and arranged in a radiating manner round a low centre. A little below the margin, their individuality is lost in the deposition of rough calcareous matter. . . . The general form is more or less cylindrical, commonly wider at the top than just above the bottom. . . . This is but the skeleton ; and though it is a very pretty object, those who are acquainted with it alone, can form but a very poor idea of the beauty of the living animal. . . . Let it, after being torn from the rock, recover its equani-mity ; then you will see a pellucid gelatinous flesh emerging from between the plates, and little exquisitely formed and coloured tentacula, with white clubbed tips fringing the sides of the cup-shaped cavity in the centre, across which stretches the oval disc marked with a star of some rich and brilliant colour, surrounding the central mouth, a slit with white crenated lips, like the orifice of one of those elegant cowry shells which we put upon our mantelpieces. The mouth is always more or less promi-nent, and can be protruded and expanded to an astonish-ing extent. The space surrounding the lips is commonly fawn colour, or rich chestnut-brown ; the star or vandyked circle rich red, pale vermilion, and sometimes the most brilliant emerald green, as brilliant as the gorget of a humming-bird."

And what does this exquisitely delicate creature do with its pretty mouth? Alas for fact ! It sips no honey-dew, or fruits from paradise.

" I put a minute spider, as large as a pin's head, into the water, pushing it down to the coral. The instant it touched the tip of a tentacle, it adhered, and was drawn in with the surrounding tentacles between the plates. With a lens I saw the small mouth slowly open, and move over to that side, the lips gaping unsymmetrically, while with a movement as imperceptible as that of the hour hand of a watch, the tiny prey was carried along between the plates to the corner of the mouth. The mouth, however, moved most, and at length reached the edges of the plates, gradually closed upon the insect, and then returned to its usual place in the centre."

Mr. Gosse next tried the fairy of the walking mouth with a house-fly, who escaped only by hard fighting; and at last the gentle creature, after swallowing and disgorging various large pieces of shell-fish, found viands to its taste in "the lean of cooked meat, and portions of earth-worms," filling up the intervals by a perpetual dessert of microscopic animalcules, whirled into that lovely avernus, its mouth, by the currents of the delicate ciliæ which clothe every tentacle. The fact is, that the Madrepore, like those glorious sea-anemones whose living flowers stud every pool, is by profession a scavenger, and a feeder on carrion; and being as useful as he is beautiful, really comes under the rule which he seems at first to break, that handsome is who handsome does.

Another species of Madrepore[1] was discovered on our Devon coast by Mr. Gosse, more gaudy, though not so delicate in hue as our Caryophyllia; three of which are at this moment pouting out their conical orange mouths and pointed golden tentacles in a vase on my table, at once grumbling and entreating for something to eat. Mr. Gosse's locality, for this and numberless other curiosities, is Ilfracombe, on the north coast of Devon. These last specimens came from Lundy Island, in the mouth of the Bristol Channel, or more properly from that curious "Rat Island" to the south of it, where still lingers the black long-tailed English rat, exterminated everywhere else by his sturdier brown cousin of the Hanoverian dynasty.

Look, now, at these tiny saucers of the thinnest ivory, the largest not bigger than a silver threepence, which contain in their centres a milk-white crust of stone, pierced, as you see under the magnifier, into a thousand cells, each with its living architect within. Here are two sorts; in one the tubular cells radiate from the centre, giving it the appearance of a tiny compound flower, daisy or groundsel; in the other they are crossed

---

[1] *Balanophyllia regia*, "Coast of Devon," p. 399.

with waving grooves, giving the whole a peculiar fretted look, even more beautiful than that of the former species. They are *Tubulipora patina* and *Tubulipora hispida ;*— and stay—break off that tiny rough red wart, and look at its cells also under the magnifier: it is *Cellepora pumicosa ;* and now, with the Madrepore you hold in your hand the principal, at least the commonest, British types of those famed coral insects, which in the tropics are the architects of continents, and the conquerors of the ocean surge.   All the world, since the publication of Darwin's delightful "Voyage of the Beagle," and of Williams's "Missionary Enterprises," knows, or ought to know, enough about them: for those who do not, there are a few pages in the beginning of Dr. Landsborough's "British Zoophytes," well worth perusal.

There are a few other true cellepore corals round the coast.   The largest of all, Cervicornis, may be dredged a few miles outside on the Exmouth bank, with a few more Tubulipores; but all tiny things, the lingering, and, as it were, expiring remnants of that great coral-world, which, through the abysmal depths of past ages, formed here in Britain our limestone hills, storing up for generations yet unborn the materials of agriculture and architecture.   Inexpressibly interesting, even solemn, to those who will think, is the sight of these puny parasites, which, as it were, connect the ages and the zones : yet not so solemn and full of meaning as that tiny relic of an older world, the little pear-shaped Turbinolia (cousin of the Madrepores and Sea-anemones), found fossil in the Suffolk Crag, and yet still lingering here and there alive in the deep water off Scilly and the west coast of Ireland, possessor of a pedigree which dates, perhaps, from ages before the day in which it was said, "Let us make man in our image, after our likeness."   To think that the whole human race, its joys and its sorrows, its virtues and its sins, its aspirations and its failures, has been rushing out of eternity and into eternity again, as Arjoon in the Bhagavad Gita beheld the race of men, issuing from Kreeshna's flaming mouth, and swallowed up in it again, " as the crowds of insects swarm into the flame, as the homeless streams leap down into the ocean bed," in an everlasting heart-pulse whose blood is living souls.   And all that while, and ages before that mystery began, that humble coral, unnoticed on the dark sea-floor, has been "continuing as it was at the beginning," and fulfilling "the law which cannot be broken," while races and dynasties and generations have been

> "Playing such fantastic tricks before high heaven,
> As make the angels weep."

Yes; it is this vision of the awful permanence and perfection of the natural world, beside the wild flux and confusion, the mad struggles, the despairing cries of that world of spirits which man has defiled by sin, which would at moments crush the naturalist's heart, and make his brain swim with terror, were it not that he can see by faith, through all the abysses and the ages, not merely

> "*Hands*,
> From out the darkness, shaping man;"

but above them a living loving countenance, human and yet divine; and can hear a voice which said at first, "Let us make man in our image"; and hath said since then, and says for ever and for ever, "Lo, I am with you always, even to the end of the world."

But now, friend, who listenest, perhaps instructed, and at least amused—if, as Professor Harvey well says, the simpler animals represent, as in a glass, the scattered organs of the higher races, which of your organs is represented by that "sca'd man's head," which the Devon children more gracefully, yet with less adherence to plain likeness, call "mermaid's head,"[1] which we picked up just now on Paignton Sands? Or which, again, by its more beautiful little congener,[2] five or six of which are adhering tightly to the slab before us, a ball covered with delicate spines of lilac and green, and stuck over (cunning fellows!) with strips of dead sea-weed

---

[1] *Amphidotus cordatus.*   [2] *Echinus miliaris.*

to serve as improvised parasols? One cannot say
(though Oken and the Okenists might) that in him
we have the first type of the human skull; for the
resemblance, quaint as it is, is only sensuous and
accidental (in the logical use of that term), and not
homological, *i.e.* a lower manifestation of the same idea.
Yet how is one tempted to say, that this was Nature's
first and lowest attempt at that use of hollow globes
of mineral for protecting soft fleshy parts, which she
afterwards developed to such perfection in the skulls of
vertebrate animals. But even that conceit, pretty as
it sounds, will not hold good; for though Radiates
similiar to these were among the earliest tenants of
the abyss, yet as early as their time, perhaps even before
them, had been conceived and actualised, in the sharks,
and in Mr. Hugh Miller's pets the old red sandstone
fishes, that very true vertebrate skull and brain, of which
this is a mere mockery.[1]   Here the whole animal, with
his extraordinary feeding mill (for neither teeth nor jaws
is a fit word for it), is enclosed within an ever-growing
limestone castle, to the architecture of which the
Eddystone and the Crystal Palace are bungling heaps;
without arms or legs, eyes or ears, and yet capable,
in spite of his perpetual imprisonment, of walking,
feeding, and breeding, doubt it not, merrily enough.
But this result has been attained at the expense of
a complication of structure, which has baffled all human
analysis and research into final causes. As much con-
cerning this most miraculous of families as is needful to
be known, and ten times more than is comprehended,
may be read in Professor Harvey's Sea-side Book,
pp. 142–148—pages from which you will probably arise
with a dizzy sense of the infinity of nature, and a
conviction that The Creative Word, so far from having
commenced, as some fancy, with the simplest, and, as it
were, easiest forms of life, took delight, as it were,
in solving the most difficult and complicated problems

---

[1] See Professor Sedgwick's last edition of the Discourses on
the Studies of Cambridge.

first of all, with a certain divine prodigality of wisdom and of power; and that before the mountains were brought forth, or ever the earth and the world was made, He was God from everlasting, the same yesterday, to-day, and for ever. Conceive a Crystal Palace (for mere difference in size, as both the naturalist and the metaphysician know, has nothing to do with the wonder), whereof each separate joist, girder, and pane grows continually without altering the shape of the whole; and you have conceived only one of the miracles embodied in that little sea-egg, which The Divine Word has, as it were to justify to man His own immutability, furnished with a shell capable of enduring fossil for countless ages, that we may confess Him to have been as great when first His spirit brooded on the deep, as He is now, and will be through all worlds to come.

But we must make haste; for the tide is rising fast, and our stone will be restored to its eleven hours' bath, long before we have talked over half the wonders which it holds. Look though, ere you retreat, at one or two more.

What is that little brown fellow whom you have just taken off the rock to which he adhered so stoutly by his sucking-foot? A limpet? Not at all: he is of quite a different family and structure; but, on the whole, a limpet-like shell would suit him well enough, so he had one given him: nevertheless, owing to certain anatomical peculiarities, he needed one aperture more than a limpet; so one, if you will examine, has been given him at the top of his shell.[1] This is one instance among a thousand of the way in which a scientific knowledge of objects must not obey, but run counter to, the impressions of sense; and of a custom in nature which makes this caution so necessary, namely, the repetition of the same form, slightly modified, in totally different animals, sometimes as if to avoid waste (for why should not the same conception be used in two different cases, if it will suit in

---

[1] *Fissurella græca.*

both?) and sometimes (more marvellous by far), when an organ fully developed and useful in one species, appears in a cognate species, but feeble, useless, and, as it were, abortive; and gradually, in species still farther removed, dies out altogether; placed there, it would seem, at first sight, merely to keep up the family likeness. I am half jesting; that cannot be the only reason, perhaps not the reason at all; but the fact is one of the most curious, and notorious also, in comparative anatomy.

Look, again, at those sea-slugs. One, some three inches long, of a bright lemon-yellow, clouded with purple; another of a dingy grey;[1] another (exquisite little creature) of a pearly French white,[2] furred all over the back with what seem arms, but are really gills, of ringed white and grey and black. Put that yellow one into water, and from his head, above the eyes, arise two serrated horns, while from the after part of his back springs a circular Prince-of-Wales's-feather of gills—they are almost exactly like those which we saw just now in the white *Cucumaria*. Yes; here is another instance of that same custom of repetition. The *Cucumaria* is a low radiate animal—the sea-slug a far higher mollusc; and every organ within him is formed on a different type; as indeed are those seemingly identical gills, if you come to examine them under the microscope, having to oxygenate fluids of a very different and more complicated kind; and, moreover, the *Cucumaria's* gills were put round his mouth; the *Doris's* feathers round the other extremity; that grey *Eolis's*, again, are simple clubs, scattered over his whole back, and in each of his nudi-branch congeners these same gills take some new and fantastic form; in *Melibæa* those clubs are covered with warts; in *Scyllæa*, with tufted bouquets; in the beautiful *Antiopa*[3] they are transparent bags; and in many other English species they take every conceivable form of leaf, tree, flower, and branch, bedecked with every colour of

---

[1] *Doris tuberculata* and *bilineata*.   [2] *Eolis papillosa*.
[3] Grosse's "Naturalist in Devon," p. 325.

the rainbow, as you may see them depicted in Messrs. Alder and Hancock's unrivalled Monograph on the Nudibranch Mollusca.

And now, worshipper of final causes and the mere useful in Nature, answer but one question—Why this prodigal variety? All these Nudibranchs live in much the same way: why would not the same mould have done for them all? And why, again (for we must push the argument a little further), why have not all the butterflies, at least all who feed on the same plant, the same markings? Of all unfathomable triumphs of design (we can only express ourselves thus, for honest induction, as Paley so well teaches, allows us to ascribe such results only to the design of some personal will and mind), what surpasses that by which the scales on a butterfly's wing are arranged to produce a certain pattern of artistic beauty beyond all painter's skill? What a waste of power, on any utilitarian theory of nature! And once more, why are those strange microscopic atomies, the *Diatomaceæ* and *Infusoria*, which fill every stagnant pool, which fringe every branch of sea-weed, which form banks hundreds of miles long on the Arctic sea-floor, and the strata of whole moorlands, which pervade in millions the mass of every iceberg, and float aloft in countless swarms amid the clouds of the volcanic dust—why are their tiny shells of flint as fantastically various in their quaint mathematical symmetry, as they are countless beyond the wildest dreams of the Pantheist? Mystery inexplicable on all theories of evolution by necessary laws, as well as on the conceited notion which, making man forsooth the centre of the universe, dares to believe that variety of forms has existed for countless ages in abysmal sea-depths and untrodden forests, only that some few individuals of the western races might, in these latter days, at last discover and admire a corner here and there of the boundless realms of beauty. Inexplicable, truly, if man be the centre and the object of their existence; explicable enough to him who believes that God has created all things for Himself, and rejoices in His own handiwork, and that the material universe is, as the wise man says, "A platform whereon His eternal Spirit sports and makes melody." Of all the blessings which the study of nature brings to the patient observer, let none, perhaps, be classed higher than this;—that the further he enters into those fairy gardens of life and birth, which Spenser saw and described in his great poem, the more he learns the awful and yet most comfortable truth, that they do not belong to him, but to one greater, wiser, lovelier than he; and as he stands, silent with awe, amid the pomp of nature's ever-busy rest, hears, as of old, "The Word of the Lord God walking among the trees of the garden in the cool of the day."

One sight more, and we have done. We had something to say, had time permitted, on the ludicrous element which appears here and there in nature. There are animals, like monkeys and crabs, which seem made to be laughed at; by those at least who possess that most indefinable of faculties, the sense of the ridiculous. As long as man possesses muscles especially formed to enable him to laugh, we have no right to suppose (with some) that laughter is an accident of our fallen nature; or to find (with others) the primary cause of the ridiculous in the perception of unfitness or disharmony. And yet we shrink (whether rightly or wrongly, we can hardly tell) from attributing a sense of the ludicrous to the Creator of these forms. It may be a weakness on our part; at least we will hope it is a reverent one: but till we can find something corresponding to what we conceive of the Divine Mind in any class of phænomena, it is perhaps better not to talk about them at all, but observe stoic "epoché," waiting for more light, and yet confessing that our own laughter is uncontrollable, and therefore we hope not unworthy of us, at many a strange creature and strange doing which we meet, from the highest ape to the lowest polype.

But, in the meanwhile, there are animals in which results so strange, fantastic, even seemingly horrible, are produced, that fallen man may be pardoned, if he shrinks from them in disgust. That, at least, must be a consequence of our own wrong state; for everything is beautiful and perfect in its place. It may be answered, " Yes, in its place; but its place is not yours. You had no business to look at it, and must pay the penalty for intermeddling." I doubt that answer; for surely, if man have liberty to do anything, he has liberty to search out freely his heavenly Father's works; and yet every one seems to have his antipathic animal; and I know one bred from his childhood to zoology by land and sea, and bold in asserting, and honest in feeling, that all without exception is beautiful, who yet cannot, after handling and petting and admiring all day long every uncouth and venomous beast, avoid a paroxysm of horror at the sight of the common house-spider. At all events, whether we were intruding or not, in turning this stone, we must pay a fine for having done so; for there lies an animal as foul and monstrous to the eye as "hydra, gorgon, or chimæra dire," and yet so wondrously fitted to its work, that we must needs endure for our own instruction to handle and to look at it. Its name I know not (though it lurks here under every stone), and should be glad to know. It seems some very " low " Ascarid or Planarian worm. You see it ? That black, shiny, knotted lump among the gravel, small enough to be taken up in a dessert spoon. Look now, as it is raised and its coils drawn out. Three feet— six—nine, at least: with a capability of seemingly endless expansion; a slimy tape of living caoutchouc, some eighth of an inch in diameter, a dark chocolate-black, with paler longitudinal lines. Is it alive? It hangs helpless and motionless, a mere velvet string across the hand. Ask the neighbouring Annelids and the fry of the rock fishes, or put it into a vase at home, and see. It lies motionless, trailing itself among the gravel; you cannot tell where it begins or ends; it may be a dead strip of sea-weed, *Himanthalia lorea* perhaps, or *Chorda filum;* or even a tarred string. So thinks the little fish who plays over and over it, till he touches at last what is too surely a head. In an instant a bell-shaped sucker mouth has fastened to his side. In another instant, from one lip, a concave double proboscis, just like a tapir's (another instance of the repetition of forms), has clasped him like a finger ; and now begins the struggle : but in vain. He is being "played" with such a fishing-line as the skill of a Wilson or a Stoddart never could invent ; a living line, with elasticity beyond that of the most delicate fly-rod, which follows every lunge, shortening and lengthening, slipping and twining round every piece of gravel and stem of sea-weed, with a tiring drag such as no Highland wrist or step could ever bring to bear on salmon or on trout. The victim is tired now ; and slowly, and yet dexterously, his blind assailant is feeling and shifting along his side, till he reaches one end of him ; and then the black lips expand, and slowly and surely the curved finger begins packing him end-foremost down into the gullet, where he sinks, inch by inch, till the swelling which marks his place is lost among the coils, and he is probably macerated to a pulp long before he has reached the opposite extremity of his cave of doom. Once safe down, the black murderer slowly contracts again into a knotted heap, and lies, like a boa with a stag inside him, motionless and blest.

There ; we must come away now, for the tide is over our ankles ; but touch, before you go, one of those little red mouths which peep out of the stone. A tiny jet of water shoots up almost into your face. The bivalve [1] who has burrowed into the limestone knot (the softest part of the stone to his jaws, though the hardest to your chisel) is scandalised at having the soft mouths of his siphons so rudely touched, and taking your finger for some bothering Annelid, who wants to nibble him, is defending himself ; shooting you, as naturalists do hum-ming-birds, with water. Let him rest in peace ; it will cost you ten minutes' hard work, and much dirt, to extract him : but if you are fond of shells, secure one or two of those beautiful pink and straw-coloured scallops,[2] who have gradually incorporated the layers of their lower valve with the roughnesses of the stone, destroying thereby the beautiful form which belongs to their race, but not their delicate colour. There are a few more bivalves too,

---

[1] *Saxicava rugosa.*   [2] *Pecten pusio.*

adhering to the stone, and those rare ones, and two or three delicate *Mangeliæ* and *Nasæ* are trailing their graceful spires up and down in search of food.   That little bright red and yellow pea, too, touch it—the brilliant coloured cloak is withdrawn, and, instead, you have a beautifully ribbed pink cowry,[1] our only European representative of that grand tropical family.   Cast one wandering glance, too, at the forest of zoophytes and corals, *Lepraliæ* and *Flustræ*, and those quaint blue stars, set in brown jelly, which are no zoophytes, but respectable molluscs, each with his well-formed mouth and intestines,[2] but combined in a peculiar form of Communism, of which all one can say is, that one hopes they like it; and that, at all events, they agree better than the heroes and heroines of Mr. Hawthorne's Blithedale Romance.

Now away, and as a specimen of the fertility of the water-world, look at this rough list of species,[3] the greater part of which are on this very stone, and all of which you might obtain in an hour, would the rude tide wait for zoologists; and remember, that the number of individuals

---

[1] *Cypræa Europœa.*

[3] *Molluscs.*
Doris tuberculata.
—— Bilineata.
Eolis papillosa.
Pleurobranchus plumula.
Neritina.
Cypræa.
Trochus—2 species.
Mangelia.
Triton.
Trophon.
Nasa—2 species.
Cerithium.
Sigaretus.
Fissurella.
Arca lactea.
Pecten pusio.
Tapes pullastra.
Kellia suborbicularis.
Sphænia Binghami.
Saxicava rugosa.
Gastrochœna pholadia.
Pholas parva.

Anomiæ — 2 or 3 species.
Cynthia—2 species.
Botryllus,   do.
Sydinum ?

Annelids.
Phyllodoce, and other Nereid worms.
Polynoe squamata.

Crustacea.
4 or 5 species.

Echinoderms.
Echinius miliaris.
Asterias gibbosa.
Ophiocoma neglecta.
Cucumaria Hyndmanni.
—— communis.

Polypes.
Sertularia pumila.
—— rugosa.

[2] *Botrylli.*
Sertularia fallax.
—— filicula.
Plumularia falcata.
—— setacea.
Laomedea geniculata.
Campanularia volubilis.
Actinia mesembryanthemum.
—— clavata.
—— anguicoma.
—— crassicornis.
Tubulipora patina.
—— hispida.
—— serpens.
Crisia eburnea.
Cellepora pumicosa.
Lepraliæ—many species.
Membranipora pilosa.
Cellularia ciliata.
—— scruposa.
—— reptans.
Flustra membranacea, &c.

of each species of polype must be counted by tens of thousands, and also, that, by searching the forest of sea-weeds which covers the upper surface, we should probably obtain some twenty minute species more.

A goodly catalogue this, surely, of the inhabitants of three or four large stones ; and yet how small a specimen of the multitudinous nations of the sea. From the bare rocks above high-water mark, down to abysses deeper than ever plummet sounded, is life, everywhere life ; fauna after fauna, and flora after flora, arranged in zones, according to the amount of light and warmth which each species requires, and to the amount of pressure which they are able to endure. The crevices of the highest rocks, only sprinkled with salt spray in spring-tides and high gales, have their peculiar little univalves, their crisp lichen-like sea-weeds, in myriads ; lower down, the region of the *Fuci* (bladder-weeds) has its own tribes of peri-winkles and limpets ; below again, about the neap-tide mark, the region of the corallines and *Algæ* furnishes food for yet other species who graze on its watery meadows ; and beneath all, only uncovered at low spring-tide, the zone of the *Laminariæ* (the great tangles and oar-weeds) is most full of all of every imaginable form of life. So that as we descend the rocks, we may compare ourselves (likening small things to great) to those who, descending the Andes, pass in a single day from the vegetation of the Arctic zone to that of the Tropics. And here and there, even at half-tide level, deep rock-basins, shaded from the sun and always full of water, keep up in a higher zone the vegetation of a lower one, and afford in miniature an analogy to those deep "barrancos" which split the high table-land of Mexico, down whose awful cliffs, swept by cool sea-breezes, the traveller looks from among the plants and animals of the temperate zone, and sees far below, dim through their everlasting vapour-bath of rank hot steam, the mighty forms and gorgeous colours of a tropic forest.

"I do not wonder," says Mr. Gosse, in his charming "Naturalist's Rambles on the Devonshire Coast,"[1] "that

[1] Page 187.

when Southey had an opportunity of seeing some of those
beautiful quiet basins hollowed in the living rock, and
stocked with elegant plants and animals, having all the
charm of novelty to his eye, they should have moved
his poetic fancy, and found more than one place in the
gorgeous imagery of his oriental romances.   Just listen
to him :—

> " ' It was a garden still beyond all price,
>   Even yet it was a place of paradise ;
> .   .   .   .
>   And here were coral bowers,
>   And grots of madrepores,
>   And banks of sponge, as soft and fair to eye
>   As e'er was mossy bed
>   Whereon the wood-nymphs lie
> With languid limbs in summer's sultry hours.
>   Here, too, were living flowers,
>   Which, like a bud compacted,
>   Their purple cups contracted ;
>   And now in open blossom spread,
> Stretch'd, like green anthers, many a seeking head.
>   And arborets of jointed stone was there,
>   And plants of fibres fine as silkworm's thread ;
>   Yea, beautiful as mermaid's golden hair
>   Upon the waves dispread.
>   Others that, like the broad banana growing,
> Raised their long wrinkled leaves of purple hue,
>   Like streamers wide outflowing.'
>   —*Kehama*, xvi. 5.

" A hundred times you might fancy you saw the type,
the very original of this description, tracing, line by line,
and image by image, the details of the picture ; and ac-
knowledging, as you proceed, the minute truthfulness
with which it has been drawn.   For such is the loveliness
of nature in these secluded reservoirs, that the accom-
plished poet, when depicting the gorgeous scenes of
eastern mythology— scenes the wildest and most extra-
vagant that imagination could paint, drew not upon the
resources of his prolific fancy for imagery here, but was
well content to jot down the simple lineaments of nature
as he saw her in plain, homely England.

" It is a beautiful and fascinating sight for those who
have never seen it before, to see the little shrubberies of

pink coralline—'the arborets of jointed stone'—that
fringe those pretty pools. It is a charming sight to see
the crimson banana-like leaves of the *Delesseria* waving
in their darkest corners; and the purple fibrous tufts of
Polysiphoniæ and *Ceramia*, 'fine as silkworm's thread.'
But there are many others which give variety and impart
beauty to these tide-pools. The broad leaves of the
Ulva, finer than the finest cambric, and of the brightest
emerald-green, adorn the hollows at the highest level,
while, at the lowest, wave tiny forests of the feathery
Ptilota and *Dasya*, and large leaves, cut into fringes and
furbelows, of rosy *Rhodymeniæ*. All these are lovely to
behold; but I think I admire as much as any of them,
one of the commonest of our marine plants, *Chondrus
crispus*. It occurs in the greatest profusion on this coast,
in every pool between tide-marks; and everywhere—
except in those of the highest level, where constant exposure to light dwarfs the plant, and turns it of a dull
umber-brown tint—it is elegant in form and brilliant in
colour. The expanding fan-shaped fronds, cut into seg-
ments, cut, and cut again, make fine bushy tufts in a deep
pool, and every segment of every frond reflects a flush
of the most lustrous azure, like that of a tempered sword-
blade."—Gosse's "Devonshire Coast," pp. 187–189.

And the sea bottom, also, has its zones, at different
depths, and its peculiar forms in peculiar spots, affected
by the currents and the nature of the ground, the riches
of which have to be seen, alas! rather by the imagination than the eye; for such spoonfuls of the treasure as
the dredge brings up to us, come too often rolled and
battered, torn from their sites and contracted by fear,
mere hints to us of what the populous reality below
is like. And often, standing on the shore at low tide,
has one longed to walk on and in under the waves,
as the water-ousel does in the pools of the mountain
burn, and see it all but for a moment; and a solemn
beauty and meaning has invested the old Greek fable
of Glaucus the fisherman, how he ate of the herb which
gave his fish strength to leap back into their native
element, was seized on the spot with a strange longing

to follow them under the waves, and became for ever a companion of the fair semi-human forms with which the Hellenic poets peopled their sunny bays and firths, feeding his "silent flocks" far below on the green Zostera beds, or basking with them on the sunny ledges in the summer noon, or wandering in the still bays on sultry nights amid the choir of Amphitrite and her sea-nymphs,

"Joining the bliss of the gods, as they waken the coves with their
    laughter,"

in nightly revels, whereof one has sung,—

"So they came up in their joy; and before them the roll of the
    surges
Sank, as the breezes sank dead, into smooth green foam-flecked
    marble
Awed; and the crags of the cliffs, and the pines of the mountains
    were silent.
So they came up in their joy, and around them the lamps of the
    sea-nymphs
Myriad fiery globes, swam heaving and panting, and rainbows,
Crimson and azure and emerald, were broken in star-showers,
    lighting
Far in the wine-dark depths of the crystal, the gardens of Nereus,
Coral and sea-fan and tangle, the blooms and the palms of the
    ocean.
So they went on in their joy, more white than the foam which they
    scattered,
Laughing and singing and tossing and twining, while eager, the
    Tritons
Blinded with kisses their eyes, unreproved, and above them in
    worship
Fluttered the terns, and the sea-gulls swept past them on silvery
    pinions,
Echoing softly their laughter; around them the wantoning dolphins
Sighed as they plunged, full of love; and the great sea-horses
    which bore them
Curved up their crests in their pride to the delicate arms of their
    riders,
Pawing the spray into gems, till a fiery rainfall, unharming,
Sparkled and gleamed on the limbs of the maids, and the coils
    of the mermen.
So they went on in their joy, bathed round with the fiery coolness,
Needing nor sun nor moon, self-lighted, immortal: but others
Pitiful, floated in silence apart; on their knees lay the sea-boys

Whelmed by the roll of the surge, swept down by the anger
    of Nereus ;
Hapless, whom never again upon quay or strand shall their
    mothers
Welcome with garlands and vows to the temples ; but wearily
    pining,
Gaze over island and main for the sails which return not ; they
    heedless
Sleep in soft bosoms for ever, and dream of the surge and the
    sea-maids.
So they past by in their joy, like a dream, down the murmuring
    ripples."

Such a rhapsody may be somewhat out of order, even
in a popular scientific book ; and yet one cannot help
at moments envying the old Greek imagination, which
could inform the soulless sea-world with a human life
and beauty. For after all, star-fishes and sea-anemones
are dull substitutes for Sirens and Tritons ; the lamps
of the sea-nymphs, those glorious phosphorescent medusæ
whose beauty Mr. Gosse sets forth so well with pen and
pencil, are not as attractive as the sea-nymphs themselves
would be ; and who would not, like Menelaus, take the
grey old man of the sea himself asleep upon the rocks,
rather than one of his seal-herd, probably too with the
same result as the world-famous combat in the Antiquary,
between Hector and Phoca ? And yet—is there no
human interest in these pursuits, more human, ay,
and more divine, than there would be even in those
Triton and Nereid dreams, if realised to sight and
sense ? Heaven forbid that those should say so, whose
wanderings among rock and pool have been mixed up
with holiest passages of friendship and of love, and
the intercommunion of equal minds and sympathetic
hearts, and the laugh of children drinking in health
from every breeze, and instruction at every step, running
ever and anon with proud delight to add their little
treasure to their parents' stock, and of happy friendly
evenings spent over the microscope and the vase, in
examining, arranging, preserving, noting, down in the
diary the wonders and the labours of the happy, busy
day. No ; such short glimpses of the water world as
our present appliances afford us, are full enough of

pleasure; and we will not envy Glaucus; we will not even be over-anxious for the success of his only modern imitator, the French naturalist who is reported to have just fitted himself with a waterproof dress and breathing apparatus, in order to walk the bottom of the Mediterranean, and see for himself how the world goes on at the fifty-fathom line. We will be content with dredging next year as we dredged this; and in the meanwhile let Mr. Gosse tell us some of the pleasures of that little-known amusement :—

"The dredge is a strong bag with an iron frame around the mouth, which is drawn over the sea-bottom by a rope. The rudest form of the instrument is that used for procuring oysters. The bag is generally made of iron rings linked together, and one of the longer sides of the frame is turned up to make a scraping-lip.

"But the naturalists' dredge is an improvement upon this form : the oyster-dredge, with all the care employed in heaving, will frequently turn over in sinking, so that the unlipped side of the frame which will not scrape is on the ground. Hence we have each of the two long sides of the mouth made into a scraping-lip, so that the instrument cannot fall wrong. Instead of rings our body is made of spun-yarn (a sort of small rope), or fishing-line, netted with a small mesh; or which is still better, of a raw hide (such as those which the tobacconists receive from South America inclosing tobacco, the hides of the wild cattle of the Pampas), cut into thongs, and netted in like manner. Sometimes the bag is made of coarse sackcloth, or of canvas, but the former soon wears out, and the latter is not sufficiently pervious to water; an important point, for if there be not a free current through the bag, while on the bottom, it embraces nothing, merely driving everything before it, and coming up empty. The hide-net is almost indestructible.

"To the two ends, or short sides of the frame, which forms an oblong square, are attached by a hinge two long triangles, which, meeting in front at some distance from the mouth, are connected by a swivel-joint. To this the dragging rope is bent, which must be long

enough to allow thrice as much at least to be overboard
as the perpendicular depth would require; if you are
dredging in ten fathoms, you must use at least thirty
fathoms of line, or your dredge will make long jumps
over the ground instead of steadily raking it. The
inward end of the rope having been made fast to one of
the thwarts, the dredge is hove to windward, and the
boat is put before the wind, or at least allowed a flowing
sheet.

"But before we ran down to our dredging ground, my
master of the ceremonies proposed that we should haul
up a point or two, and have a scrape on the Zostera beds
that cover many acres of shallow water in the bight of
Preston Valley. But let me introduce my man to you.
A clever fellow is Jone, and though only bred as a fisherman, he is quite an amateur naturalist. There is nobody
else in Weymouth harbour that knows anything about
dredging ; (I have it from his own lips, so you may rely
upon it ;) but *he* is familiar with the feel of almost every
yard of bottom from Whitenose to Church-Hope, and
from St. Aldham's Head to the Bill. He follows dredging
with the zest of a *savant ;* and it is amusing really to
hear how he pours forth the crackjaw, the sesquipedalian
nomenclature. 'Now, Sir, if you do want a *Gastrochœna,*
I can just put down your dredge upon a lot of 'em ; we'll
bring up three and four in a stone.' 'I'm in hopes we
shall have a good *Cribella* or two off this bank, if we
don't get choked up with them 'ere *Ophiocomas.*' He
tells me in confidence that he has been sorely puzzled to
find a name for his boat, but has at length determined to
appellate her 'The Turritella ; just to astonish the fishermen, you know, Sir,'—with an accompanying wink and
chuckle, and a patronising nudge in my ribs. Jone is a
proud man when he gets a real *savant* alone in a boat ;
and he talks with delight of the feats which he has
achieved in the dredging line for Mr. Bowerbank, Mr.
Hanley, and Professor Forbes.

"Well, here we are in the bight, just off the mouth of

Preston Valley, the only bit of pretty scenery anywhere near. This, however, is a little gem; a verdant dell opening to the sea, through which a streamlet runs, with the sides and bottom covered with woods, a rare feature in this neighbourhood. We are over the Zostera: the beds of dark green grass are waving in the heave of the swell, and we can make out the long and narrow blades by closely looking down beneath the shadow of the boat. Here then is the place for the keer-drag. Down it goes and sinks into the long grass, while we slowly drag it for a couple of hundred yards or so.

"When disposed to try our luck, we hauled on the rope till we got the mouth of the drag to the top of the water; a turn or hitch was then taken round a belaying pin, with the two side lines of the bridle, and the point of the net only was then hauled on board, put into a pan of water and untied. Here was congregated the chief part of the prey taken, and hence the need of having the meshes so small in this part. Out swam in a moment a good many little fishes that haunt the grass-bed; as Pipe-fishes (*Syngnathus*) of several species, Gobies (*Gobius unipunctatas*, &c., &c.) and bright blue Conners (*Labrus* and *Crenilabrus*). With these were two or three active and charming Cuttles (*Sepiola*); and clinging to the meshes of the net in various parts, were several species of Nudibranch Mollusca, creatures of remarkable elegance and beauty.

.   .   .   .   .

"Meanwhile we put the boat before the wind, and run along the inhospitable coast on our left. We leave the pleasant vale behind, and skim swiftly by the black rocks of Ratcliff Head, and the distorted and confused strata of Goggin's Berrow. We pass Osmington Mills, where a rather ample sheet of water is poured in a foaming cascade over the low cliffs, and where those curious circular blocks of grit-stone, flat on one side and conical on the other, are imbedded with regularity on the sandy face of the precipice: and leave on our quarter the rocks, where the abundance of iron pyrites and sulphur has more than once presented the strange phenomenon of spontaneous fire ; a phenomenon distinctly remembered still by the inhabitants of Weymouth, who night after night used to gaze out with wonder on the burning cliffs.

"At length we are under Whitenose, that bold chalk cliff that is so prominent an object as the eye roves along the coast line from Weymouth. Here we turn the boat's edge to the southward, and throw the dredge overboard in fourteen fathoms. And while I am enjoying with the line in my hand, what a dredger particularly likes to feel, the vibration produced by the instrument as it rumbles and scrapes over a moderately rough bottom, telling that it is doing its work well—we will gaze with admiration on this magnificent precipice of dazzling white that rears its noble head behind us. It is the termination of that range of chalk hills which, with some few interruptions, intersect the kingdom from the Yorkshire coast to Dorset : and stands in simple majesty, the snowy whiteness of its vast face unvaried, except by the slanting lines which mark the dipping strata running across it, and which look so fine and so regular, as if they had been drawn by the pen of a geometrician.

"But up with the dredge ; let us see our success. It feels pretty heavy as it mounts, and here, as it breaks the surface, we can already see some bright-hued and active creatures in its capacious bag. A wide board, resting on two thwarts, serves for a table, and on this— a few of the more delicate things, that appear at a glance, having been first taken out—the whole contents are poured. The empty dredge is returned to the deep for another haul, while we set eagerly to work with fingers and eyes on the heap before us.

"What a pleasure it is to examine a tolerably prolific dredge-haul! I am not going to enumerate all the things that we found ; it would make a pretty long list. Numbers of rough stones, and of old worm-eaten shells, half a broken bottle, and other strange matters, were there—every one, however rude, worthy of close examination, because studded with elegant zoophytes, the tubes of serpulæ and other annelidæ, bright-coloured pellucid ascidians, graceful nudibranch molluscæ, the spawn of fishes, and endless other things.   Brittle-stars, by scores, were twining their long spiny arms, like lizard's tails, among the tangled mass, arrayed in the most varied and most gorgeous hues of all varieties of kaleidoscope patterns (see plate IV.),[1] and sandstars not a few.   The latter are much more delicate in constitution than the former, being very difficult to keep alive, and also much more brittle ; the former, notwithstanding their English name, I have not found so particularly fragile.   Among other members of this wonderful class of animals, we obtained, in the course of our day's work, several of that fine but common one, the twelve-rayed sun-star (*Solaster papposa*), a showy creature, dressed in rich scarlet livery, some eight inches in diameter.   Two or three of a species usually counted rare also occurred, the bird's foot (*Palmipes membranaceus*), more curious, and equally beautiful.   (See plate III.)   It resembles a pentagonal piece of thin leather, with the angles a little produced, and regularly pointed.   The central part of this disc is scarlet, and a double line of scarlet proceeds from this to each angle, while the whole is margined by a narrow band of the same gorgeous hue.   The remainder of the surface is of a pale yellow or cream colour, and covered, in the most elegant manner, with tufts of minute spines, arranged in lines which cross each other, lozenge-fashioned, near the middle of the disc, and run parallel to each other, at right angles to the margin, between the points.

" Not less attractive was another star-fish, the Eyed Cribella (*Cribella oculata*).   It consists of five finger-like rays, tapering to a blunt point, and cleft nearly to the centre, the consistence stiffly fleshy, or almost cartilaginous.   The hue of both disc and rays, or the superior surface, is a fine rosy purple.   (See plate III.)

" All these are very attractive occupants of an aquarium. They are active and restless, though slow in movement,

---

[1] Gosse's " Aquarium."

continually crawling about the rocks, and round the
sides of the tank, by a gliding motion produced by the
attachment and shifting of hundreds of sucker feet,
which are protruded at will through minute pores in the
calcareous integument. Their showy colours are ex-
hibited to advantage on the dark rocks, around the pro-
jections and angles of which they wind their flexible
bodies, now and then turning back a ray, from which
the pellucid suckers are seen stretching and sprawling;
and as they mount the glass, not only can their hues be
admired, but the exquisite structure of their spines, and
the mechanism of their suckers, can be studied at
leisure.

"Every haul of the dredge brought up several univalve
shells, tenanted, not by their original constructors and
proprietors, but by their busy intruder, the soldier crab
(*Pagurus*). Several species of this curious creature
occurred. . . . I shall only just allude to the beautiful
cloak anemone (*Adamsia palliata*), and several other
species of this charming family. Long legged spider
crabs, of the genera Stenorynchus, Inachus, &c., were
abundant, sprawling their slender limbs like bristles, to
an unconscionable distance, tempting us to think that,
if we had legs like these, we might cover the ground in a
style that would put to shame the old giant slayer's
seven-league boots.

"But as I have said, time and space would fail me if
I were to attempt an enumeration of all the objects
of interest that were brought to view in the course of
a good day's dredging. Mollusca, both naked and
shelled, both univalve and bivalve, and crabs, prawns and
shrimps, worms, sponges, sea-weeds, all presented claims
to notice, and all contributed representatives to my
stock, in the successive emptyings of the dredge ; for we
worked pretty nearly all the way home. And when we
came to bring on shore the bottles, jars, pans, pails, and
tubs, we found them all well tenanted with strange
creatures, the greater part of which were despatched
on their way to London by the same evening mail train."
—Gosse's "Aquarium," pp. 55, 58, 59, 63.

But if you cannot afford the expense of your own dredge and boat, and the time and trouble necessary to follow the occupation scientifically, yet every trawler and oyster boat will afford you a tolerable satisfaction. Go on board one of these; and while the trawl is down, spend a pleasant hour or two in talking with the simple, honest, sturdy fellows who work it, from whom (if you are as fortunate as we have been for many a year past) you may get many a moving story of danger and sorrow, as well as many a shrewd practical maxim, and often, too, a living recognition of God, and the providence of God, which will send you home, perhaps, a wiser and more genial man. And when the trawl is hauled, wait till the fish are counted out, and packed away, and then kneel down and inspect (in a pair of Mackintosh leggings, and your oldest coat) the crawling heap of shells and zoophytes which remains behind about the decks, and you will find, if a landsman, enough to occupy you for a week to come. Nay, even if it be too calm for trawling, condescend to go out in a coble, and help to haul some honest fellow's deep-sea lines and lobster-pots, and you will find more and stranger things about them than even fish or lobsters : though they, to him who has eyes to see, are strange enough.

We speak from experience ; for it was but the other day that, in the north of Devon, we found sermons, not indeed in stones, but in a creature reputed among the most worthless of sea-vermin. I had been lounging about all the morning on the little pier, waiting, with the rest of the village, for a trawling breeze which would not come. Two o'clock was past, and still the red mainsails of the skiffs hung motionless, and their images quivered head downwards in the glassy swell,

> " As idle as a painted ship
> Upon a painted ocean."

It was neap-tide, too, and therefore nothing could be done among the rocks. So, in despair, finding an old coast-guard friend starting for his lobster-pots, I determined to save the old man's arms, by rowing him up the shore ; and then paddled homeward again, under the high green northern wall, five hundred feet of cliff furred to the water's edge with rich oak woods, against whose base the smooth Atlantic swell died whispering, as if curling itself up to sleep at last within that sheltered nook, tired with its weary wanderings. The sun sank lower and lower behind the deer-park point ; the white stair of houses up the glen was wrapt every moment deeper and deeper in hazy smoke and shade, as the light faded ; the evening fires were lighted one by one ; the soft murmur of the waterfall, and the pleasant laugh of children, and the splash of homeward oars, came clearer and clearer to the ear at every stroke : and as we rowed on, arose the recollection of many a brave and wise friend, whose lot was cast in no such western paradise, but rather in the infernos of this sinful earth, toiling even then amid the festering alleys of Bermondsey and Bethnal Green, to palliate death and misery which they had vainly laboured to prevent, watching the strides of that very cholera which they had been striving for years to ward off, now re-admitted in spite of all their warnings, by the carelessness, and laziness, and greed of sinful man.　　And as I thought over the whole hapless question of sanatory reform, proved long since a moral duty to God and man, possible, easy, even pecu- niarily profitable, and yet left undone; there seemed a sub- lime irony, most humbling to man, in some of Nature's processes, and in the silent and unobtrusive perfection with which she has been taught to anticipate, since the foundation of the world, some of the loftiest discoveries of modern science, of which we are too apt to boast as if we had created the method by discovering its possibility. Created it ?　　Alas for the pride of human genius, and the autotheism which would make man the measure of all things, and the centre of the universe !　All the in- valuable laws and methods of sanatory reform at best are but clumsy imitations of the unseen wonders which every animalcule and leaf have been working since the world's foundation, with this slight difference between them and us, that they fulfil their appointed task, and we do not.

The sickly geranium which spreads its blanched leaves against the cellar panes, and peers up, as if imploringly, to the narrow slip of sunlight at the top of the narrow alley, had it a voice, could tell more truly than ever a doctor in the town, why little Bessy sickened of the scarlatina, and little Johnny of the hooping-cough, till the toddling wee things who used to pet and water it were carried off each and all of them one by one to the churchyard sleep, while the father and mother sat at home, trying to supply by gin that very vital energy which fresh air and pure water, and the balmy breath of woods and heaths, were made by God to give ; and how the little geranium did its best, like a heaven-sent angel, to right the wrong which man's ignorance had begotten, and drank in, day by day, the poisoned atmosphere, and formed it into fair green leaves, and breathed into the children's faces from every pore, whenever they bent over it, the life-giving oxygen for which their dulled blood and festered lungs were craving in vain ; fulfilling God's will itself, though man would not, too careless or too covetous to see, after six thousand years of boasted progress, why God had covered the earth with grass, herb, and tree, a living and life-giving garment of perpetual health and youth.

It is too sad to think long about, lest we become very Heraclituses. Let us take the other side of the matter with Democritus, try to laugh man out of a little of his boastful ignorance and self-satisfied clumsiness, and tell him, that if the House of Commons would but summon one of the little Paramecia from any Thames' sewermouth, to give his evidence before their next Cholera Committee, sanatory blue-books, invaluable as they are, would be superseded for ever and a day, and Sir William Molesworth would no longer have to confess, as he did last year, that he knew of no means of stopping the smells which were driving the members out of the House, and the judges out of Westminster Hall.

Nay, in the boat at the minute of which I have been speaking, silent and neglected, sat a fellow-passenger, who was a greater adept at removing nuisances than the

whole Board of Health put together ; and who had done
his work, too, with a cheapness unparalleled ; for all his
good deeds had not as yet cost the State one penny.
True, he lived by his business ; so do other inspectors of nuisances : but nature, instead of paying Maia
Squinado, Esquire, some five hundred pounds sterling
per annum for his labour, had contrived, with a sublime
simplicity of economy which Mr. Hume might have
envied and admired afar off, to make him do his work
gratis, by giving him the nuisances as his perquisites,
and teaching him how to eat them.   Certainly (without
going the length of the Caribs, who uphold Cannibalism
because, they say, it makes war cheap, and precludes
entirely the need of a commissariat), this cardinal virtue
of cheapness ought to make Squinado an interesting
object in the eyes of the present generation, especially as
he was at that moment a true sanatory martyr, having,
like many of his human fellow-workers, got into a fearful
scrape by meddling with those existing interests, and
"vested rights which are but vested wrongs," which have
proved fatal already to more than one Board of Health.
For last night, as he was sitting quietly under a stone in
four fathoms water, he became aware (whether by sight,
smell, or that mysterious sixth sense, to us unknown,
which seems to reside in his delicate feelers) of a pal-
pable nuisance somewhere in the neighbourhood ; and,
like a trusty servant of the public, turned out of his bed
instantly, and went in search ; till he discovered, hanging among what he judged to be the stems of tangle
(*Laminaria*), three or four large pieces of stale thorn-
back, of most evil savour, and highly prejudicial to the
purity of the sea, and the health of the neighbouring
herrings.   Happy Squinado !   He needed not to discover the limits of his authority, to consult any lengthy
Nuisances' Removal Act, with its clauses, and counter-
clauses, and exceptions, and explanations of interpretations, and interpretations of explanations.   Nature, who
can afford to be arbitrary, because she is perfect, and
to give her servants irresponsible powers, because she
has trained them to their work, had bestowed on him

and on his forefathers, as general health inspectors, those very summary powers of entrance and removal in the watery realms, for which common-sense, public opinion, and private philanthropy, are still entreating vainly in the terrestrial realms; so finding a hole, in he went, and began to remove the nuisance, without "waiting twenty-four hours," "laying an information," "serving a notice," or any other vain delay. The evil was there,—and there it should not stay; so having neither cart nor barrow, he just began putting it into his stomach, and in the meanwhile, set his assistants to work likewise. For suppose not, gentle reader, that Squinado went alone; in his train were more than a hundred thousand as good as he, each in his office, and as cheaply paid; who needed no cumbrous baggage train of force-pumps, hose, chloride of lime packets, white-wash, pails or brushes, but were every man his own instrument; and to save expense of transit, just grew on Squinado's back. Do you doubt the assertion? Then lift him up hither, and putting him gently into that shallow jar of salt-water, look at him through the hand-magnifier, and see how nature is *maxima in minimis.*

There he sits, twiddling his feelers (a substitute, it seems, with crustacea for biting their nails when they are puzzled), and by no means lovely to look on in vulgar eyes;—about the bigness of a man's fist; a round-bodied, spindle-shanked, crusty, prickly, dirty fellow, with a villainous squaint, too, in those little bony eyes which never look for a moment both the same way. Never mind: many a man of genius is ungainly enough; and nature, if you will observe, as if to make up to him for his uncomeliness, has arrayed him as Solomon in all his glory never was arrayed, and so fulfilled one of the few rational proposals of old Fourier, that scavengers, chimney-sweeps, and other workers in disgusting employments, should be rewarded for their self-sacrifice in behalf of the public weal by some peculiar badge of honour, or laurel crown. Not that his crown, like those of the old Greek games, is a mere useless badge; on the contrary, his robe of state is composed of his fellow-servants. His whole back is covered with a little grey forest of branching hairs, fine as the spider's web, each branchlet carrying its little pearly ringed club, each club its rose-crowned polype, like (to quote Mr. Gosse's comparison) the unexpanded buds of the acacia.[1]

On that leg grows, amid another copse of the grey polypes, a delicate straw-coloured Sertularia, branch on branch of tiny double combs, each tooth of the comb being a tube containing a living flower; on another leg another Sertularia, coarser, but still beautiful; and round it again has trained itself, parasitic on the parasite, plant upon plant of glass ivy, bearing crystal bells,[2] each of which, too, protrudes its living flower; on another leg is a fresh species, like a little heather-bush of whitest ivory,[3] and every needle leaf a polype cell—let us stop before the imagination grows dizzy with the contemplation of those myriads of beautiful atomies. And what is their use? Each living flower, each polype mouth is feeding fast, sweeping into itself, by the perpetual currents caused by the delicate fringes upon its rays (so minute these last, that their motion only betrays their presence), each tiniest atom of decaying matter in the surrounding water, to convert it, by some wondrous alchemy, into fresh cells and buds, and either build up a fresh branch in their thousand-tenanted tree, or form an egg-cell, from whence when ripe may issue, not a fixed zoophyte, but a free swimming animal.

And in the meanwhile, among this animal forest, grows a vegetable one of delicatest sea-weeds, green and brown and crimson, whose office is, by their everlasting breath, to reoxygenate the impure water, and render it fit once more to be breathed by the higher animals who swim or creep around.

Mystery of mysteries! Let us jest no more—Heaven forgive us if we have jested too much on so simple a matter as that poor spider-crab, taken out of the

---

[1] *Coryne Ramosa.*
[2] *Campanularia Integra.*
[3] *Crisidia Eburnea.*

lobster-pots, and left to die at the bottom of the boat, because his more aristocratic cousins of the blue and purple armour will not enter the trap while he is within.

I am not aware whether the surmise, that these tiny zoophytes help to purify the water by exhaling oxygen gas, has yet been verified. The infusorial animalcules do so, reversing the functions of animal life, and instead of evolving carbonic acid gas, as other animals do, evolve pure oxygen. So, at least, says Liebig, who states that he found a small piece of matchwood, just extinguished, burst out again into a flame on being immersed in the bubbles given out by these living atomies.

I myself should be inclined to doubt that this is the case with zoophytes, having found water in which they were growing (unless, of course, sea-weeds were present) to be peculiarly ready to become foul : but it is difficult to say whether this is owing to their deoxygenating the water while alive, like other animals, or to the fact that it is very rare to get a specimen of zoophyte in which a large number of the polypes have not been killed in the transit home, or at least so far knocked about, that (in the Anthozoa, which are far the most abundant) the polype—or rather living mouth, for it is little more— is thrown off to decay, pending the growth of a fresh one in the same cell.

But all the sea-weeds, in common with other vege- tables, perform this function continually, and thus main- tain the water in which they grew in a state fit to support animal life.

This fact, first advanced by Priestley and Ingenhousz, and though doubted by the great Ellis, satisfactorily ascertained by Professor Daubeny, Mr Ward, Dr. Johnston, and Mr. Warington, gives an answer to the question, which I hope has ere now arisen in the minds of some of my readers.

How is it possible to see these wonders at home ? Beautiful and instructive as they may be, can they be meant for any but dwellers by the seaside ? Nay more, even to them, must not the glories of the water-world be always more momentary than those of the rainbow, a mere Fata Morgana which breaks up and vanishes before the eyes? If there were but some method of making a miniature sea-world for a few days; much more of keeping one with us when far inland.

This desideratum has at last been filled up; and science has shown, as usual, that by simply obeying nature we may conquer her, even so far as to have our miniature sea, of artificial salt-water, filled with living plants and sea-weeds, maintaining each other in perfect health, and each following, as far as is possible in a confined space, its natural habits.

To Dr. Johnston is due, as far as is known, the honour of the first accomplishment of this as of a hundred other zoological triumphs. As early as 1842, he proved to himself the vegetable nature of the common pink coralline, which fringes every rock-pool, by keeping it for eight weeks in unchanged salt-water, without any putrefaction ensuing. The ground, of course, on which the proof rested in this case was, that if the coralline were, as had often been thought, a zoophyte, the water would become corrupt, and poisonous to the life of the small animals in the same jar; and that its remaining fresh argued that the coralline had reoxygenated it from time to time, and was therefore a vegetable.

In 1850, Mr. Robert Warington communicated to the Chemical Society the results of a year's experiments, "On the Adjustment of the Relations between the Animal and Vegetable Kingdoms, by which the vital functions of both are permanently maintained." The law which his experiments verified was the same as that on which Mr. Ward, in 1842, founded his invaluable proposal for increasing the purity of the air in large towns, by planting trees, and cultivating flowers in rooms, *that the animal and vegetable respirations might counterbalance each other;* the animal's blood being purified by the oxygen given off by the plants, the plants fed by the carbonic acid breathed out by the animals.

On the same principle, Mr. Warington first kept, for

many months, in a vase of unchanged water, two small
gold fish and a plant of *Vallisneria spiralis;* and two
years afterwards began a similar experiment with sea-
water, weeds, and anemones, which were, at last, as
successful as the former ones. Mr. Gosse had, in the
meanwhile, with tolerable success, begun a similar
method, unaware of what Mr. Warington had done;
and now the beautiful and curious exhibition of fresh
and salt-water tanks, opened last year in the Zoological
Gardens in London, bids fair to be copied in every
similar institution, and we hope in many private houses,
throughout the kingdoms.

To this subject Mr. Gosse's last book, " The Aquarium," is principally devoted, though it contains, besides,
sketches of coast scenery, in his usual charming style,
and descriptions of rare sea-animals, with wise and godly
reflections thereon.   One great object of interest in the
book is the last chapter, which treats fully of the making
and stocking these salt-water " Aquaria"; and the various
beautifully coloured plates, which are, as it were, sketches
from the interior of tanks, are well fitted to excite the
desire of all readers to possess such gorgeous living
pictures, if as nothing else, still as drawing-room orna-
ments, flower-gardens which never wither, fairy lakes of
perpetual calm which no storm blackens,—

$$\text{οὔτ' ἐν θέρει, οὔτ' ἐν ὀπώρῃ.}$$

Those who have never seen one of them can never
imagine (and neither Mr. Gosse's pencil nor our clumsy
words can ever describe to them) the gorgeous colouring
and the grace and delicacy of form which these subaqueous
landscapes exhibit.

As for colouring,—the only bit of colour which I can
remember even faintly resembling them (for though
Corregio's Magdalene may rival them in greens and
blues, yet even he has no such crimsons and purples), is
the Adoration of the Shepherds, by that "prince of
chlorists"—Palma Vecchio, which hangs on the left-
hand side of Lord Ellesmere's great gallery.   But as for

the forms,—where shall we see their like? Where, amid
miniature forests as fantastic as those of the tropics,
animals whose shapes outvie the wildest dreams of the
old German ghost painters which cover the walls of the
galleries of Brussels or Antwerp? And yet the un-
couthest has some quaint beauty of its own, while most
—the star-fishes and anemones, for example—are nothing
but beauty. The brilliant plates in Mr. Gosse's "Aquarium" give, after all, but a meagre picture of the reality,
as it may be seen either in his study, or in the tank-house
at the Zoological Gardens; and as it may be seen also,
by any one who will follow carefully the directions given
at the end of his book, stock a glass vase with such
common things as he may find in an hour's search at
low-tide, and so have an opportunity of seeing how truly
Mr. Gosse says, in his valuable preface, that—

"The habits" (and he might well have added, the
marvellous beauty) "of animals will never be thoroughly
known till they are observed in detail. Nor is it sufficient to mark them with attention now and then; they
must be closely watched, their various actions carefully
noted, their behaviour under different circumstances, and
especially those movements which seem to us mere
vagaries, undirected by any suggestible motive or cause,
well examined. A rich fruit of result, often new and
curious and unexpected, will, I am sure, reward any one
who studies living animals in this way. The most interesting parts, by far, of published Natural History are
those minute, but graphic particulars, which have been
gathered up by an attentive watching of individual
animals."

Mr. Gosse's own books, certainly, give proof enough of
this. We need only direct the reader to his exquisitely
humorous account of the ways and works of a captive
soldier-crab,[1] to show them how much there is to be
seen, and how full nature is also of that ludicrous element
of which we spoke above. And, indeed, it is in this form
of Natural History: not in mere classification, and the

[1] "Aquarium," p. 163.

finding out of names, and quarrelings as to the first discovery of that beetle or this butter-cup,—too common,
alas! among mere closet-collectors,—"endless genea-
logies," to apply St. Paul's words by no means irrever-
ently or fancifully, "which do but gender strife;"—not
in these pedantries is that moral training to be found,
for which we have been lauding the study of Natural
History: but in healthful walks and voyages out of doors,
and in careful and patient watching of the living animals
and plants at home, with an observation sharpened by
practice, and a temper calmed by the continual practice
of a naturalist's first virtues—patience and perseverance.

Practical directions for forming an " Aquarium " may
be found in Mr. Grosse's book bearing that name, at pp.
101, 255, *et sqq.;* and those who wish to carry out the
notion thoroughly, cannot do better than buy his book,
and take their choice of the many different forms of vase,
with rockwork, fountains, and other pretty devices which
he describes.

But the many, even if they have Mr. Gosse's book,
will be rather inclined to begin with a small attempt;
especially as they are probably half sceptical of the possibility of keeping sea-animals inland without changing
the water. A few simple directions, therefore, will not
come amiss here. They shall be such as any one can
put into practice, who goes down to stay in a lodging-
house at the most cockney of watering-places.

Buy at any glass-shop a cylindrical glass jar, some six
inches in diameter and ten high, which will cost you
from three to four shillings; wash it clean, and fill it
with clean salt water, dipped out of any pool among the
rocks, only looking first to see that there is no dead
fish or other evil matter in the said pool, and that no
stream from the land runs into it. If you choose to
take the trouble to dip up the water over a boat's side,
so much the better.

So much for your vase; now to stock it.

Go down at low spring-tide to the nearest ledge of
rocks, and with a hammer and chisel chip off a few
pieces of stone covered with growing sea-weed. Avoid

the common and coarser kinds (fuci) which cover the surface of rocks ; for they give out under water a slime which will foul your tank : but choose the more delicate species which fringe the edges of every pool at low-water mark ; the pink coralline, the dark purple ragged dulse (*Rhodymenia*), the Carrageen moss (*Chondrus*), and above all, the commonest of all, the delicate green Ulva, which you will see growing everywhere in wrinkled fan-shaped sheets, as thin as the finest silver-paper. The smallest bits of stone are sufficient, provided the sea-weeds have hold of them ; for they have no real roots, but adhere by a small disc, deriving no nourishment from the rock, but only from the water. Take care, meanwhile, that there be as little as possible on the stone, beside the weed itself. Especially scrape off any small sponges, and see that no worms have made their twining tubes of sand among the weed-stems ; if they have, drag them out ; for they will surely die, and as sure spoil all by sulphuretted hydrogen, blackness, and evil smells.

Put your weeds into your tank, and settle them at the bottom ; which last some say should be covered with a layer of pebbles : but let the beginner leave it as bare as possible ; for the pebbles only tempt cross-grained annelids to crawl under them, die, and spoil all by decaying : whereas if the bottom of the vase is bare, you can see a sickly or dead inhabitant at once, and take him out (which you must do) instantly. Let your weeds stand quietly in the vase a day or two before you put in any live animals ; and even then, do not put any in if the water does not appear perfectly clear : but lift out the weeds, and renew the water ere you replace them.

Now for the live stock. In the crannies of every rock you will find sea-anemones (Actiniæ) ; and a dozen of these only will be enough to convert your little vase into the most brilliant of living flower-gardens. There they hang upon the under side of the ledges, apparently mere rounded lumps of jelly : one is of a dark purple dotted with green ; another of a rich chocolate ; another of a delicate olive ; another sienna-yellow ; another all

but white. Take them from their rock; you can do it
easily by slipping under them your finger-nail, or the
edge of a pewter spoon. Take care to tear the sucking
base as little as possible (though a small rent they will
darn for themselves in a few days, easily enough), and
drop them into a basket of wet sea-weed; when you get
home, turn them into a dish full of water and leave them
for the night, and go to look at them to-morrow. What
a change! The dull lumps of jelly have taken root and
flowered during the night, and your dish is filled from
side to side with a bouquet of chrysanthemums; each has
expanded into a hundred-petalled flower, crimson, pink,
purple, or orange; touch one, and it shrinks together
like a sensitive plant, displaying at the root of the petals
a ring of brilliant turquoise beads. That is the commonest of all the Actiniæ (*Mesembryanthemum*); you
may have him when and where you will: but if you will
search those rocks somewhat closer, you will find even
more gorgeous species than him. See in that pool some
dozen noble ones, in full bloom, and quite six inches
across, some of them. If their cousins whom we found
just now were like chrysanthemums, these are like quilled
dahlias. Their arms are stouter and shorter in proportion than those of the last species, but their colour is
equally brilliant. One is a brilliant blood-red; another
a delicate sea-blue, striped with pink; but most have
the disc and the innumerable arms striped and ringed
with various shades of grey and brown. Shall we get
them? By all means, if we can. Touch one. Where
is he now? Gone? Vanished into air, or into stone?
Not quite. You see that knot of sand and broken shell
lying on the rock, where your dahlia was one moment
ago. Touch it, and you will find it leathery and elastic.
That is all which remains of the live dahlia. Never
mind; get your finger into the crack under him, work
him gently but firmly out, and take him home, and he
will be as happy and as gorgeous as ever to-morrow.

Let your Actiniæ stand for a day or two in the dish,
and then, picking out the liveliest and handsomest, detach
them once more from their hold, drop them into your

vase, right them with a bit of stick, so that the sucking base is downwards, and leave them to themselves thenceforth.

These two species (*Mesembryanthemum* and *Crassi-cornis*) are quite beautiful enough to give a beginner amusement ; but there are two others which are not un-common, and of such exceeding loveliness, that it is worth while to take a little trouble to get them.   The one is *Bellis*, the sea-daisy, of which there is an excellent description and plates in Mr. Gosse's " Rambles in Devon," pp. 24 to 32.

It is common at Ilfracombe, and at Torquay; and indeed everywhere where there are cracks and small holes in limestone or slate rock.   In these holes it fixes its base, and expands its delicate brown-grey star-like flowers on the surface : but it must be chipped out with hammer and chisel, at the expense of much dirt and patience ; for the moment it is touched it contracts deep into the rock, and all that is left of the daisy flower some two or three inches across, is a blue knot of half the size of a marble. But it will expand again, after a day or two of captivity, and well repay all the trouble which it has cost.

The other is *Dianthus ;* which you may find adhering to fresh oysters in any dredger or trawler's skiff, a lengthened mass of olive, pale rose, or snow-white jelly. The rose and the white are the more beautiful ; the very maiden queens of all the beautiful tribe.   If you find one, clear the shell on which it grows of everything else (you may leave the oyster inside if you will), and watch it expand under water into a furbelowed flower, furred with innumerable delicate tentacula ;[1] and in the centre, a mouth of the most brilliant orange; altogether one of the loveliest gems, in the opinion of him who writes, with which it has pleased God to bedeck His lower world.

But you will want more than these anemones, both for your own amusement, and for the health of your tank. Microscopic animals will breed, and will also die ; and

[1] See Gosse's "Aquarium," Plate V., p. 192.

you need for them some such scavenger as our poor friend Squinado, to whom you were introduced a few pages back. Turn, then, a few stones which lie piled on each other at extreme low-water mark, and five minutes' search will give you the very animal you want—a little crab, of a dingy russet above, and on the underside like smooth porcelain. His back is quite flat, and so are his large angular fringed claws, which, when he folds them up, lie in the same plane with his shell, and fit neatly into its edges. Compact little rogue that he is, made especially for sideling in and out of cracks and crannies, he carries with him such an apparatus of combs and brushes as Isidor or Floris never dreamed of; with which he sweeps out of the sea-water at every moment shoals of minute animalcules, and sucks them into his tiny mouth. Mr. Gosse will tell you more of this marvel, in his "Aquarium," p. 48.

Next, your sea-weeds, if they thrive as they ought to do, will sow their minute spores in millions around them; and these, as they vegetate, will form a green film on the inside of the glass, spoiling your prospect; you may rub it off for yourself, if you will, with a rag fastened to a stick, but if you wish at once to save yourself trouble, and to see how all emergencies in nature are provided for, you will set three or four live shells to do it for you, and to keep your subaqueous lawn close mown.

That last word is no figure of speech. Look among the beds of sea-weed for a few of the bright yellow or green sea-snails (*Nerita*), or Conical Tops (*Trochus*), especially that beautiful pink one spotted with brown (*Ziziphinus*), which you are sure to find about shaded rock-ledges at dead low tide, and put them into your aquarium. For the present, they will only nibble the green ulvæ, but when the film of young weed begins to form, you will see it mown off every morning as fast as it grows, in little semicircular sweeps, just as if a fairy's scythe had been at work during the night.

And a scythe has been at work; none other than the tongue of the little shell-fish; a description of its extraordinary mechanism (too long to quote here, but which is well worth reading) may be found in Gosse's "Aquarium." [1]

A prawn or two, and a few minute star-fish, will make your aquarium complete; though you may add to it endlessly, as one glance at the salt-water tanks of the Zoological Gardens and the strange and beautiful forms which they contain will prove to you sufficiently.

You have two more enemies to guard against; dust, and heat. If the surface of the water becomes clogged with dust, the communication between it and the life-giving oxygen of the air is cut off; and then your animals are liable to die, for the very same reason that fish die in a pond which is long frozen over, unless a hole be broken in the ice to admit the air. You must guard against this by occasional stirring of the surface (it should be done once a day, if possible), and by keeping on a cover. A piece of muslin tied over will do; but a better defence is a plate of glass, raised on wire some half-inch above the edge, so as to admit the air. I am not sure that a sheet of brown paper laid over the vase is not the best of all, because that by its shade also guards against the next evil, which is heat. Against that you must guard by putting a curtain of muslin or oiled paper between the vase and the sun, if it be very fierce, or simply (for simple expedients are best) by laying a handkerchief over it till the heat is past. But if you leave your vase in a sunny window long enough to let the water get tepid, all is over with your pets. Half-an-hour's boiling may frustrate the care of weeks. And yet, on the other hand, light you must have, and you can hardly have too much. Some animals certainly prefer shade, and hide in the darkest crannies; and for them, if your aquarium is large enough, you must provide shade, by arranging the bits of stone into piles and caverns. But without light, your sea-weeds will neither thrive, nor keep the water sweet. With plenty of light you will see, to quote Mr. Gosse once more,[2] "thousands of tiny globules forming on every plant, and even all over the stones, where the infant

[1] Page 34.   [2] Page 259.

vegetation is beginning to grow; and these globules presently rise in rapid succession to the surface all over the vessel, and this process goes on uninterruptedly as long as the rays of the sun are uninterrupted.

"Now these globules consist of *pure oxygen*, given out by the plants under the stimulus of light; and to this oxygen the animals in the tank owe their life. The difference between the profusion of oxygen-bubbles produced on a sunny day, and the paucity of those seen on a dark cloudy day, or in a northern aspect, is very marked." Choose, therefore, a south or east window, but draw down the blind, or throw a handkerchief over all if the heat become fierce. The water should always feel cold to your hand, let the temperature outside be what it may.

Next, you must make up for evaporation by *fresh* water. A very little will suffice, as often as in summer you find the water in your vase sink below its original level, and prevent the water from getting too salt. For the salts, remember, do not evaporate with the water, and if you left the vase in the sun for a few weeks, it would become a mere brine pan.

But how will you move your treasures up to town?

The simplest plan which I have found successful is an earthen jar. You may buy them with a cover which screws on with two iron clasps. If you do not find such, a piece of oilskin tied over the mouth is enough. But do not fill the jar full of water; leave about a quarter of the contents in empty air, which the water may absorb, and so keep itself fresh. And any pieces of stone, or oysters, which you send up, hang by a string from the mouth, that they may not hurt tender animals by rolling about the bottom. With these simple precautions, anything which you are likely to find will well endure forty-eight hours of travel.

What if the water fails after all?

Then Mr. Gosse's artificial sea water will form a perfect substitute. You may buy the requisite salts (for there are more salts than "salt" in sea water) from any chemist to whom Mr. Gosse has entrusted his discovery, and according to his directions, make sea water for yourself.[1]

One more hint before we part. If, after all, you are not going down to the seaside this year, and have no opportunities of testing " the wonders of the shore," you may still study Natural History in your own drawing-room, by looking a little into "the wonders of the pond."

I am not jesting ; a fresh-water aquarium, though by no means as beautiful as a salt-water one, is even more easily established. A glass jar, floored with two or three inches of pond-mud (which should be covered with fine gravel to prevent the mud washing up); a specimen of each of two water-plants which you may buy now at any good shop in Covent Garden, *Vallisneria spiralis* (which is said to give to the Canvas-backed duck of America its peculiar richness of flavour), and *Anacharis alsinastrum*, that magical weed which, lately introduced from Canada among timber, has multiplied, self-sown, to so prodigious an extent, that it bids fair in a few years to choke the navigation not only of our canals and fen-rivers, but of the Thames itself :—these (in themselves, from the transparency of their circulation, interesting microscopic objects) for oxygen-breeding vegetables ; and for animals, the pickings of any pond. A minnow or two, an eft ; some of those caddis-baits (walking tubes of straw, sticks, and shells) and water-crickets, which you may find under any stone ; a few of the delicate pond-snails (unless they devour your *Vallisneria* too rapidly), water-beetles, of activity inconceivable, and that wondrous bug the Notonecta, who lies on his back all day, rowing about his boat-shaped body, with one long pair of oars, in search of animalcules, and the moment the lights are out, turns head over heels, rights himself, and opening a pair of handsome wings, starts to fly about the dark room in company with his friend the water-beetle, and (I suspect) catch

[1] Mr. W. Bolton, Chemist, of 146, Holborn Bars, London, will furnish the materials.

flies; and then slips back demurely into the water with the first streak of dawn. These animals, their habits, their miraculous transformations, as the caddis-baits appear at the top of the water as alder-flies and sedge-flies (*Phryganeæ*) and the water-crickets as duns and drakes (*Ephemeræ*) of the most delicate beauty, might give many an hour's quiet amusement to an invalid, laid on a sofa, or imprisoned in a sick-room, and debarred from reading, unless by some such means, any page of that great green book outside, whose pen is the finger of God, whose covers are the fire kingdoms and the star kingdoms, and its leaves the heather-bells, and the polypes of the sea, and the gnats above the summer stream.

And, now, how can this desultory little treatise end more usefully than in recommending a few books on Natural History, fit for the use of young people? Not that this list will contain all the best; but simply the best of which the writer knows; let, therefore, none feel aggrieved, if, as it may chance, opening these pages, they find their books omitted.

First and foremost, certainly, come Mr. Gosse's books. There is a playful and genial spirit in them, a brilliant power of word-painting, combined with deep and earnest religious feeling, which makes them as morally valuable as they are intellectually interesting. Since White's "History of Selborne," few or no writers on Natural History, save Mr. Gosse and poor Mr. E. Forbes, have had the power of bringing out the human side of science, and giving to seemingly dry disquisitions and animals of the lowest type, by little touches of pathos and humour, that living and personal interest, to bestow which is generally the special function of the poet: not that Waterton and Jesse are not excellent in this respect, and authors who should be in every boy's library: but they are rather anecdotists than systematic or scientific inquirers; while Mr. Gosse, in his "Naturalist on the Shores of Devon," his "Tour in Jamaica," and his "Canadian Naturalist," has done for those three places what White did for Selborne, with all the improved appliances of a science which has widened and deepened tenfold since White's time.

Miss Anne Pratt's "Things of the Sea-coast" is excellent ; and still better is Professor Harvey's "Seaside Book," of which it is impossible to speak too highly ; and most pleasant it is to see a man of genius and learning thus gathering the bloom of his varied knowledge, to put it into a form equally suited to a child and to a *savant.* Seldom, perhaps, has there been a little book in which so vast a quantity of facts has been compressed into so small a space, and yet told so gracefully, simply, without a taint of pedantry or cumbrousness—an excellence which is the sure and only mark of a perfect mastery of the subject.

Two little "Popular" Histories, one of British Zoophytes, the other of British Sea-weeds, by Dr. Landsborough (lately dead of cholera, at Saltcoats, the scene of his energetic and pious ministry), are very excellent ; and are furnished, too, with well-drawn and coloured plates, for the comfort of those to whom a scientific nomenclature (as liable as any other human thing to be faulty and obscure) conveys but a vague conception of the objects. These may serve well for the beginner, as introductions to Professor Harvey's large work on the British Algæ, and to the new edition of Professor Johnston's invaluable "British Zoophytes."

For general Zoology the best books for beginners are, perhaps, as an introduction to comparative anatomy, Professor Rymer Jones's "Animal Kingdom"; and for systematic Zoology, Mr. Gosse's four little books, on Mammals, Birds, Reptiles, and Fishes, published, with many plates, by the Christian Knowledge Society, at a marvellously cheap rate. For microscopic animalcules, Miss Agnes Catlow's "Drops of Water" will teach the young more than they will ever remember, and serve as a good introduction to those teeming abysses of the unseen world, which must be afterwards traversed under the guidance of Hassall and Ehrenberg.

For Ornithology, there is no book, after all, like dear old Bewick, *passé* though he may be in a scientific point of view. There is a good little British ornithology, too, published in Sir W. Jardine's "Naturalist's Library," and another by Mr. Gosse. And Mr. Knox's "Ornithological Rambles in Sussex," with Mr. St. John's "Highland Sports" and "Tour in Sutherlandshire," are the monographs of naturalists, gentlemen, and sportsmen, which remind one at every page (and what higher praise can one give?) of White's "History of Selborne." These last, with Mr. Gosse's "Canadian Naturalist," and his little book "The Ocean," not forgetting Darwin's delightful "Voyage of the Beagle and Adventure," ought to be in the hands of every lad who is likely to travel to our colonies.

For general Geology, Professor Anstey's Introduction is excellent; while, as a specimen of the way in which a single district may be thoroughly worked out, and the universal method of induction learnt from a narrow field of objects, what book can, or perhaps ever will, compare with Mr. Hugh Miller's "Old Red Sandstone"?

For this last reason, I especially recommend to the young the Rev. C. A. Johns's "Week at the Lizard," as teaching a young person how much there is to be seen and known within a few square miles of these British Isles. But, indeed, all Mr. Johns's books are good (as they are bound to be, considering his most accurate and varied knowledge), especially his "Flowers of the Field," the best cheap introduction to systematic botany which has yet appeared. Trained, and all but self-trained, like Mr. Hugh Miller, in a remote and narrow field of observation, Mr. Johns has developed himself into one of our most acute and persevering botanists, and has added many a new treasure to the Flora of these isles; and one person, at least, owes him a deep debt of gratitude for first lessons in scientific accuracy and patience,—lessons taught, not dully and dryly at the book and desk, but livingly and genially, in adventurous rambles over the bleak cliffs and ferny woods of the wild Atlantic shore,—

> " Where the old fable of the guarded mount
> Looks toward Namancos and Bayona's hold."

And so I end this little book, hoping, even praying, that it may encourage a few more labourers to go forth into a vineyard, which those who have toiled in it know to be full of ever-fresh health, and wonder, and simple joy, and the presence and the glory of Him whose name is Love.

MADE AT THE TEMPLE PRESS LETCHWORTH IN GREAT BRITAIN

EVERYMAN'S LIBRARY

A LIST OF THE 925 VOLUMES
ARRANGED UNDER AUTHORS

Anonymous works are given under titles.
Anthologies, Dictionaries, etc. are arranged at the end of the list.

Abbott's Rollo at Work, etc., 275
Addison's Spectator, 164-7
Æschylus's Lyrical Dramas, 62
Æsop's and Other Fables, 657
Aimard's The Indian Scout, 428
Ainsworth's Tower of London, 400
   „   Old St. Paul's. 522
   „   Windsor Castle. 709
   „   Rookwood, 870
   „   The Admirable Crichton, 894
A Kempis's Imitation of Christ, 484
Alcott's Little Women, and Good
   Wives, 248
   „   Little Men, 512
Alpine Club: Peaks, Passes and
   Glaciers, 778
Andersen's Fairy Tales, 4
   „   More Fairy Tales, 822
Anglo-Saxon Chronicle, 624
Anson's Voyages, 510
Aristophanes' Acharnians, etc., 344
   „   Frogs, etc., 516
Aristotle's Nicomachaen Ethics, 547
   „   Politics, 605
   „   Poetics, and Demetrius
      on Style, etc., 901
Armour's Fall of the Nibelungs,
   312
   „   Gudrun, 880
Arnold's (Matthew) Essays, 115
   „   Poems, 334
   „   Study of Celtic Literature,
      etc., 458
Aucassin and Nicolette, 497
Augustine's (Saint) Confessions,
   200
Aurelius's (Marcus) Meditations, 9
Austen's (Jane) Sense and Sensi-
   bility, 21
   „   Pride and Prejudice, 22
   „   Mansfield Park, 23
   „   Emma, 24
   „   Northanger Abbey, and
      Persuasion, 25

Bacon's Essays, 10
   „   Advancement of Learning.
      719
Bagehot's Literary Studies, 520, 521
Baker's (Sir S. W.) Cast up by the
   Sea, 539
Ballantyne's Coral Island, 245
   „   Martin Rattler, 246
   „   Ungava, 276
Balzac's Wild Ass's Skin, 26
   „   Eugénie Grandet, 169
   „   Old Goriot, 170
   „   Atheist's Mass, etc., 229
   „   Christ in Flanders, etc., 284
   „   The Chouans, 285
   „   Quest of the Absolute, 286
   „   Cat and Rachet, etc., 349
   „   Catherine de Medici, 419
   „   Cousin Pons, 463
   „   The Country Doctor, 530
   „   Rise and Fall of César
      Birotteau, 596
   „   Lost Illusions, 656
   „   The Country Parson, 686
   „   Ursule Mirouet, 733
Barbusse's Under Fire, 798
Barca's (Mme C. de la) Life in
   Mexico, 664
Bates's Naturalist on the Amazon,
   446
Baxter's (Richard) Autobiography,
   868
Beaumont and Fletcher's Selected
   Plays, 506
Beaumont's (Mary) Joan Seaton, 597
Bede's Ecclesiastical History, 479
Belt's Naturalist in Nicaragua, 561
Bennett's The Old Wives' Tale, 919
Berkeley's (Bishop) Principles of
   Human Knowledge, New Theory
   of Vision, etc., 483
Berlioz (Hector), Life of, 602
Binns's Life of Abraham Lincoln,
   783

...'s Plays, 625, 696
Blackmore's Lorna Doone, 304
,,   Springhaven, 350
Blackwell's Pioneer Work for
    Women, 667
Blake's Poems and Prophecies, 792
Boccaccio's Decameron, 845, 846
Boehme's The Signature of All
    Things, etc., 569
Bonaventura's The Little Flowers,
    The Life of St. Francis, etc., 485
Borrow's Wild Wales, 49
,,   Lavengro, 119
,,   Romany Rye, 120
,,   Bible in Spain, 151
,,   Gypsies in Spain, 697
Boswell's Life of Johnson, 1, 2
,,   Tour to the Hebrides, 387
Boult's Asgard and Norse Heroes,
    689
Boyle's The Sceptical Chymist, 559
Bright's (John) Speeches, 252
Brontë's (A.) The Tenant of Wild-
    fell Hall, and Agnes Grey, 685
Brontë's (C.) Jane Eyre, 287
,,   Shirley, 288
,,   Villette, 351
,,   The Professor, 417
Brontë's (E.) Wuthering Heights,
    243
Brown's (Dr. John) Rab and His
    Friends, etc., 116
Browne's (Frances) Grannie's Won-
    derful Chair, 112
Browne's (Sir Thos.) Religio Medici,
    etc., 92
Browning's Poems, 1833–44, 41
,,   ,, 1844–64, 42
,,   The Ring and the Book,
    502
Buchanan's Life and Adventures
    of Audubon, 601
Bulfinch's The Age of Fable, 472
,,   Legends of Charlemagne,
    556
Bunyan's Pilgrim's Progress, 204
,,   Grace Abounding, and
    Mr. Badman, 815
Burke's American Speeches and
    Letters, 340
,,   Reflections on the French
    Revolution, etc., 460
Burnet's History of His Own Times,
Burney's Evelina, 352   [85
Burns's Poems and Songs, 94
Burton's East Africa, 500
Burton's (Robert) Anatomy of
    Melancholy, 886–8
Butler's Analogy of Religion, 90
Butler's (Samuel) Erewhon and
    Erewhon Revisited, 881
Butler's The Way of All Flesh, 895
Buxton's Memoirs, 773
Byron's Complete Poetical and
    Dramatic Works. 486–8

Cæsar's Gallic War, etc., 702
Calderon's Plays, 819

Canton's Child's Book of Saints, 61
,,   Invisible Playmate, etc., 566
Carlyle's French Revolution, 31, 32
,,   Letters, etc., of Crom-
    well, 266–8
,,   Sartor Resartus, 278
,,   Past and Present, 608
,,   Essays, 703, 704
,,   Reminiscences, 875
Carroll's (Lewis) Alice in Wonder-
    land, etc., 836
Castiglione's The Courtier, 807
Cellini's Autobiography, 51
Cervantes' Don Quixote, 385, 386
Chaucer's Canterbury Tales, 307
Chesterfield's Letters to his Son, 823
Chesterton's Stories, Essays, and
    Poems, 913
Chrétien de Troyes's Arthurian
    Romances, 698
Cibber's Apology for his Life, 668
Cicero's Select Letters and Ora-
    tions, 345
Clarke's Tales from Chaucer, 537
,, Shakespeare's Heroines, 109–11
Cobbett's Rural Rides, 638, 639
Coleridge's Biographia, 11
,, Golden Book of Poetry, 43
,, Lectures on Shakspeare, 162
Collins's Woman in White, 464
Collodi's Pinocchio, 538
Conrad's Lord Jim, 925
Converse's Long Will, 328
,,   House of Prayer, 923
Cook's (Captain) Voyages, 99
Cooper's The Deerslayer, 77
,,   The Pathfinder, 78
,,   Last of the Mohicans, 79
,,   The Pioneer, 171
,,   The Prairie, 172
Cowper's Letters. 774
,,   Poems, 872
Cox's Tales of Ancient Greece, 721
Craik's Manual of English Litera-
    ture, 346
Craik (Mrs.). See Mulock.
Creasy's Fifteen Decisive Battles,
    300
Crèvecœur's Letters from an Amer-
    ican Farmer, 640
Curtis's Prue and I, and Lotus, 418

Dana's Two Years Before the
    Mast, 588
Dante's Divine Comedy, 308
Darwin's Origin of Species, 811
,,   Voyage of the Beagle, 104
Dasent's Story of Burnt Njal, 558
Daudet's Tartarin of Tarascon, 423
Defoe's Robinson Crusoe, 59
,,   Captain Singleton, 74
,,   Memoirs of a Cavalier, 283
,,   Journal of Plague, 289
,,   Tour through England and
    Wales, 820, 821
,,   Moll Flanders, 837
De Joinville's Memoirs of the
    Crusades, 333

Demosthenes' Select Orations, 546
Dennis's Cities and Cemeteries of Etruria, 183, 184
De Quincey's Lake Poets, 163
　　,,　　　Opium-Eater, 223
　　,,　　　English Mail Coach, etc., 609
De Retz (Cardinal), Memoirs of, 735, 736
Descartes' Discourse on Method, 570
Dickens's Barnaby Rudge, 76
　　,,　　Tale of Two Cities, 102
　　,,　　Old Curiosity Shop, 173
　　,,　　Oliver Twist, 233
　　,,　　Great Expectations, 234
　　,,　　Pickwick Papers, 235
　　,,　　Bleak House, 236
　　,,　　Sketches by Boz, 237
　　,,　　Nicholas Nickleby, 238
　　,,　　Christmas Books, 239
　　,,　　Dombey and Son, 240
　　,,　　Martin Chuzzlewit, 241
　　,,　　David Copperfield, 242
　　,,　　American Notes, 290
　　,,　　Child's History of England, 291
　　,,　　Hard Times, 292
　　,,　　Little Dorrit, 293
　　,,　　Our Mutual Friend, 294
　　,,　　Christmas Stories, 414
　　,,　　Uncommercial Traveller, 536
　　,,　　Edwin Drood, 725
　　,,　　Reprinted Pieces, 744
Disraeli's Coningsby, 535
Dodge's Hans Brinker, 620
Donne's Poems, 867
Dostoevsky's Crime and Punishment, 501
　　,, The House of the Dead, 533
　　,, Letters from the Underworld, etc., 654
　　,, The Idiot, 682
　　,, Poor Folk, and the Gambler, 711
　　,, The Brothers Karamazov, 802, 803
　　,, The Possessed, 861, 862
Dowden's Life of R. Browning, 701
Dryden's Dramatic Essays, 568
　　,,　　　Poems, 910
Dufferin's Letters from High Latitudes, 499
Dumas' The Three Musketeers, 81
　　,, The Black Tulip, 174
　　,, Twenty Years After, 175
　　,, Marguerite de Valois, 326
　　,, The Count of Monte Cristo, 393, 394
　　,, The Forty-Five, 420
　　,, Chicot the Jester, 421
　　,, Vicomte de Bragelonne, 593-5
　　,, Le Chevalier de Maison Rouge, 614
Du Maurier's Trilby, 863
Duruy's Heroes of England, 471
　　,,　　History of France, 737, 738

Eddington's Nature of the Physical World, 922
Edgar's Cressy and Poictiers, 17
　　,,　　Runnymede and Lincoln Fair, 320
Edgeworth's Castle Rackrent, etc., 410
Eighteenth-Century Plays, 818
Eliot's Adam Bede, 27
　　,,　　Silas Marner, 121
　　,,　　Romola, 231
　　,,　　Mill on the Floss, 325
　　,,　　Felix Holt, 353
　　,,　　Scenes of Clerical Life, 468
　　,,　　Middlemarch, 2 vols., 854-5
Elyot's Gouernour, 227
Emerson's Essays, 12
　　,, Representative Men, 279
　　,, Nature, Conduct of Life, etc., 322
　　,, Society and Solitude, etc., 567
　　,, Poems, 715
Epictetus's Moral Discourses, 404
Erckmann-Chatrian's The Conscript and Waterloo, 354
　　,,　　Story of a Peasant, 706, 707
Euclid's Elements, 891
Euripides' Plays, 63, 271
Evans's Holy Graal, 445
Evelyn's Diary, 220, 221
Everyman and other Interludes, 381
Ewing's (Mrs.) Mrs. Overtheway's Remembrances, etc., 730
　　,, Jackanapes, Daddy Darwin's Dovecot, and The Story of a Short Life, 731

Faraday's Experimental Researches in Electricity, 576
Ferrier's (Susan) Marriage, 816
Fielding's Tom Jones, 355, 356
　　,,　　Amelia, 2 vols., 852-3
　　,,　　Joseph Andrews, 467
　　,,　　Jonathan Wild and the Journal of a Voyage to Lisbon, 877
Finlay's Byzantine Empire, 33
　　,, Greece under the Romans, 185
Flaubert's Madame Bovary, 808
　　,,　　Salammbo, 869
Fletcher's (Beaumont and) Selected Plays, 506
Ford's Gatherings from Spain, 152
Forster's Life of Dickens, 781, 782
Fox's (George) Journal, 754
Fox's (Charles James) Selected Speeches, 759
Francis's (Saint), The Little Flowers, etc., 485
Franklin's Journey to the Polar Sea, 447
Freeman's Old English History for Children, 540
French Mediaeval Romances, 557

Froissart's Chronicles, 57
Froude's Short Studies, 13, 705
  „   Henry VIII. 372-4
  „   Edward VI, 375
  „   Mary Tudor, 477
  „   History of Queen Eliza-
        beth's Reign, 583-7
  „   Life of Benjamin Disraeli,
        Lord Beaconsfield, 666

Galsworthy's The Country House,
  917
Galt's Annals of the Parish, 427
Galton's Inquiries into Human
  Faculty, 263
Gaskell's Cranford, 83
  „   Life of Charlotte Brontë,
        318
  „   Sylvia's Lovers, 524
  „   Mary Barton, 598
  „   Cousin Phillis, etc., 615
  „   North and South, 680
Gatty's Parables from Nature, 158
Geoffrey of Monmouth's Histories
  of the Kings of Britain, 577
George's Progress and Poverty, 560
Gibbon's Roman Empire, 434-6,
        474-6
  „   Autobiography, 511
Gilfillan's Literary Portraits, 348
Giraldus Cambrensis, Wales, 272
Gleig's Life of Wellington, 341
  „   The Subaltern, 708
Goethe's Faust. 335
  „   Conversations with Ecker-
        mann, 851
  „   Wilhelm Meister, 599, 600
Gogol's Dead Souls, 726
  „   Taras Bulba, 740
Goldsmith's Vicar of Wakefield, 295
  „   Poems and Plays, 415
  „   Citizen of the World,
        etc., 902
Goncharov's Oblomov, 878
Gore's Philosophy of the Good Life,
  924
Gorki's Through Russia, 741
Gotthelf's Ulric the Farm Servant,
  228
Gray's Poems and Letters, 628
Green's Short History of the Eng-
  lish People, 727, 728. The cloth
  edition is in 2 vols. All other
  editions are in 1 vol.
Grettir Saga, 699
Grimm's Fairy Tales, 56
Grote's History of Greece, 186-197
Guest's (Lady) Mabinogion, 97

Hahnemann's The Organon of the
  Rational Art of Healing, 663
Hakluyt's Voyages, 264, 265, 313,
  314, 338, 339, 388, 389
Hallam's Constitutional History,
  621-3
Hamilton's The Federalist, 519
Harte's Luck of Roaring Camp, 681
Harvey's Circulation of Blood, 262

Hawthorne's Wonder Book, 5
  „   The Scarlet Letter, 122
  „   House of Seven Gables,
        176
  „   The Marble Faun, 424
  „   Twice Told Tales, 531
  „   Blithedale Romance, 592
Hazlitt's Characters of Shakespeare's
        Plays, 65
  „   Table Talk, 321
  „   Lectures, 411
  „   Spirit of the Age and Lec-
        tures on English Poets,
        459
  „   Plain Speaker, 814
Hebbel's Plays, 694
Heimskringla: the Olaf Sagas, 717
  „   Sagas of the Norse
                Kings, 847
Heine's Prose and Poetry, 911
Helps' (Sir Arthur) Life of Colum-
        bus, 332
Herbert's Temple, 309
Herodotus, 405, 406
Herrick's Hesperides, 310
Hobbes's Leviathan, 691
Holinshed's Chronicle, 800
Holmes's Life of Mozart, 564
Holmes's (O. W.) Autocrat, 66
  „   Professor, 67
  „   Poet, 68
Homer's Iliad, 453
  „   Odyssey, 454
Hooker's Ecclesiastical Polity, 201,
        202
Horace's Complete Poetical Works,
        515
Houghton's Life and Letters of
        Keats, 801
Howard's (E.) Rattlin the Reefer,
        857
Howard's (John) State of the
        Prisons, 835
Hughes's Tom Brown's Schooldays,
        58
Hugo's (Victor) Les Misérables, 363,
        364
  „   Notre Dame, 422
  „   Toilers of the Sea, 509
Hume's Treatise of Human Nature,
        etc., 548, 549
Hunt's (Leigh) Selected Essays, 829
Hutchinson's (Col.) Memoirs, 317
Huxley's Man's Place in Nature, 47
  „   Select Lectures and Lay
        Sermons, 498

Ibsen's The Doll's House, etc., 494
  „   Ghosts, etc., 552
  „   Pretender, Pillars of Society,
        Rosmersholm, 659
  „   Brand, 716
  „   Lady Inger, etc., 729
  „   Peer Gynt, 747
Ingelow's Mopsa the Fairy, 619
Irving's Sketch Book, 117
  „   Conquest of Granada, 478
  „   Life of Mahomet, 513

Italian Short Stories, 876

James's (G. P. R.) Richelieu, 357
James' (Henry) The Turn of the Screw and The Aspern Papers, 912
James (Wm.), Selections from, 739
Jefferies' (Richard) Bevis, 850
Johnson's (Dr.) Lives of the Poets, 770-1
Jonson's (Ben) Plays, 489, 490
Josephus's Wars of the Jews, 712

Kalidasa's Shakuntala, 629
Kant, Critique of Pure Reason, 909
Keats's Poems, 101
Keble's Christian Year, 690
King's Life of Mazzini, 562
Kinglake's Eothen, 337
Kingsley's (Chas.) Westward Ho! 20
   „   Heroes, 113
   „   Hereward the Wake, 296
   „   Hypatia, 230
   „   Water Babies, and Glaucus, 277
   „   Alton Locke, 462
   „   Yeast, 611
   „   Madam How and Lady Why, 777
   „   Poems, 793
Kingsley's (Henry) Ravenshoe, 28
   „   Geoffrey Hamlyn, 416
Kingston's Peter the Whaler, 6
   „   Three Midshipmen, 7
Kirby's Kalevala, 259-60
Koran, 380

Lamb's Tales from Shakespeare, 8
   „   Essays of Elia, 14
   „   Letters, 342, 343
Landor's Imaginary Conversations and Poems, 890
Lane's Modern Egyptians, 315
Langland's Piers Plowman, 571
Latimer's Sermons, 40
Law's Serious Call. 91
Lawrence's The White Peacock, 914
Layamon's (Wace and) Arthurian Chronicles, 578
Lear (Edward). See under Anthologies
Leibniz' Philosophical Writings, 905
Le Sage's Gil Blas, 437, 438
Leslie's Memoirs of John Constable, 563
Lessing's Laocoön, etc., 843
Lever's Harry Lorrequer, 177
Lewes' Life of Goethe, 269
Lincoln's Speeches. etc., 206
Livy's History of Rome, 603, 609, 670, 749, 755, 756
Locke's Civil Government, 751
Lockhart's Life of Napoleon, 3
   „   Life of Scott, 55
   „   Life of Burns, 156
Longfellow's Poems, 382
Lönnrott's Kalevala, 259, 260
Loti's Iceland Fisherman, 920

Lover's Handy Andy, 178
Lowell's Among My Books. 607
Lucretius's Of the Nature of Things, 750
Lützow's History of Bohemia, 432
Lyell's Antiquity of Man, 700
Lytton's Harold, 15
   „   Last of the Barons, 18
   „   Last Days of Pompeii, 80
   „   Pilgrims of the Rhine, 390
   „   Rienzi, 532

Macaulay's England, 34-6
   „   Essays, 225, 226
   „   Speeches on Politics, etc., 399
   „   Miscellaneous Essays, 439
MacDonald's Sir Gibbie, 678
   „   Phantastes. 732
Machiavelli's Prince. 280
   „   Florence, 376
Maine's Ancient Law, 734
Malory's Le Morte D'Arthur. 45, 46
Malthus on the Principles of Population, 692, 693
Mandeville's Travels, 812
Manning's Sir Thomas More, 19
   „   Mary Powell, and Deborah's Diary, 324
Marlowe's Plays and Poems, 383
Marryat's Mr. Midshipman Easy, 82
   „   Little Savage, 159
   „   Masterman Ready, 160
   „   Peter Simple, 232
   „   Children of New Forest, 247
   „   Percival Keene, 358
   „   Settlers in Canada, 370
   „   King's Own, 580
   „   Jacob Faithful, 618
Martineau's Feats on the Fjords, 429
Martinengo-Cesaresco's Folk-Lore and other Essays, 673
Marx's Capital, 848, 849
Maupassant's Short Stories, 907
Maurice's Kingdom of Christ, 146-7
Mazzini's Duties of Man, etc., 224
Melville's Moby Dick, 179
   „   Typee, 180
   „   Omoo, 297
Meredith's The Ordeal of Richard Feverel, 916
Mérimée's Carmen, etc., 834
Merivale's History of Rome, 433
Mickiewicz's Pan Tadeusz, 842
Mignet's French Revolution, 713
Mill's Utilitarianism, Liberty, Representative Government, 482
   „   Rights of Woman, 825
Miller's Old Red Sandstone, 103
Milman's History of the Jews, 377, 378
Milton's Areopagitica and other Prose Works, 795
   „   Poems, 384
Molière's Comedies, 830-1

Mommsen's History of Rome, 542-5
Montagu's (Lady) Letters, 69
Montaigne's Essays, 440-2
More's Utopia, and Dialogue of Comfort against Tribulation, 461
Morier's Hajji Baba, 679
Morris's (Wm.) Early Romances, 261
,, Life and Death of Jason, 575
Morte D'Arthur Romances, 634
Motley's Dutch Republic, 86-8
Mulock's John Halifax, 123

Neale's Fall of Constantinople, 655
Newcastle's (Margaret, Duchess of) Life of the First Duke of Newcastle, etc., 722
Newman's Apologia Pro Vita Sua, 636
,, On the Scope and Nature of University Education, and a Paper on Christianity and Scientific Investigation, 723
Nietzsche's Thus Spake Zarathustra, 892

Oliphant's Salem Chapel, 244
Omar Khayyam, 819
Osborne (Dorothy), Letters of, 674
Owen's (Robert) A New View of Society, etc., 799

Paine's Rights of Man, 718
Palgrave's Golden Treasury, 96
Paltock's Peter Wilkins, 676
Park's (Mungo) Travels, 205
Parkman's Conspiracy of Pontiac, 302, 303
Pascall's Pensees, 874
Paston Letters, 752, 753
Pater's Marius the Epicurean, 903
Peacock's Headlong Hall, 327
Penn's The Peace of Europe, Some Fruits of Solitude, etc., 724
Pepys's Diary, 53, 54
Percy's Reliques, 148, 149
Pitt's Orations, 145
Plato's Republic, 64
,, Dialogues, 456, 457
Plutarch's Lives, 407-409
,, Moralia, 565
Poe's Tales of Mystery and Imagination, 336
,, Poems and Essays, 791
Polo's (Marco) Travels, 306
Pope's Complete Poetical Works, 760
Prescott's Conquest of Peru, 301
,, Conquest of Mexico, 397, 398
Prévost's Manon Lescaut, etc., 834
Procter's Legends and Lyrics, 150
Pushkin's The Captain's Daughter, etc., 898

Quiller-Couch's Hetty Wesley, 864

Rabelais's Gargantua and Pantagruel, 826, 827
Radcliffe's (Mrs. Ann) The Mysteries of Udolpho, 865, 866

Ramayana and Mahabharata, 403
Reade's The Cloister and the Hearth, 29
Reade's Peg Woffington, 299
Reid's (Mayne) Boy Hunters of the Mississippi, 582
,, The Boy Slaves, 797
Renan's Life of Jesus, 805
Reynold's Discourses, 118
Ricardo's Principles of Political Economy and Taxation, 590
Richardson's Pamela, 683, 684
,, Clarissa, 882-5
Roberts' (Morley) Western Avernus, 762
Robertson's Religion and Life, 37
,, Christian Doctrine, 38
,, Bible Subjects, 39
Robinson's (Wade) Sermons, 637
Roget's Thesaurus, 630, 631
Rossetti's (D. G.) Poems, 627
Rousseau's Emile, 518
,, Social Contract and other Essays, 660
,, Confessions, 859, 860
Ruskin's Seven Lamps of Architecture, 207
,, Modern Painters, 208-212
,, Stones of Venice, 213-215
,, Unto this Last, etc., 216
,, Elements of Drawing, etc., 217
,, Pre-Raphaelitism, etc., 218
,, Sesame and Lilies, 219
,, Ethics of the Dust, 282
,, Crown of Wild Olive, and Cestus of Aglaia, 323
,, Time and Tide, etc., 450
,, The Two Boyhoods, 683
Russell's Life of Gladstone, 661

Sand's (George) The Devil's Pool, and François the Waif, 534
Scheffel's Ekkehard, 529 [710
Scott's (M.) Tom Cringle's Log,
Scott's (Sir W.) Ivanhoe, 16
,, Fortunes of Nigel, 71
,, Woodstock, 72
,, Waverley, 75
,, The Abbot, 124
,, Anne of Geierstein, 125
,, The Antiquary, 126
,, Highland Widow, and Betrothed, 127
,, Black Dwarf, Legend of Montrose, 128
,, Bride of Lammermoor, 129
,, Castle Dangerous, Surgeon's Daughter, 130
,, Robert of Paris, 131
,, Fair Maid of Perth, 132
,, Guy Mannering, 133
,, Heart of Midlothian, 134
,, Kenilworth, 135
,, The Monastery, 136
,, Old Mortality, 137
,, Peveril of the Peak, 138
,, The Pirate, 139

Scott's (Sir W.) Quentin Durward, 140
„ Redgauntlet, 141
„ Rob Roy, 142
„ St. Ronan's Well, 143
„ The Talisman, 144
„ Lives of the Novelists, 331
„ Poems and Plays, 550, 551
Seebohm's Oxford Reformers, 665
Seeley's Ecce Homo. 305
Sewell's (Anna) Black Beauty, 748
Shakespeare's Comedies, 153
„ Histories, etc., 154
„ Tragedies, 155
Shchedrin's The Golovlyov Family, 908
Shelley's Poetical Works, 257, 258
Shelley's (Mrs.) Frankenstein, 616
„ Rights of Women, 825
Sheppard's Charles Auchester, 505
Sheridan's Plays, 95
Sienkiewicz's Tales, 871
Sismondi's Italian Republics, 250
Smeaton's Life of Shakespeare, 514
Smith's Wealth of Nations, 412, 413
Smith's (George) Life of Wm. Carey, 395
Smollett's Roderick Random, 790
„ Peregrine Pickle, 838, 839
Sophocles' Dramas, 114
Southey's Life of Nelson, 52
Spectator, 104 7
Speke's Source of the Nile, 50
Spencer's (Herbert) Essays on Education, 503
Spenser's Faerie Queene, 443, 444
„ The Shepherd's Calendar, 879
Spinoza's Ethics, etc., 481
Spyri's Heidi, 431
Stanley's Memorials of Canterbury, 89
„ Eastern Church, 251
Steele's The Spectator, 164-7
Sterne's Tristram Shandy, 617
„ Sentimental Journey and Journal to Eliza, 796
Stevenson's Treasure Island and Kidnapped, 763
„ Master of Ballantrae and the the Black Arrow, 764
„ Virginibus Puerisque and Familiar Studies of Men and Books, 765
„ An Inland Voyage, Travels with a Donkey, and Silverado Squatters, 766
„ Dr. Jekyll and Mr. Hyde, The Merry Men, etc., 767
„ Poems, 768
„ In the South Seas and Island Nights' Entertainments,769
„ St. Ives, 904
St. Francis, The Little Flowers of, etc., 485
Stow's Survey of London, 589
Stowe's Uncle Tom's Cabin, 371
Strickland's Queen Elizabeth, 100

Surtees' Jorrocks' Jaunts, 817
Swedenborg's Heaven and Hell, 379
„ Divine Love and Wisdom, 635 [653
„ Divine Providence,
„ The True Christian Religion. 893
Swift's Gulliver's Travels, 60
„ Tale of a Tub, etc., 347
„ Journal to Stella, 757
Swiss Family Robinson, 430
Tacitus's Annals, 273
„ Agricola and Germania, 274
Taylor's Words and Places, 517
Tennyson's Poems, 44, 626
Thackeray's Esmond, 73
„ Vanity Fair, 298
„ Christmas Books, 359
„ Pendennis, 425, 426
„ Newcomes, 465, 466
„ The Virginians, 507, 508
„ English Humorists, and The Four Georges, 610
„ Roundabout Papers, 687
Thierry's Norman Conquest, 198, 199
Thoreau's Walden, 281
Thucydides' Peloponnesian War, 455
Tolstoy's Master and Man, and Other Parables and Tales, 469
„ War and Peace, 525-7
„ Childhood, Boyhood and Youth, 591
„ Anna Karenina, 612, 613
Trench's On the Study of Words and English Past and Present, 788
Trollope's Barchester Towers, 30
„ Framley Parsonage, 181
„ The Warden, 182
„ Dr. Thorne, 360
„ Small House at Allington 361
„ Last Chronicles of Barset, 391, 392
„ Golden Lion of Granpere, 761
„ Phineas Finn, 832-3
Trotter's The Bayard of India, 396
„ Hodson of Hodson's Horse, 401
„ Warren Hastings, 452
Turgenev's Virgin Soil, 528
„ Liza, 677
„ Fathers and Sons, 742
Tyndall's Glaciers of the Alps, 98
Tytler's Principles of Translation, 168
Vasari's Lives of the Painters, 784-7
Verne's (Jules) Twenty Thousand Leagues under the Sea, 319
„ Dropped from the Clouds, 367
„ Abandoned, 368
„ The Secret of the Island, 369
„ Five Weeks in a Balloon, and Around the World in Eighty Days, 779

Virgil's Æneid, 161
,, Eclogues and Georgics, 222
Voltaire's Life of Charles XII, 270
,, Age of Louis XIV, 780
Wace and Layamon's Arthurian Chronicles, 578
Wakefield's Letter from Sydney, etc., 828
Walpole's Letters, 775
Walpole's (Hugh) Mr. Perrin and Mr. Traill, 918
Walton's Compleat Angler, 70
Waterton's Wanderings in South America, 772
Webster and Ford's Selected Plays, 899
Wells' The Time Machine and The Wheels of Chance, 915
Wesley's Journal, 105-108
White's Selborne, 48
Whitman's Leaves of Grass, and Democratic Vistas, etc., 573
Whyte-Melville's Gladiators, 523
Wilde's Plays, Prose Writings and Poems, 858
Wood's (Mrs. Henry) The Channings, 84
Woolman's Journal, etc., 402
Wordsworth's Shorter Poems, 203
,, Longer Poems, 311
Xenophon's Cyropædia, 67

Yellow Book, 503
Yonge's The Dove in the Eagle's Nest, 329
,, The Book of Golden Deeds, 330
,, The Heir of Redclyffe, 362
,, The Little Duke, 470
,, The Lances of Lynwood, 579
Young's (Arthur) Travels in France and Italy, 720

Zola's Germinal, 897

Anthologies, Dictionaries, etc.:

A Book of English Ballads, 572
A Book of Heroic Verse, 574
A Book of Nonsense, by Edward Lear, and Others, 806
A Century of Essays. An Anthology, 653
American Short Stories of the Nineteenth Century, 840
A New Book of Sense and Nonsense, 813
An Anthology of English Prose: From Bede to Stevenson, 675
An Encyclopædia of Gardening, by Walter P. Wright, 555

Ancient Hebrew Literature, 4 vols., 253-6
Anglo-Saxon Poetry, 794
Annals of Fairyland, 365, 366, 541
Anthology of British Historical Speeches and Orations, 714
Atlas of Classical Geography, 451
Atlases, Literary and Historical: Europe, 496; America, 553; Asia, 633; Africa and Australasia, 662
Dictionary, Biographical, of English Literature, 449
,, Biographical, of Foreign Literature, 900
,, of Dates, 554
,, Everyman's English, 776
,, of Non-Classical Mythology, 632
,, Smaller Classical, 495
,, of Quotations and Proverbs, 809-10
English Short Stories. An Anthology, 743
Fairy Gold, 157
Fairy Tales from the Arabian Nights, 249
French Short Stories, 896
Golden Book of Modern English Poetry, 921
Golden Treasury of Longer Poems, 746
Minor Elizabethan Drama, 491, 492
Minor Poets of the Eighteenth Century, 844
Minor Poets of the 17th Century, 873
Mother Goose, 473
Muses' Pageant, The, 581, 606, 671
New Golden Treasury, 695
New Testament, The, 93
Poetry Book for Boys and Girls, 894
Political Liberty, a Symposium, 745
Prayer Books of King Edward VI. 1st and 2nd, 448
Prelude to Poetry, 789
Reader's Guide to Everyman's Library, by R. Farquharson Sharp and E. Rhys, 889
Restoration Plays, 604
Russian Short Stories, 758
Shorter Novels: Elizabethan, 824
,, Jacobean and Restoration, 841
,, Eighteenth Century, 856
Table Talk, 906
Theology in the English Poets, 493
Thesaurus of English Words and Phrases, Roget's, 630, 631

NOTE—The following numbers are at present out of print:

89, 110, 111, 146, 227, 228, 244, 275, 315, 317, 346, 350, 390, 418, 432, 450, 480, 493, 540, 541, 559, 565, 574, 597, 634, 641-52, 661, 664, 679

LONDON: J. M. DENT & SONS LTD.
NEW YORK: E. P. DUTTON & CO. INC.

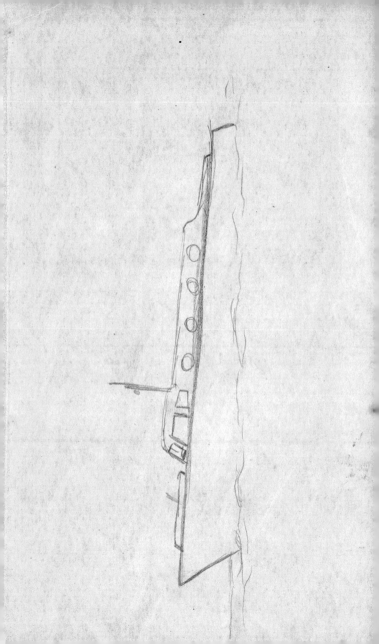

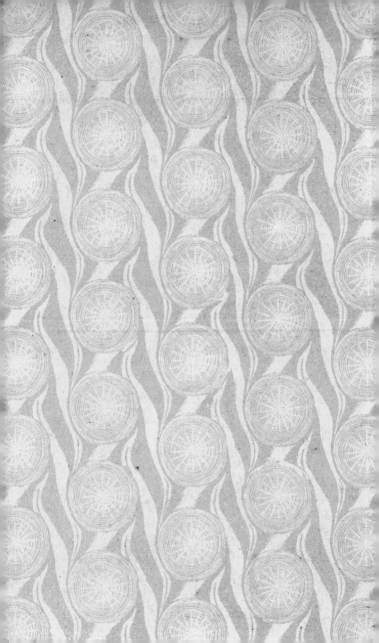